CEE CEE LOOKED AT HER WATCH AND ALREADY FELT AS IF SOMEONE HAD KICKED HER IN THE STOMACH . . .

. . . just thinking about having to say good-bye to this little girl whose screaming entry into the world she had watched in the hospital delivery room so long ago. All right, so she'd only watched part of the time, until she realized how bloody it was going to be, and then she'd fainted so the nurses had to peel her up off the floor in the middle of the whole thing. But that was just a detail. The point was that she and Nina were connected very deeply from way back.

'I think we'd better hit the road, kiddo,' Cee Cee said, hearing the lack of conviction in her own voice . . . This really is the best thing for her, Cee Cee thought. For now this is the best thing. But it was hard to convince herself when she looked at Nina's tiny face, because what she really wanted to do was to zip the kid inside of her Wind-breaker and hide her there forever.

IRIS RAINER DART

I'll Be There

A SIGNET BOOK

SIGNET

Published by the Penguin Group
Penguin Books Ltd, 27 Wrights Lane, London w8 5tz, England
Penguin Books USA Inc., 375 Hudson Street, New York, New York 10014, USA
Penguin Books Australia Ltd, Ringwood, Victoria, Australia
Penguin Books Canada Ltd, 10 Alcorn Avenue, Toronto, Ontario, Canada m4v 3b2
Penguin Books (NZ) Ltd, 182–190 Wairau Road, Auckland 10, New Zealand

Penguin Books Ltd, Registered Offices: Harmondsworth, Middlesex, England

First published in the USA by Little, Brown and Company 1991
Published in Signet 1992
3 5 7 9 10 8 6 4

The acknowledgements that appear at the end of the book constitute an extension
of this copyright page

Typeset by DatIX International Limited, Bungay, Suffolk
Printed in England by Clays Ltd, St Ives plc

This book is dedicated to every member of my beloved, crazy, brilliant, outspoken, opinionated family. With gratitude for the support, the laughs, the inspiration, and the love you each give so willingly and so well. Particularly my husband, Stephen Dart, who never fails to be there for all of us.

I.R.D.

L.T.B.

As long as there's the two of us
We've got the world and all its charms
And when the world is through with us
We've got each other's arms.

from 'The Glory of Love'
by Billy Hill

'Making a living is getting.
Making a life is giving.'

from a magnet on my
Aunt Sylvia's refrigerator

Thank Yous

Elaine Markson

Arthur Klebanoff

Bobbi Vogel M.F.C.C.

Rabbi Scott Sperling

Meg Sivitz

Chad Saffro

Arlene Saffro

Jeff Galpin

Howard Allen

Vicki Gold Levi

Sandy Ferguson

Richard Grossman

David Steinberg

Joyce Brotman

Artie Butler

Barry Adelman

Dave McIntyre

Mary Blann

François R. Brenot

Sandy Cope

Andrew Fishmann

Stephen Crain

Josh Winston

Patricia Lienesch

Charlotte and
   Amanda Brown

Helen Lasley

Doctor Ramsey Kyriakas

Marcia, Nicole, and
   David Harrow

Jim and Gail Andrews

Megan

Paul Livedary

Phil Stutz

Gregory Michael Wolf

Sandi, my hero

My love, and thanks, and prayers
for the many anonymous parents and kids
who shared their stories with me.

And a special thank you to my editor
Fredrica Friedman for the faith, the confidence,
the constancy, the accessibility and
above all, the grace to make some of the
little yellow slips contain love notes.

I'LL BE THERE

LOS ANGELES, CALIFORNIA

August 1990

Once Cee Cee told Bertie if anyone ever wanted to torture her, they could tie her up and make her watch herself on television. Now it was Sunday night at seven thirty-eight, and while she sat watching a clip from one of her old television appearances she remembered that conversation. *60 Minutes* was using the tape as part of a feature story on Hal Lieberman, and they intercut the old shots of Cee Cee singing, with current shots of Hal talking about the days when he was her rehearsal pianist and accompanist.

There she was, singing her heart out on *The Ed Sullivan Show*, with a beehive of teased hair, eye makeup Cleopatra would kill for, and my dear, the way those voluminous bazooms were fighting their way out of that slutty little sequined dress, it was a wonder Standards and Practices hadn't called to say, 'Kindly tuck in your tits.'

Not to mention the fact that the chestnut of a song was about the same vintage as Ed Sullivan's tie. But the best part was the way Hal, a blurry image just behind her on the screen, wearing a tux he had obviously borrowed from a maître d' two sizes smaller, swayed along joyously, plunking away at the Steinway, grinning and mouthing the words with Cee Cee as she sang.

> Nights are long since you went away
> I think about you all through the day
> My buddy, my buddy
> Nobody quite so true.

It was truly a toss-up as to which was schmaltzier, the singer or the song, but considering how nervous she used to get on those shows, she had to admit her voice sounded pretty damn good. Now they cut away to the interview they'd shot at her house last spring, where Mike Wallace was asking her to talk about her relationship with Hal, and *that* part made her sound like a Miss America Pageant reject.

'Hal Lieberman is truly the sweetest man in the world, and I love him very much.' Oh please, she thought. Why in the hell when the people from *60 Minutes* called, hadn't she told them to shove it? After all the times she'd seen that show make dogmeat out of so many people, the way they could make a genius look like a bimbo just by the camera angles they used and the clips they chose, why didn't she say, 'Sorry, folks,' and hang up on them? Well, she should have. And if it had been for anybody but Hal, she would have.

Naturally Hal came off great in *his* interview. He was charming and bright and so funny he even made that stiff Mike Wallace laugh, which was what was supposed to happen since the segment *was* about him, not about Cee Cee. Go figure, she thought. My former rehearsal pianist, Harold J. Lieberman, has become the man being honored for saving the American musical theater from extinction. Three hit shows on Broadway in five years.

'I played in piano bars endlessly,' Hal said, now in a two-shot with Mike Wallace. 'Then, thanks to a friend of mine who was supposed to have the job and got sick, I started playing backup for Cee Cee Bloom, and just because she'd kill me if I did, I won't tell you what year that was . . . but one of our gigs was George Burns's bar mitzvah.' Hal laughed at his own joke and Mike Wallace smiled.

'Oh, Harold, you need new writers,' Cee Cee said out loud to the television. But she was laughing.

'I became her accompanist, in fact most of the time I was her whole band, and boy did we work some dives.' Then as Hal let himself truly remember the past, Cee Cee saw his expression turn soft. 'Of course nobody could compare to Cee Cee even then,' he said. 'I believe she's the greatest performer since Judy Garland.'

'She really put your songs on the map, too,' Mike Wallace said.

'She did. She always sang a few of my tunes in her act, which gave me confidence in the songs and myself. Then years later, when she had her own television show, she insisted they make me the musical director, and the security of that job gave me the luxury to start composing in earnest, so I'm very grateful to her.'

'You're welcome,' Cee Cee said, feeling a chill and hugging herself to get warm, because she knew if she went to get a sweater she'd miss the end of the interview, which sounded as if it was winding down now, and she promised herself that the second it was over she would call Hal and gush. Then, of course, she would have to tell him the news.

'And now you have three shows running on Broadway all at once,' Mike Wallace said to Hal, as they cut to shots of the three marquees above the Broadway theaters where Hal's shows were playing. Then there was an extreme close-up of Hal smiling that philosophical smile of his Cee Cee knew so well. How she loved his funny dear face. The Hirschfeld drawing in the *New York Times* last month had captured it perfectly. The bushy eyebrows over the sad eyes, the too-large bumpy nose, and the pouting, wonderful mouth. 'It's been a very good year,' he said. 'A very good life, actually. I've been very lucky.' Then there was a freeze frame on him, and they cut to a commercial.

'Me too,' Cee Cee said. 'Me too.' And she punched Hal's number into the phone, but the line was busy, so she turned down the volume on the television and watched the commercials without the sound. After a while she tried his number again, and then again a few minutes after that. By the fourth try the busy signal started to sound like a taunt. Jeezus, *60 Minutes* had been on three hours earlier in New York. You'd think by now she could get through to him.

She considered calling the operator and asking her to break in on the call, but Hal was so nuts, if an operator said the word *emergency* to him, he'd probably panic and think something had happened to his eighty-year-old mother, so instead she kept pushing the buttons and getting more and more pissed off by the minute, while she waited for him to get through with all the well-wishers and F.B.s.

F.B.s. That had been one of her jokes with Bertie. One night, when was it? A million years ago, she and Bertie were yakking on the phone and Bertie asked about a guy Cee Cee had been dating for a month or two. Maybe it was that bozo Zack. 'You won't be hearing me mention *that* lowlife again, because it's all over with him,' Cee Cee reported.

'Ahh, Cee, I'm sorry,' Bertie had said with that sincere concern she could get in her voice. 'You were so excited about a future with him. What happened?'

'I found out he was an F.B.'

'Well, knowing you as I do,' Bertie said, 'I already know what the F stands for, so let's see. Is he an F bastard, or an F bullshitter?'

'I don't know why I let you use language like that in front of a lady like me, Bert,' Cee Cee had said, putting on her most dignified voice. 'All I was trying to say is that the guy turned out to be an F.B. A phony baloney.' Bertie had laughed a big 'Oh, Cee Cee' laugh at that, and from then on, anyone who was the least bit full of it, which applied to a lot of people they both knew, was referred to as an F.B.

Cee Cee dialed Hal again, and this time, instead of the immediate busy signal, there was a long hesitation and her heart raced, because she wondered how he would react when she told him what she was going to do, but then there was the busy signal again and she had a reprieve. A few more minutes to decide how she would say it, phrase it, break the news. For a long time she continued to sit and alternately press the buttons on the telephone and the buttons on the TV remote control, cursing the busy signal and seeing the images flash by her. A cough medicine commercial with a worried mother sitting on her little girl's bed reminded her of the first of many nights she had spent with Nina after Bertie died.

'Will you stay in my room until I fall asleep?' Nina would ask her when it was time to turn off the lights, and Cee Cee would say, 'Of course I will.' Then in the child's room, lit only by a night light, she would sit quietly at the foot of the bed wondering where in the hell she was ever going to get the strength to pull off raising a kid, and watching as the ruffle on the front of one of those night-before-Christmas flannel night-gowns Nina always wore rose and fell with her breathing until the little girl was in a deep sleep. Many nights Cee Cee, still drained from the past many months, would fall asleep too and wake, surprised to find herself still at the bottom of Nina's bed, in the early morning.

Hal's phone was finally ringing, and when Cee Cee

glanced at the clock, she realized she'd been trying him for so long it was nine o'clock. Midnight in New York.

'Savior of the Great White Way,' he said when he picked up the phone, instead of hello. It was how they had described him on *60 Minutes*.

'Harold,' was all Cee Cee said.

'Cee, are you okay?'

'I'm okay,' she said, 'I'm just calling to add my name to the list of people who thought you were great on *60 Minutes*. And to thank you for thanking me in front of the entire country.'

'I could have gone on about you for hours,' he said so sweetly it made her want to cry. 'In fact I *did* go on about you for hours when they interviewed me, but they cut most of it.'

There was a long moment of only the shush of the long-distance line, the way it sounded when she put a seashell against her ear, until Cee Cee said, 'Hal, I need you to come out to Los Angeles right away. It's very important to me that you be here.'

'Say no more. I'm on a plane. I'll be in Los Angeles tomorrow, and you don't even have to tell me why.'

'I *will* tell you why,' Cee Cee said, 'but you'd better sit down.' Hal was already sitting, on the bench of the baby grand piano in the living room of his high-ceilinged, Art Deco Park Avenue apartment. And as Cee Cee told him why he had to drop everything and come to Los Angeles, he was so overwhelmed with emotion he sat shaking his head with his eyes closed. And when she'd finished, he promised he was on his way and would see her as soon as possible. Then he hung up the telephone, and stayed where he was for a while, picking out a few bars of 'I'm Bad,' because it used to be one of Nina's favorite songs in those days that seemed so long ago.

CARMEL, CALIFORNIA

August 1983

Even when she wore a big hat and dark glasses because she thought they would make her look dramatically different, the disguise didn't do her any good at all, because what everyone recognized about her to begin with was her nose and her bright red hair and her funny little walk. So on those days when she was going out in public, she'd put on the hat, then the glasses, and within minutes people would still come right up to her on the street, or stop her when she and Nina were walking on the beach and ask, 'Aren't you Cee Cee Bloom?'

Most of the time it was okay with her to be approached by fans, but on days when she wasn't in the mood, she could be impatient or abrupt with them, and on those days Nina would overhear the people when they walked away saying things like 'What a bitch,' after Cee Cee had autographed their chocolate-smeared paper napkin from Mrs Field's Cookies, or a deposit slip from a checkbook, which was sometimes all the paper the people had with them.

Today, when Cee Cee and Nina took a long silent walk on the beach, nobody came over to talk. Maybe because it was just a day when everyone was too busy with their friends and their dogs and their kites to notice them walking arm in arm. Or it could have been that people did notice them but sensed this was a very bad time. Bertie had died exactly two weeks ago today and later this morning Cee Cee was taking Nina to the boarding school in Santa Cruz, which Bertie's tight-ass lawyer decided was the best place for the kid to be.

So this was the last walk they would take together on the Carmel beach they had grown to depend on for solace over the last few months.

In an effort to make sure she was doing everything right, Cee Cee had called the lawyer a few days after Bertie's death, weighted down with a grief so heavy she could barely talk. But that didn't seem to matter to the all-business lawyer who did most of the talking anyway, while Cee Cee, trying to focus through her acute pain, only understood about half of the legal bullshit he was spouting, and during the other half she said, 'Uh huh' and 'Yeah' a lot so he'd think she got it all. The part she *did* get was that his law firm in Sarasota, Florida, was the 'guardian of the estate,' which meant they were in charge of the money Bertie had left to Nina.

'And you, Mizz Bloom,' he said, putting a real buzz on the *Mizz*, the way some men did to show they'd rather say Miss, and didn't go for what they thought was some made-up feminist bullshit title, 'are the guardian of the person.' End of sentence, she thought, but no such luck. 'Provided, of course, the guardianship isn't contested by anyone else,' he had added in a snarky voice that made her clutch. Who in the hell was he talking about? Who was gonna contest it? Bertie picked *her* and that's the way it would stay. Wasn't it?

'Since Mrs Barron's verbal nomination of you as Nina's guardian, I've made some inquiries into the school situation, and have a strong suggestion as to the most appropriate private school for Nina,' was what he said next, and Cee Cee, who had been so racked with sadness watching Bertie leave this life, trying desperately through it all to hold herself and Nina together, had to admit she sure as hell hadn't thought as far as where she was going to put the kid in school.

'Isn't it summer?' she blurted out, then felt dumb when he answered.

'It's August. Long past the time to apply. School begins in two weeks.'

The body ain't even cold yet, asshole, was what she wanted to say, but instead, probably because the little putz had thrown her off with that stuff about somebody contesting her right to Nina, she laid off and tried to be obliging. 'Well then . . . suggest away,' she said, picturing some pompous little pain-in-the-wazoo lawyer sitting in Florida deciding what was best for a kid he'd probably never even met. And it was clear as glass he wasn't just 'suggesting,' because then he said that as soon as Bertie told him how after she died she wanted Cee Cee to be Nina's guardian, he'd located 'the perfect boarding school' for the kid, 'situated conveniently in the foothills of the Santa Cruz mountains. And,' he added, while Cee Cee sat there, knowing things were going very wrong but feeling unable to stop them, 'I've already sent the school a deposit in order to hold a place for the child, since I was certain you'd agree.'

Boarding school, she wanted to scream. Who the fuck goes to boarding school, you heartless little prick? Maybe Oliver Twist, and all those other characters from Shakespeare. Not *my* kid. Her kid. Now that's what was the hardest to believe about all this. To really get it into her head that this funny little pain-in-the-ass creature, this little lost soul of a girl, who was an amazing combination of Bertie's beauty and Michael's steel-jawed iciness, was now in the care of Cee Cee not-exactly-the-odds-on-favorite-for-Mother-of-the-Year Bloom. And here she was, already proving she was no good at it by caving like an empty beer can at a fraternity party, and by her silence, agreeing to let Nina go to boarding school.

Yeah, it was definitely because the snotty little lawyer had scared her with that stuff about contesting her right to Nina, filled her head with terrors of courtroom scenes where she had to fight Bertie's ex-husband or Bertie's aunt, two people who would jump at the chance of flinging a little mud about Cee Cee's past. And it was the vision of those two coming after her that had made her sit there on the phone with the guy like some spineless blob, never saying what she should have, afraid to challenge him, and now it was killing her.

Filling her with guilt, because she knew that implicit in her pitch to Bertie to give the kid to her was a deathbed promise to show Nina a world filled with the kind of passion and spontaneity Bertie knew only Cee Cee could provide. And now, because she'd let the lawyer walk all over her, she wouldn't even be around the kid, except during school vacations. Of course those other two phone calls she'd made during that first week hadn't exactly helped her confidence in herself either. One of them was to her agent at the William Morris office, Larry Gold, and the other one was to her business manager, Wayne Gordon.

Each of them had been real sympathetic and sweet about her friend's dying. And why wouldn't they be? Their percentage of her earnings over the many years they'd represented her would put all of their kids through college. But after the words of sympathy, each of them had warned her in an ominous voice that her exit, in the middle of production, from her television special a few months earlier had damaged her career. And now that she was coming home, if she couldn't make peace with the network, she could find herself in a tough spot.

'They're pissed off, Cee Cee. You walked out on

them, and there's a real good chance they'll say they don't want to be in the Cee Cee Bloom business anymore.' If that was true, she'd definitely have some big financial problems. Have to live off her savings for a while and sell some of her stock and hustle a little to get work. And that could mean traveling anywhere the work was happening. Maybe to make a movie in some far-off place, or worse yet put together an act to take on the road, which was not exactly the life for somebody raising a kid. Which was another reason why, even though it felt so shitty, she had agreed to let Nina go to that boarding school. At least for now.

When they had reached the southernmost end of the Carmel Beach Cee Cee looked at her watch and already felt as if someone had kicked her in the stomach, just thinking about having to say goodbye to this little girl whose screaming entry into the world she had watched in the hospital delivery room so long ago. All right, so she'd only watched part of the time, until she realized how bloody it was going to be, and then she'd fainted so the nurses had to peel her up off the floor in the middle of the whole thing. But that was just a detail. The point was that she and Nina were connected very deeply from way back.

'I think we'd better hit the road, kiddo,' Cee Cee said, hearing the lack of conviction in her own voice. An old lady wearing faded jeans and a fisherman's knit sweater walked by with two little dogs the size of mice on leashes, and one of the dogs stopped, lifted its little leg, and peed in the sand. 'Good boy,' the lady said, and they walked on. Nina stood looking down at her own pretty little toes as they curled up to scrunch bunches of sand under and between them and then released the sand and did it again. This really is the best thing for her, Cee Cee thought. For now this is the best thing. But it was hard to convince herself when she looked at Nina's tiny face, because what she really wanted to do was to zip the kid inside of her Windbreaker and hide her there forever.

Last night they'd spent hours packing up the house Bertie had rented in Carmel. First they organized their own things and then they went through all of Bertie's. Her personal effects. 'Is there any of this you want to wear now?' Cee Cee had asked Nina, sorting through some of Bertie's jewelry, while a kind of slide show of the times she remembered Bertie wearing each piece played itself out in her mind.

Nina took a bracelet of seed pearls out of the box and looked at it for a while, then handed it to Cee Cee, who opened the clasp and looped the delicate thing carefully around the girl's wrist, which she needn't have done because Nina could have easily slipped her tiny hand and wrist into the bracelet without opening it. Then both of them looked back into the box at what was clearly the most special piece of jewelry there. It was the ring Bertie had worn every day of her life since 1970, when Rosie, her own mother, died and left it to her.

It had a platinum band and a small round emerald that was such a brilliant green it always used to catch the eye of people who saw it on Bertie's long slim finger. Nina slipped the ring over her own ring finger. 'Much too big,' she said, disappointed.

'Nina, the ring is yours, and it's insured. It's very valuable, but if you want to wear it, I have a chain with a good safety clasp in the back, and you could wear it hanging from the chain, at least for now.'

Nina thought about it and then turned the ring over and over in her hand. 'I'd like that,' she said.

Cee Cee found her chain, slipped the ring onto it,

and had Nina hold her hair up so that she could fasten the chain around her neck.

'How do I look?' she asked Cee Cee, and stood to see herself in the oval pine mirror above the dresser. She was so much the picture of Bertie at that moment Cee Cee had to take a deep breath before she answered.

'More beautiful than anything I've ever seen.'

This morning when they got back to the house and squirted the sand from their feet with the hose at the side door, Cee Cee went inside and found her car keys on the hall table, then she picked up the small suitcases they had piled up last night in the hallway near the front door and carried them out to the car, with Nina following her carrying another, her two hands wrapped around the handle as the suitcase bumped against her legs.

When the car was loaded she climbed into the passenger seat, and Cee Cee went back to lock the front door of the house, remembering the first day she arrived, summoned by Bertie, not knowing then what the reason was for the urgency, never imagining it would be months before she would leave. With Nina and without Bertie. 'Goodbye, house,' she said softly. Then she got into the car, made sure Nina was belted in, fastened the seat belt around herself, and started the engine of the big Chevy she'd rented the day she arrived.

'I gotta get gas,' she said, looking at the gauge on the dashboard as she pulled away from the curb, then turned the car up to Ocean Avenue, and after a while made a right turn and drove a few blocks down one of the streets of Hansel and Gretel shops, to the gas station.

'It's a good thing we're getting out of this place,'

Cee Cee said. 'I'm about to overdose on quaint. What about you?'

Nina didn't answer. The gas station was busy and they waited in line behind a camper with the bumper sticker that said PROTECTED BY SMITH AND WESSON.

'How do I get to Santa Cruz?' Cee Cee asked the gas station attendant while he was cleaning the windshield. She had mostly used the big clunky car to take Bertie from the house down the few blocks to the Carmel Beach after the time had come during the illness when Bertie was too weak to walk that far. Now the gas station attendant had to push down hard on the scraper because the windshield was thick with a residue of salt air and leaves as a result of the car sitting unused for so long.

'You go up to Highway One, then get on it going north and you can't miss it.'

'Got any maps?'

In a few minutes the man came back with a map and Cee Cee opened it, turned it and folded it, then unfolded it and muttered to herself, because she didn't have a clue how to read it. All those little blue and red lines and numbers and letters were the same blur they always were when she looked at maps.

'Where the effing hell is Santa Cruz?' she said impatiently. 'The guy must have brought me the wrong map because it's not on here.'

'May I help?' Nina asked, and she spotted Santa Cruz on the map before the map was even in her hands, but politely took a minute to act as if she was searching for it so Cee Cee wouldn't feel too stupid.

'Here it is,' Nina said, holding the map so Cee Cee could see it.

'Oh yeah,' Cee Cee said. While the gas station attendant was processing her Master Charge, she tried a couple of times to refold the map to the original size, but finally she gave up and tossed the large open piece of paper over her shoulder into the backseat and started the car. Nina wasn't saying a word, and Cee Cee knew it was up to her to say something first, something important or reassuring, but she couldn't think of anything so she drove through Carmel in silence.

Just as they reached the end of one of the long tree-lined residential streets and drove around the bend, the stone dome of the adobe Carmel Mission rose against the blue sky ahead of them. The mission was the place they had chosen a few days ago to have their own little memorial service for Bertie. Janice Carnes, the lady from the hospice, had been there and Jessica, the nurse who had been hired to take care of Bertie before Cee Cee came to take over, showed up too, and Madeline, the cleaning girl, arrived carrying a little bouquet of flowers from her garden for Nina.

As they all sat together in the mission courtyard among the pink and lavender hydrangeas, each one told a story about something nice Bertie had done for her. At the end they stood in a circle with their arms around one another and held tightly for a long time. Now Nina pressed the automatic window button, and as it opened she closed her eyes to let the clean cool air blow against her curly bangs and serious face.

You have to talk to this child, Cee Cee thought to herself as the big Chevy rumbled and rattled up the highway. *You were so busy every day trying not to lose control and to get all the details out of the way, then every night you collapsed and fell asleep, so this is your last chance to say something to her before you dump her like a hot potato. Speak up, girl.* But all she could get out was the question 'You hungry?'

'No,' Nina answered and sighed a deep sigh. She

15

wasn't even looking out the window at the farms they were passing covered with neat green rows of leafy artichokes; instead she sat slumped low in the seat, and with great concentration picked at the cuticle of her right thumb with the curled index finger of her right hand. Kids. You had to be so careful with them. Their little minds were so delicate, if you did the wrong thing you could screw them up royally forever. In fact raising kids *these* days was a science. Cee Cee couldn't believe her eyes a couple of weeks ago when she noticed a whole wall of books about it in Books, Inc.

It was on one of the rare outings she'd allowed herself to take during Bertie's last days when she'd wandered numbly into the busy bookstore in the Carmel Plaza, and for a few minutes she'd stood in front of the wide rack of magazines, running her aching eyes past their splashy, glossy covers, seeing only the colors. Then, thinking she should buy one or two but too confused by all the choices, she started to leave empty-handed, until on the way out she found herself passing through the section on child care. Child care. She stopped and picked up one then another of the books whose titles intrigued her, and stood paging through them, skimming chapters that promised answers, and by the time she got to the checkout counter she was carrying a stack of books on child care.

Some of the books had titles about children and death, some had the words *positive* or *winning* in their titles, and all of them had pictures of kids on the covers. Kids whose huge smiles were obviously supposed to be evidence of their mental health. Back at the house, while Bertie slept Cee Cee had thumbed through the books, stopping to read long sections of each of them before she'd had the guts to ask Bertie to give her custody of Nina. In fact, she thought now, maybe it was reading those books that had made her think she'd be able to raise a kid. Made her wonder if it could be like following a recipe – first you do this, then you do that, and if you followed the recipe carefully, the kid would turn out just right. Like a cake. Of course she'd never baked a cake in her life.

The thing she decided she'd better read about first in those books, while she'd sat next to Bertie's bed holding her hand and listening for every breath, was how to handle kids and death.

> Most children find it difficult to mourn, unless they have been raised to express their feelings freely. . . . Share with them your own feelings of unhappiness, hurt, loneliness, abandonment, and even anger and this will make it easier for them.

'Your mother was the most special person I ever knew,' she said, finally breaking the silence in the car, 'and she was *different* than everybody else I knew. I needed her in my life because when it came to me, she had X-ray vision. She saw through all the stuff I put on for the rest of the world, like so many different outfits from my closet.'

'What do you mean?' Nina asked, looking at Cee Cee.

'Well, let's see. There was my I'm-Cee-Cee-the-Famous-Star-So-Give-Me-Whatever-I-Want outfit. Or my I-Can't-Handle-This-So-Somebody-Do-It-*for*-Me outfit. I could pull those things off with other people, but never with her. Because she wouldn't fall for it. She'd always look me in the eye and say, "No, Cee, that's not going to work." You get what I'm saying?' Nina nodded.

'There's a song from a great Broadway show,' Cee

Cee went on, 'and the lyrics are "Who else but your bosom buddy will tell you the whole stinkin' truth?" Well, your mother always told it to me. Whether I liked it or not, and I needed it to be told. Everybody does, but especially if you're famous, because then what happens is that people start telling you only what they think you want to hear.'

'Why?'

'Lots of reasons. To keep you happy. To keep their jobs, if they work for you. To get you to like them so they can hang around with a star.'

'Those are dumb reasons.'

'So now every time it hits me that she's not going to be here to tell me the truth anymore, I get mad at her. Real mad that my one true friend is gone. Is that how *you* feel? Mad that she left you?'

Now Nina couldn't look at her. She turned her face to the passenger window, but after a moment Cee Cee heard her answer, 'Yes,' in a very small voice.

'I lost my mom too, a long time ago, and my husband, John . . . he left me . . . and after that I figured it was just my fate to get left by anyone I loved,' Cee Cee said. 'Matter of fact, once when I lived in New York I had this cat named Tuffy. She was orange with a bushy tail, and believe me when I tell you I'm no animal lover but I was crazy about her. Anyhow, one day she just walked across the fire escape into my neighbor's apartment and never came back. I couldn't believe it. I even tried to bribe her by leaving out some caviar some guy I was dating gave me, but she came by that morning, sniffed it, turned her little whiskers up, and walked away, and I cried my eyes out. Can you imagine?' she asked. 'Abandoned by a cat?'

The memory made her laugh now, with a giggle that built into a guffaw, and the laughter felt good for a minute, but then she felt guilty about laughing until she saw Nina's back shaking with giggles too and when Nina turned to look at her, the child's eyes were wet, but her mouth was smiling.

'Well, you know *I'm* not going to leave you because *I've* got no place else to go,' the little girl said.

'And I'm not going to ever leave you either, honey,' Cee Cee said, and just as she did the sun went behind a cloud and the sky dimmed and Cee Cee felt more guilt shoot through her, as if the sun disappearing just then was God's way of saying, You're lying, Bloom. Because the truth was she was already *about* to leave the kid, at some hootsy-snootsy boarding school, and she felt her mouth starting to turn down involuntarily the way it sometimes did just before she cried.

Where the fuck was my mind when I begged Bert to give me this child? she thought. *Shallow me was thinking about going out to buy pink party dresses and patent leather shoes for her as if that was what being a mother was all about. I was already imagining how cute we were gonna look together at the celebrity mother-and-daughter luncheon. But how in the hell can I be a mother to somebody else when I'm bleeding to death myself? Maybe by the time her first school vacation comes along I'll be feeling a little better.*

'We'll go away somewhere together on your first school break. Thanksgiving. I'll take you anywhere you want to go,' she said, knowing Nina had to be able to tell how forced this life-is-just-a-bowl-of-cherries voice was that she was using. But if she did, she didn't say anything, in fact she seemed to perk up at the idea of a shared vacation.

'What about Vail?' she asked.

'Huh?'

'On the break?'

'Where?'

'Vail, Colorado. Three years ago my mom took me there.'

'Great, we'll do it. I promise. Whatever you want.'

'Ever been skiing?' Nina asked, and she took her dark glasses out of her little purse and put them on as the car chugged into the sunny day.

'*Moi?* Are you joking? The thinnest book in the world is called *Jewish Downhill Racers*. May I quote my beloved friend Joan Rivers, who said, "I won't participate in any sport that has an ambulance waiting at the bottom of the hill."'

'Then I guess Vail's out,' Nina said quietly.

God, I'm a rat, Cee Cee thought. Like Miss Hannigan in *Annie*, or Maleficent in *Sleeping Beauty*. One of those villains in children's stories who treat kids like dirt, but what in the hell else can I do? Santa Cruz. It'll have to be okay. Just for now. She would explore the school with Nina, look it over, help her unpack, maybe even have lunch with her, and by the time she called tonight, the kid would be all settled in, with roommates and a whole new crew of pals, and that's how it was supposed to be. Other parents did this. Families with real mothers and fathers sent kids away to school all the time because they thought it was good for the kids.

'Ever snorkeled?' Nina asked.

'Is that where they stick a tank on your back and you dive down and look at a fish?'

'No. That's scuba diving. Snorkeling is easy. You wear a little mask with a breathing tube, and mostly float on the surface of the water. It's like watching fish on television.'

'If I want to watch fish on television I'll tune into *The Undersea World of Jacques Cousteau*,' Cee Cee joked.

'So much for Hawaii,' Nina said quietly.

They were nearly at the turnoff to the school before Nina spoke again.

'Well, what *are* we going to do?' she asked with real concern in her voice.

'About what?'

'Thanksgiving break.'

'You know, I'll bet you're not going to believe this,' Cee Cee said, 'but at that time of year? November? There are very few places that can compare to Las Vegas.'

Nina looked at Cee Cee's face, and when she realized she'd been teasing, she smiled, and Cee Cee did too, and they held hands over the console.

'We'll work it out, kiddo,' Cee Cee told her. 'I swear to God, we'll work it out.'

The school in the foothills of the Santa Cruz Mountains, on its acres of land with its college-like grounds, intimidated Cee Cee. Just the idea of a place where all those kids knew so much more than she did made her uneasy. In her own life, school had always been the place where she was either in trouble with the teachers because she'd been cutting to go into the city to auditions, or where she was thought of as a tap-dancing weirdo by the other kids. That was why she was quiet during the entire tour today, worrying the whole time that the headmistress who led them from building to building might ask her some question she couldn't answer. Nina, as always, was aloof, her little face strained with feigned interest.

'The amphitheater. Our productions of the classics are known for the authenticity of their costume and scene design. Recently we had productions of both Sophocles' and Anouilh's *Antigone*s. I'm sure, Miss

Bloom, that you, with your theatrical orientation, would have appreciated the detail and care with which they were mounted.'

Yeah, sure. Sophocles and Anouilh, Cee Cee thought. I never got past Dick and Jane.

'Are you interested in the theater?' Miss McCullough asked Nina.

'I like movies better.'

'We have a film society here. And what film is your favorite?'

'*Jilted*, starring Cee Cee Bloom,' Nina said, and Cee Cee wanted to kiss her cute face.

'Private bathrooms,' Cee Cee said after the tour. She was sitting on the chair across from the bed in Nina's new dormitory room. She could see the sprawling campus all green and lush through the open window, and the parking lot in the distance, where the Chevy and its contents waited for her.

'Cee Cee, they just showed us a huge science hall, a polo field, a language lab, and a big amphitheater, and all you keep talking about is the fact that the dorm rooms have private bathrooms.'

'Hey, I'm impressed. You're looking at someone who didn't have a bathroom to herself till she was twenty-nine.'

Nina was slowly and painstakingly making the single bed, lifting each corner of the light mattress in order to tuck in the hospital corners. Bertie had taught her to do that and everything else perfectly. Cee Cee tried to imagine the proper and orderly life Nina would live here just to console herself, but still she felt like a rotten shit.

Earlier in the week Cee Cee had called Hal Lieberman in Los Angeles. He was house-sitting at her place in Brentwood and she told him the news about Bertie's death, knowing he was someone she could trust with her raw feelings. A *mensch*, her mother would have called him.

'Cee, I'm sorry,' he said. 'Is there anything I can do to make your return here easier?' Hal's own home was a studio apartment containing a bed, a chest of drawers, and the baby grand his grandfather gave him for his bar mitzvah, so he had readily accepted the assignment to stay at Cee Cee's big, roomy rented house.

'Keep the porchlight burning,' she told him. 'I'm dropping Nina at school and coming home to try and glue my life back together. Am I still in the business?'

'Are you kidding? You *are* the business,' he joked, then added gently: 'Don't be too tough on yourself. Everything will shake out and be okay.' Shake out and be okay. No chance. She was copping out on her promise to an orphan, how could anything make that okay?

'Neen, this place is lovely,' she said, sounding like Jayne Meadows describing a float in the Rose Bowl Parade. 'The classrooms are fancy, the other kids look great, you'll wear the lovely plaid uniform so you don't have to think about clothes every day. And that lovely woman who gave us the tour, seemed so . . .'

'Cee,' Nina said stone-faced, 'I'm sorry to interrupt you, but anytime *you* use the word *lovely* three times in one breath . . . I know you're freaked out. But it's okay. I'll settle in here. I'll be with lots of kids, and you can call and tell me all your adventures, and I'll mark off the days on the calendar until our trip to Las Vegas. You'd better pull yourself together or you're going to hurt your career even more.'

That little face. Those big-girl words coming out of that little sweet face, that look in her eyes which, now that Nina had removed the sunglasses, Cee Cee could see looked too old for someone so young.

'You're amazing,' Cee Cee said. 'So amazing you make me feel like a complete jackass. And it must be in your blood, because your mother had a way of doing that to me too. On a regular basis.' She walked to Nina and hugged her and gave her a little kiss on the top of the head, and as she did she inhaled the sweet clean smell of the little girl's hair. Then she held her at arm's length and said, 'I promise I'll call you every day,' then, trying not to make a big deal out of it, she turned and walked out of the room. When she was about halfway down the hall, she thought she heard Nina say, in a voice that sounded like it was pushing to come off as cavalier, 'Once a week will probably do it.' But she kept walking and when she got outside the building and moved toward her car, she could feel in the back of her neck that Nina was watching her from the window.

For a while she sat behind the wheel, looking back at the school buildings, so torn apart she couldn't even start the car. Finally she did and she drove slowly away, back to Highway 1 and south, this time toward the Monterey Peninsula Airport, with the memory of Nina's little face lodged in the front of her brain and a burr of sadness stuck in her heart.

According to the clock on the dashboard of the Chevy she was early, so she pulled into the parking lot of Del Monte Aviation, where she sat for a while looking out at all of the airplanes, then with a resigned deep breath she made herself get out of the car and walk around to the trunk, which she opened so she could take out the box wrapped in white paper.

'Dying and flying,' she said, 'my two biggest phobias, and *you*, the woman who called herself my best friend, have managed to make sure I had to deal with both of them at the same time. Well, don't worry, Bert. I fully intend to get back at you for this, as soon as I find out how to reach you from Shirley MacLaine.' Then she got back into the car, put the box on the passenger seat, and sat looking out at the rows of private airplanes parked just beyond the fence, and finally too aware of its presence to ignore it, she looked at the box again, leaned over, and tore at the wrapping paper to uncover the package inside. Then, with a mixture of horror and curiosity, she pulled up the lid, and unwound the top of the plastic bag inside the box.

The color. The first thing that struck her was the color. Not black or gray the way she pictured it would look. Not at all like cigarette ashes. But a light color. Like chopped coral, or seashells. Coarse and uneven pieces of what looked like . . . oh God. Bones. She closed her eyes.

'Bert,' she said, 'I always told you I loved you to pieces, but I didn't mean as small as these.' Hearing herself say that made her laugh, a horrified laugh at her own black humor. The kind Bertie loved. And she knew Bertie would have laughed her ass off at that. What would ever be funny again? Hysterical, the way things used to be when she was with Bertie. Even things that didn't seem funny when she was alone, somehow, when they were together, could make them both laugh like idiots. Like that dopey running gag they had for years where Cee Cee would say, 'If one of us dies, *I'm* moving to Miami Beach.' It had been Nathan and Leona's joke that Cee Cee used to overhear all the time when she was a kid. And after she told it to Bertie, the two of them had adopted it as their own.

One night when she wasn't kidding, but long before she ever got sick, Bertie said, 'Cee, you know I was thinking recently, I hope I die before you do.' It must

25

have been one of those times Cee Cee was visiting her in Sarasota. Yeah. It was one of those conversations they had until four in the morning. Bertie was real maudlin that night, probably because she was pregnant and her hormones were on the fritz. And after talking the night away they had decided to make some popcorn because it was a low-calorie snack. Of course they'd smothered it in butter and Cee Cee had washed hers down with a little Sara Lee chocolate cake she'd found in the freezer and defrosted in the oven. 'Because if you ever died first and I was still on this earth without you, I'd be miserable.'

'I'll tell you what, kiddo,' Cee Cee had offered, polishing off the last bite of the cake, 'just to make sure *that* doesn't happen, if I ever get real sick . . . we'll have *you* killed.' Bertie had laughed a lot at that one. So look what happened. She got her wish. She died first and it was Cee Cee who was left to go on without *her*. And now they wouldn't get old together the way they always swore they would, from the time they had noticed two little old ladies together, walking arm and arm down a street, maybe it was in Hawaii.

One of the ladies walked with the help of a cane, and the other one was very rounded forward at the shoulders, so it wasn't exactly clear which of the two was holding the other up, and Bertie had elbowed Cee Cee, making her stop and look at the ladies, and whispered, 'That's *us* in fifty years.' Now there wouldn't be any Bertie in fifty years to hold her up and walk slowly with her when nobody else wanted to. No Bertie who would remind her to suck in her stomach when she forgot, or to tell her when she had lipstick on her teeth, or food on her chin, or to point out that one of her shoulder pads had slipped back so far she looked like Quasimodo, or that she was acting too desperate with some man, or spending too much money on dumb things. No Bertie who believed in her, and always had from the day they met. She used to sign her letters *YOUR FAN CLUB, B.W.B.* And it wasn't just because she believed in Cee Cee's future as a star the way Leona did. Bertie believed in Cee Cee as a person. Bertie had pressured her to stop snorting cocaine. Shrieked at her in an un-Bertie-like way to stop destroying herself because she had too much to offer the world, and Cee Cee had stopped.

Well, maybe she'd slid back to it after that once or twice, but it was always Bertie's letters to her begging PLEASE, CEE, YOUR TALENT IS SO BIG, DON'T DO SOMETHING THAT WILL EAT AWAY AT IT! that had helped her to feel strong, knowing in order to accomplish what she wanted to do, she had to force herself to be more disciplined. It had changed her life having Bertie out there to remind her, pound into her head the reasons she needed to stay away from cocaine, avoid pig-outs on food, and be sure to keep the list of passionate strangers short, though that one was the easiest to control, since the number of volunteers was so small.

'Do what I do,' Bertie said, advising her about men.

'I *do* do what you do, honey, and it's lonelier than hell.'

'Find other outlets. For example two nights a week, I'm taking a course on how to repair my car.'

'The only way they'll get me under a car is with the mechanic,' Cee Cee said. 'Look for our feet locked together in love.'

Bertie laughed. 'You are such a slut.'

'Talk is cheap,' Cee Cee said, 'and so, dear girl, am I.' But teasing aside, finally Bertie had proven without a doubt how much she believed in Cee Cee by changing her will and declaring Cee Cee Nina's guardian, instead of the aunt and uncle in Miami Beach. So what if, in a way, Cee Cee had pushed her into making that decision? There was no doubt in the world it was the right one for the kid, and Cee Cee would prove it to anyone who didn't think so.

'Bert,' she said to the box of ashes, 'I swear you did the right thing by giving me Nina. I promise I won't smother her the way Leona did me. I'll be understanding, but I won't spoil her, I'll be tough, but I won't lean on her too much. In fact I've been reading a lot about what to do with kids because I know somewhere up there you're worried that I won't be able to pull this off. But you're wrong, Bert, because I'm here to tell you that I'll be such a good influence you'll think I'm Mary Fucking Poppins. Hah!' That made her laugh. That and the fact that she was talking animatedly to a box. Dear God, this was bizarre. Now she patted the box warmly.

'Ahh, Bert, if this wasn't so sad it would be truly hilarious. If you were here with me, I mean really here, we'd be killing ourselves laughing the way we always did about this kind of stuff. You always loved those sick jokes I made when you were on the way out of this life, like when I said we should date two ambulance drivers just in case, or that maybe I should do it with a mortician so we could get a discount.' That brought a laugh which caught in her throat and turned into a cry she tried to hold inside. Dear God, this was too weird, too fucking over-the-top weird. This was not exactly your run-of-the-mill way to pass the time, sitting in a car talking to a box full of your dead best friend. Finally she wiped away the crying tears and the laughing tears with the sleeve of her sweatshirt, looked at her watch, and saw it was time to go into the charter office.

'I figure if you're graying at the temples, you must have been doing this for a long time,' she said to the pilot, noticing how high-pitched and nervous her voice sounded as the two of them walked out through the glass doors to the tarmac. He was a husky man in his fifties who hadn't said a word but 'Howdy' when they were introduced, and if he knew or cared who Cee Cee was she couldn't see it in his eyes. Now, as they made the long walk across the airfield, she jabbered unthinkingly in her terror, trying to elicit some assurance from him, but there wasn't a shot this guy was gonna make it easy for her.

'I'm a real white-knuckler,' she tried. 'I worry about every noise. Once on a flight to New York, I heard this snap and then a hiss and I grabbed my piano player's hand and said, "Oh my God. What was that sound?" and he said, really calmly, "It was the sound of the stewardess opening a cola can!" Hah! Of course there probably won't be any stewardesses on *this* flight though, so I guess I don't have to worry.'

They were moving in the direction of a herd of small planes grouped together like a bunch of seagulls on the beach. Their whiteness flashed the sun's glare in Cee Cee's eyes, and when she could make them out clearly she said eeny meeny miney mo, trying to figure out which one of those metal pieces of crap was about to fly her out over the ocean.

'The plane's a Cessna one seventy-two,' the pilot said, stopping at a funny-looking little job with the wings high up on the top. The silly little son-of-a-bitch airplane was almost as tiny as a toy. Not exactly the streamlined craft in which she thought she'd be sitting slouched tragically in the co-pilot's seat when she'd pictured herself doing this, and it occurred to her there was still time to back out of it. To hand the pilot the box of ashes and a big wad of dough, say, 'Good luck to you,' then drive down the coast to Big Sur and watch as he flew over.

'We'll fly out down the coast, somewhere over Big Sur, and that's probably the best place to do what you want to do,' he said, unlocking the door on his side first.

'What are *those* things?' Cee Cee asked pointing to two small wheels that extended on either side of the plane.

'That's the landing gear.'

'Thank God,' Cee Cee said. 'I thought they were training wheels.' She laughed. The pilot didn't.

'We're taking this particular airplane up,' he said, 'because the passenger window opens, and in my instructions it says you wanted to disperse the ashes yourself rather than have me or one of my assistants do it. So when it's time for the dispersal, I'll slow down the speed of the plane so you can open the window safely, and I'll teach you now how to hold the box below the window level to get the ashes to blow out to sea.'

The pilot climbed into his seat, then leaned over and unlocked the passenger door, and Cee Cee stood for a moment, afraid to get in, wondering why she couldn't just go back to L.A., stand on the Santa Monica Pier and open the box lid.

'I can assure you,' the pilot told her, seeing her expression, 'I've been flying these planes for a long time, and they're perfectly safe. Safer than your being on the freeway.'

'You've obviously *heard* about my driving,' Cee Cee said. Again he didn't crack a smile, and looked as if he wasn't planning to. Maybe ever. 'Let's go for it,' Cee Cee told him and climbed into the plane through the open passenger door, placing the box of ashes between her feet.

'Let me show you how you'll open the window once we get over the ocean and I give you the signal,' the pilot said. 'You see the window's hinged on the top, and you're going to press that small metal lever and then push very hard on the window itself. It will open far enough for you to reach out with the box in your arms, and then you're going to make sure you hold the box low, on a level under the window, because of the wind and the prop wash. Got that?'

'Got it,' Cee Cee said.

'Let's practice,' the pilot said, and closed her door. Cee Cee pulled on the metal clip, put both hands on the window and pushed. It opened. A cinch. Then she picked the box up from the floor in front of her and leaned out of the open window, moving the unopened box to a level below the window.

'Good job,' the pilot said.

Cee Cee nodded an oh-it-was-nothing nod, pulled the box back in, closed the window again, and buckled her seat belt. Not bad.

'Ready to go up?' the pilot asked, closing his door, which sounded to Cee Cee like the lightweight door of an economy car.

Ready to throw up is more like it, she thought, as she nodded. She and the pilot were sitting shoulder to shoulder, as close to one another as if they were in a tiny sports car. And in a second, he had put on his headset and the engine was running and the loud noise blasted in her ears as the Cessna began to taxi slowly toward the runway. The pilot was talking into the microphone on his headset, and Cee Cee wondered if he had a sense of humor in case she got sick all over him, which felt like a distinct possibility, and then the plane began to start down the runway slowly, picked up speed and then more speed, and as Cee Cee took a few shallow nervous breaths, the tiny airplane lifted into the clear blue Monterey sky.

In all the years she'd flown in commercial airplanes, even large private jets, she had never been anywhere near the cockpit. Always it was some magical off-limits place she didn't want to think about, probably to avoid the idea that humans who were capable of making mistakes sat in there working the big mechanical bird. But today the exhilaration she felt at the moment of takeoff thrilled her. Made her feel as if she were part of the sky. Looking right out the big front window and feeling the lift of the aircraft and seeing the ground disappear below, and seconds later having the tops of mountains at eye level, and the view of the Monterey Bay below, made her feel so elated she nearly forgot the reason she was up in the airplane to begin with.

'Now this beats the shit out of TWA!' she said very loud to the pilot, who nodded at her but probably couldn't hear her because of that headset of Mickey Mouse ears he was wearing. 'I mean I could seriously get into this. My God. Look down. You can see *everything* from here. I might even decide to get my pilot's license. Wouldn't *that* be a pisser? Amelia Earhart Bloom. Flying myself all over the place in my own plane,' she said to the pilot, who was flipping a bunch of little switches and not listening to her. 'Like Meshulam Riklis. Ever see his plane? On one side he has painted the words "Here Comes Pia!" for his wife, Pia Zadora; well, mine could say, "Boom Boom, here comes Bloom." Right?'

With relief she leaned back against the seat, proud of herself for actually pulling this off. Doing at least part of what she'd promised Bertie she would do.

Going up in a little model airplane that looked like it was made of balsa wood and Duco Cement, to disperse her ashes and to say goodbye. How 'bout *that* for an act of love?

The pilot flew south down the coast, and Cee Cee continued to look out at the mountains and the expanse of ocean below with a comfort that amazed her. For years in her therapy she had talked about the fears she had about so many things and how she hated herself for letting those fears run her, letting them determine what she would and wouldn't do. In fact the only time she was really brave was onstage. Out there when she was performing she would say anything, try anything, wear anything, and not give a rat's ass about the consequences. But in real life, she held back. Crippled and stifled by her fear.

All that stuff she had made jokes about with Nina was real. Perfect examples of her chickenshit life. She wouldn't dream of snorkeling, or be caught dead skiing, and the only time she flew was to get to a job in some faraway city. But worst of all was the way she'd even been afraid of Bertie's persnickety lawyer. Afraid if she didn't do what he said and picked a school for Nina herself, she'd fuck up and scar the kid for life. Afraid to keep the kid with her in Los Angeles, or if she had to go on the road, afraid to educate her with a tutor who came with them, terrified that her crazy unorthodox life would shock an eight-year-old girl. Well, so the fuck what? The kid was hers now, and if something about her life or somebody in her life shocked her, Nina would get over it. After all, wasn't the whole point of Cee Cee's taking the kid to put some color into her little black-and-white world? Now she was pissed off just thinking about the way she'd lamely agreed to that boarding school. Sophocles and Anouilh, my ass, she thought.

The airplane was flying out over the water, and all she could see below them was the slate blue ocean. Jesus, she thought, any minute Mister Charm would be telling her it was time to open the window. If only Leona could see her this minute, in the co-pilot's seat of some flying teakettle, she'd shit a brick. Leona, *that's* who it was who put all those bullshit fears in her head. That's whose fault it was that Cee Cee didn't even learn to ride a bike until she was a teenager because Leona said to her, 'What do you need it for? You could break a leg and then you'll never be able to be a Rockette.' 'I'm too short to be a Rockette, Ma.' 'So now you want to have *two* strikes against you?'

Leona, who also told her, 'Never trust another woman if there's a man around,' which was probably why Cee Cee had made only one real friend in her life. And of course it was Leona, that fountain of unwanted information, who had told her on at least a dozen occasions, 'Believe you me, sweetheart, when it comes down to it . . . men only want *one thing.*' Okay, Cee Cee thought . . . so *some* things the old bat *was* right about.

That thought made her chuckle, and as she did, she could feel the plane starting to slow. The moment had arrived. This was what the pilot told her would happen. He would slow the plane down so it would be okay for her to open the window, and that's what he was doing now. *Oh my God, it's my cue*, she thought, and reached down to the floor and with two hands pulled the box onto her lap. Then she removed the lid again, slowly unwound the plastic, to look long at the ashes one more time.

Okay, Bert, she thought, *here we go. I'm trying to do everything right. I'm up here like I promised, about to strew your remains over the deep blue sea like you asked me to, and I hope this cancels out the time I had that real fancy pin of your grandmother's wrapped in a Kleenex and accidentally flushed it down the toilet, or the time I yelled at you in the lobby of the hotel in Florida, or any other time you were mad at me.* Now she closed her eyes as if that would make Bertie's spirit more able to hear her, and thought about all the last minute things she wanted Bertie to know, feeling as if she needed to cram them in before she parted with the ashes.

Bert, I'm trying to make things the way I think you would have wanted them to be but I know how particular you are about stuff, so sometimes it's hard. Like for example I'm gonna keep buying Nina all those smocked little dresses you like her to wear, and that she likes too, I even took her to Saks in Monterey to buy her some more of them in spite of the fact that I personally think they're so matronly my grandmother would have returned them. But I'm trying not to be too tough on her about it. After she insisted that was what she really liked to wear, I only told her once *that she looked like a member of the D.A.R.*

'Miss Bloom,' the pilot said, and Cee Cee opened her eyes. Obviously he was about to give her the signal. Any second he would tell her to open the window, so she would have to hurry up through the rest of what she wanted Bertie to know. 'Yeah, yeah,' she said looking over at him, then she held the box close to her chest continuing her silent inner monologue to Bertie. *And that school. Bert, I've got to tell you, I hated to leave her there, because that girl was not happy. I mean she acted real brave and all . . . but see, that lawyer leaned on me and when I thought about it I guess I figured for the time being she'd be better off there than with me, and once I saw how uptown the place was I worried that you'd think so too, so I . . .*

35

'Miss Bloom, it's time,' the pilot said over the noise of the airplane.

'Okay!' Cee Cee said, feeling suddenly foolish and panicky and not sure she remembered the instructions he'd given her. The latch on the window. Turn it and push. She reached over and turned the latch on the window and pushed it open. It was hard to push now. Much harder than it had been in the airport, and the rushing wind rattled loudly through the cabin, blowing through her hair and her clothes. This was it, the last goodbye. Tears blurring her eyes, and her heart and head pounding, she looked at the pilot, who gave her the high sign, and probably because she'd been screwing up the timing talking to Bertie, the guy looked a little pissed, and he wasn't exactly the winner of the Mister Congeniality award to begin with.

'Goodbye, Bert,' she said out loud now, the overwhelming force of the wind pounding at her face. 'I sure as hell hope you think I'm doing the right thing by Nina.' And wincing from the wind, she lifted the box to the window, trying nervously to remember everything the pilot told her, and in one fast move, turned it over to dump the ashes straight down, when she instantly felt the powerful slap of an enormous gust of wind that forced Bertie's ashes back into the window at her, spraying, splattering directly into her stunned, gasping face, covering her eyes, her nostrils, her ears, her hair, her clothes while the rest of the little pellets flew wildly all around the cabin. Hastily she pulled the box back inside and grabbed for the window, which she managed to pull shut and latch.

'Oh, no. Oh, God. Oh, no,' she wailed, horrified, weak and devastated by what she'd done because she'd been too rattled to make sure her arms were in the right position.

'Goddammit,' shouted the pilot, wild-eyed with rage. 'What in the hell were you goddamned doing? Don't you remember how I told you to hold the box?' There were ashes all over *his* face and hair too, and his jacket, all over the front of his jacket. 'I don't believe what you did to my plane.' This guy is gonna kill me, Cee Cee thought. He's so bummed out he's liable to open the door and push me out, like in some James Bond movie.

'Oh, God,' she said. 'I'm sorry. I'm sorry.' The box was empty. 'Oh, Bert,' she said. 'Oh, Bert, I'm so sorry,' and then she couldn't control the bellow of a laugh that came next. The ashes were everywhere. On her, and the seats and the instrument panel, even on the pissed-off pilot who was turning the plane around now, heading back up the coast, while he brushed his hands through his hair and then over the shoulders of his jacket as if he were in a commercial for dandruff shampoo.

'Well, Bert,' Cee Cee said, trying not to laugh anymore, which only made her laugh harder as she pulled the empty cardboard box to her chest, smashing the cardboard when she did. 'I guess I should probably take that as a no!'

Back at Del Monte Aviation she had to pay an extra cleaning fee for the damage she had caused the interior of the airplane, and after that she spent a long time in the ladies bathroom in the Monterey Peninsula Airport terminal, brushing, washing, and trembling with the courage of her convictions, and soon she got into the Chevy and drove in a fever back to Highway 1 and up to Santa Cruz.

At first it looked to her as if everyone on the playing field had long brown curly hair, but when the girl she had been certain was Nina separated herself from the others to run down the field, Cee Cee realized she'd been mistaken. For a long time she watched the beautiful little girls playing. Each one was prettier than the next, their pink faces flushed with the excitement of the game. Sometimes they would whisper to one another as they huddled together on the bench or braided one another's ponytails while they watched the game, and each time a goal was scored, they all shrieked and leaped and hugged.

This is a mistake, she thought for a panicky moment. I should leave. Not even let Nina know I'm here. This is the way that child's life is supposed to be. Playing soccer at a ritzy school and having friends and wearing a proper little uniform. This was just where Bertie would have put her, not in Hollywood where the cuckoos are. It's exactly what Bertie would have wanted for her, and the ashes flying back at me was just an accident caused by my stupidity. Not a signal from Bertie. I should leave, and I'm going to.

'Cee?' When she turned, there was little Nina. Not in a soccer uniform at all, but in the plaid day uniform of the school. And the relief Cee Cee felt when she saw her renewed the certainty that had fired her as she had raced here from the airport.

'Did you forget something?' Nina asked, looking up at her.

'Neen, I came back to see you and I want to talk to you and the people at the school, because I have this really powerful feeling that maybe you shouldn't . . . maybe it would be better for you, since I'm your parent now . . . if we . . . if you didn't . . .'

'Didn't go to boarding school?' Nina finished the sentence herself, then looked into Cee Cee's face hopeful that the end of the sentence she had chosen was correct.

'Didn't go to boarding school,' Cee Cee repeated, nodding.

Nina brightened for a second, but then doubt filled her eyes. 'But what about the lawyers?' she asked.

'Honey,' Cee Cee said, 'we're just gonna do to the lawyers what lawyers have been doing to everybody else for years. And you're coming home with me. To be with me and stay with me wherever I go.'

'I am? Oh boy!' Nina said, hugging Cee Cee hard around the waist, her eyes closed and the side of her face pushed against Cee Cee's chest.

'Neen,' Cee Cee said to the top of her head, 'this isn't gonna be like anything you imagine. Especially if I don't get my television show back on the track, because maybe I'll have to go on the road, or maybe I'll have to go on location, or worst of all I could have to go off to Reno or Tahoe with an act, and that can truly be the lowest.'

'I think I can handle it,' Nina said, her eyes lit from the inside, as she held her head back so she could look up into Cee Cee's face. 'You know, a couple of times I heard my mom saying you were too much of a push-over. Is this the kind of thing she meant?'

'Sort of,' Cee Cee said, and her eyes were dancing with light too.

Miss McCullough, the headmistress who had given them the tour, responded to the news of Nina's departure in a way that Cee Cee later described as 'so cold you could hang meat.' The woman stiffly informed Cee Cee that the school would have to keep the non-refundable five-thousand-dollar deposit they had received from the child's trust fund, since Nina had occupied a place which deprived another child from entering this semester, and Cee Cee smiled a big Cee Cee smile and said, 'I'm sure you can find somewhere to put the five grand, toots.' Then she gave the woman a little wink and hustled Nina out of the office and the administration building and into the Chevy, where Nina's already repacked suitcases had been piled into the trunk and the backseat, and as she did she said out loud to herself, 'Maybe I should have phrased that another way.'

'I left one of my Cee Cee Bloom albums with my roommate, Heidi,' Nina said as she slid into the passenger seat.

'You had one of my albums with you?'

'I had all of them. They were with my things Aunt Neetie sent from Florida.'

'And that girl Heidi wanted it?' Cee Cee asked with surprise, starting the car.

Nina turned to look at her and nodded. 'After I told her who you were.'

'So you gave her yours?'

'I traded it to her. I figured I could always get another one, and she gave me a black turtleneck sweater.'

'Well, who do you think got the better deal?' Cee Cee asked, pulling out of the parking lot, so positive now that taking Nina home with her was the right thing to do, her heart seemed to lift in her chest as they sailed along Highway 1.

'Oh *she* did. Because the album was autographed.'

'What did I write on it?'

'You didn't write anything. I autographed it *for* you,' Nina told her. There was a long silence, then Cee Cee reached over and touched Nina on the top of the head.

'Thanks, kid,' she said. 'Thanks a lot.'

'You're welcome, Cee,' Nina said, grinning as the car headed toward home.

Seven hours later when they arrived in Los Angeles, it was dark, but the outside lights at Cee Cee's house were on and Hal waited for them at the front door. When he hugged Cee Cee to welcome her, she wondered if he could smell the heavy odor of death she knew had to be in her hair and her clothes. He didn't mention it. All he said was 'Welcome home.'

'This is Nina,' she told him as Nina followed behind her. Hal waved a little wave at Nina, who nodded shyly in return, and within minutes the tired-eyed little girl was bored with their conversation about telephone messages and mail and took off on her own to explore the house.

'I would have had a room ready for her,' Hal said apologetically, 'but I thought you were dropping her off at boarding school.' He was carrying some of the suitcases upstairs, with Cee Cee behind him carrying the rest.

'Boarding school did not work out,' she said as Hal dropped some of the suitcases containing Bertie's things and Cee Cee's small overnight bag in her room, and she looked around at the familiarity of it, thinking how long it had been since the last time she slept in that bed, and about all that had happened to her since then. 'It was an idea whose time had not yet arrived, and may I say it fostered hostility and fear and scads of ugly resentment.'

'No kidding?' Hal said.

'No kidding. But *I'm* all right now.' The two friends smiled. 'Nina was great about it, a trooper in fact, but I knew leaving her there would mean cheating her out of what I promised Bert I would do, and also promised myself I would do, so I figured what the hell. I keep thinking about that "Peanuts" cartoon I have pinned to the wall in the kitchen where Charlie Brown is

41

sitting against a rock saying "I've developed a new philosophy. I only dread one day at a time!" Well for the first few years, that'll be me, and then maybe I'll mellow out.'

Hal squeezed her hand. 'I'm glad you're both okay.'

They stood at the top of the stairs and shared a gentle hug, until Cee Cee pulled away to listen to the music she heard floating up from downstairs in the music room. Nina had put one of Cee Cee's albums on the turntable there and was listening to it.

> Nights are long since you went away
> I dream about you all through the day
> My buddy, my buddy
> Nobody quite so true.

Hal, who had played backup piano on the recording session of that album, listened a little mistily to the music, then nodded remembering. 'That was the first cut,' he reminded Cee Cee.

'Yeah,' Cee Cee said, sighing. 'And it's always the deepest.' Then she put her arm around Hal, and the two of them walked downstairs to be with Nina, listening to the song as it rose.

> Miss your voice, the touch of your hand
> Just long to know that you understand
> My buddy, my buddy
> Your buddy misses you.

ANDREWS, KROLL, SCHULTZ AND STEIN

Dear Cee Cee,

Per our recent telephone conversation, I reiterate how sorry I was to hear of the death of your friend Roberta Barron. Although I never met her, you told me more than once how important her friendship was to you. Regarding your role as guardian of her minor child, I am enclosing the following forms: a petition for your appointment as guardian of the person of Nina Barron and a waiver of notice and consent. Per Mrs Barron's attorney in Sarasota, I will also forward copies of the waiver to Roberta Barron's aunt Anita Bennet in Miami Beach, Florida, and the child's natural father, Michael Barron in Pittsburgh, Pennsylvania.

The petition will be filed with the State of California and a date for a hearing will be set for sometime within the next six months depending on how much independent investigation the court wishes to make before appointing a guardian. Despite what you told me on the phone about the ominous words from Mrs Barron's representatives, rest assured that the court will give great weight to Mrs Barron's nomination.

Because the firm of Barmen and Wolk in Florida has been appointed as guardian to the estate, and the child's natural father has shown no inter-

est in Nina since birth, and the aunt is elderly
and I gather relieved to be rescued from the
responsibility, I foresee no problems in closing this matter swiftly.

   Again, please accept my deepest sympathies for
your loss, and if you have any questions regarding these documents please feel free to call.

                               Sincerely,
                               Jim Andrews

Dear Cee Cee,

I got the waiver yesterday from the California court, and I signed it because I know that's what my niece said she wanted. Personally I worry about the welfare of a child who is living in that kind of environment where there are so many terrible types. (No offense meant towards you, but you know how most people in your line of work behave. Like that Cher and others I don't have to mention.) I have also put in the envelope a copy of something which I went over to the library to the copy machine to make for you. It's a letter which was sent to me by my niece, a few months before she died. You can tell by what she says in it that it was sent during the time when she still intended to give Nina to me instead of to you. I came across it last night and thought that maybe you should have it because of what it says. The handwriting in it is so poor and childlike that she must have already been very ill when she sent it off, and I'm pretty sure she wasn't really in her right mind at the end. Now and then I get a letter from Nina. If you could make her write to me more often, it would cheer me and my husband quite a bit.

Sincerely,
Anita Bennet

From the Desk of Roberta Barron

Dear Aunt Neet,

I have begun this letter to you again and again over the last few weeks, each time destroying the draft halfway through, probably to deny that eventually I would have to finish and send it, since my intention herein is to outline some of my thoughts about your future with Nina, and that brings home the very painful point that you in fact will be having a future with her, and I will not. Nevertheless, it's becoming increasingly clear that my rapidly declining physical health will soon prohibit my getting a letter of this sort off to you at all, and it's crucial to me that you understand what it is I am about to set down here.

Essentially what I want to write to you, and had the situation been otherwise would have preferred to say in person, has to do with what I will call her care and feeding after I'm gone.

To begin with, let me say that from the very first day of her somewhat unorthodox life Nina has been the dearest and best girl in the world. Yes, she is willful at times and bossy too, but I think that comes mostly as a result of being the fatherless daughter of a living father who, though he admits that she exists by sending money, continues to refuse to see her. That has never been easy for her and I'm sure it never will be. That said, I have to tell you I am terrified that her further rage at my death will tear the goodness from her. And that's why, even though I know you will do everything you can to take splendid physical care of her, educating her per my lawyers, etc., there is so much more that she will need in order to survive.

Oh, Aunt Neet, what I'm trying to say is please, please, please, love her! Try to look beyond her very proper little person façade and you won't be able to resist loving her. See the funny spark in her, appreciate her wonderful mind and indulge her wild imaginings. And as many times as you can find a moment, promise me without a doubt that you will take her in your arms and hug her long and hard. Let her feel grown-up arms around her, reassuring her that even though it seems as though events have conspired against her, she really is loved and special, and maybe that will serve to give her hope that down the line she will be able to find some happiness of her own.

I don't care if her grades in school are not the highest in the class. I don't care if her room is perfectly neat, though I realize I can't dictate the rules for your home. I don't even care if she's sometimes irreverent and more outlandish than I ever was. (Which heaven knows, wouldn't take much, after old Straight Arrow's life. The only unusual thing I ever did was to raise her alone, and I thank God for that decision every day.)

Thank you, Aunt Neetie. My memories of the times I spent with you during my childhood are many and precious to me. You were my mother's dearest sister, and she would approve of my leaving Nina in your care. The truth is, you are my only real family, and I am grateful that you have agreed to shoulder the enormous burden of raising my girl . . . my dear dear girl.

Know that I will be looking on from wherever my spirit lights, smiling with gratitude on both you and Uncle Herb.

Your niece,
Roberta

Dear Aunt Neetie:

I have only known you as Aunt Neetie, so I hope it's okay if I call you that.

I'm sending this to say thank you a lot for the copy of Bertie's letter to you. I knew about the letter but in the middle of all the stuff that's been going on here, I guess I forgot about it. What I'm trying to say is that if you look closely at the original, you'll understand that the reason I already knew about the letter is because the person with the lousy handwriting wasn't Bertie, it was me. She dictated it to me one day when I first started caring for her during her illness, and she was feeling too bad to write it herself.

The one thing I want you to know for sure is that she was not in any way out of her mind when she wrote it, or when she agreed to let me have Nina instead of sending her to you.

I'm knocking myself out to try and carry out Bert's wishes for Nina. And I promise I'll tell the kid to write you more often.

Cee Cee

We have moved
to 29 Malibu Colony Road,
Malibu, California 90265

Cee Cee Bloom
Nina Barron

LOS ANGELES, CALIFORNIA

August 1990

There was no missing Kevin in a crowd. It wasn't just his rolling walk that always stuck out so dramatically when he moved down the street with the other boys, but the high-spirited whinny of a voice ringing above the others, as he cracked endless jokes, teasing his friends mercilessly, always confident not one of them would dare to retaliate.

Cee Cee caught sight of him the minute he walked out of the front door of the school, and she watched him, surrounded by his usual gang, as they all walked down the front path. She had been sitting outside the school in her car for half an hour, waiting to tell Kevin the news face-to-face, afraid if she didn't get there early she would miss him. Her hands clutched the steering wheel at ten and two o'clock, the way her teacher at the California Driving School had taught her to do so long ago, only now she was parked.

See me, Kevie, Cee Cee thought, staring at his face, which was contorted with animation while he told a story to a few of the guys who responded with a laugh so raucous that even Cee Cee at a distance was sure it had to have been a dirty joke. *See me, Kevie*, she thought again, and then as if in answer, he looked right at her, nodded a special Kevin nod, and then moved away from the others toward her car as she opened the window on the passenger side.

'You cruising high schools now, lady?' he asked leaning in the window. 'I mean, I know a good man is hard to find . . . but really, Cee.'

Cee Cee got out of the car and walked to where he

was standing to give him a hug, startled when she did at the bony frailness under the layered clothes.

'Kevin,' she said, 'I guess you know what's been going on in our lives.'

'I've known for a long time.'

'Hey, Myers, you coming with us or what?' a voice yelled from the parking lot.

'Tell him I'm taking you home,' Cee Cee said. 'Please.'

'I've got a ride,' Kevin hollered.

'What'd you say?' the kid hollered back.

'He's got a ride,' Cee Cee shouted back toward the parking lot.

'Wow, you've got a nice set of lungs. Ever think about being a singer?' Kevin laughed at his own cuteness.

Cee Cee opened the car door for him.

'Get in,' she said to him, 'before I punch your lights out.'

'Oooh, sweet-talk me and you own me,' he said, and sank slowly onto the black leather seat of the BMW. Cee Cee walked around to her side, got in, and started the car. She drove back to the Coast Highway and when she reached the parking lot just north of the pier she made a right and pulled the car into a parking spot facing the sea. It was a clear day and there was a line of white sailboats on the horizon. Cee Cee could tell by the way Kevin's right hand held on to the open window that he was bracing himself for the worst. Bad news, otherwise why would she have come to tell him in person?

'Well,' she said, 'I thought you should hear this from me instead of on an answering machine after a beep.'

'Jesus, the suspense is killing me,' he said, laughing

51

an uncomfortable laugh, which she interrupted by telling him the news. Then the laughter stopped and she saw him try to act as if he wasn't feeling choked up, but he was.

'So can I count on you?' she asked him.

'I can't think of anything that would keep me away,' he promised, and then he reached out a hand and took hers. After a while he let out a little giggle.

'What's funny?' Cee Cee asked.

'Remembering when I met you when you first moved to Malibu. The first time I was ever in your house.' Cee Cee grinned as she remembered too, and then they reminisced, looking out at the view for so long that eventually they watched the sun, which had moved slowly down in the sky, drop like a giant orange egg yolk into the sea.

MALIBU, CALIFORNIA

October 1983

Cee Cee sat on the deck of the new house in Malibu wearing a frayed white terry cloth robe she'd had for so long it might have belonged to her ex-husband. She always pulled the now ratty thing out of the closet and wrapped herself in it when she needed to be near something familiar and homey. The breakfast tray she and Nina had shared earlier still sat on the glass and wrought-iron table piled up with their dirty breakfast dishes and the empty milk glasses they had clicked together in a toast to their own cleverness for moving to the beach.

The toast was one Nathan used to say when he drank his rare glass of schnapps on one of the Jewish holidays. 'Look out teeth, look out gums, look out kishkes, here it comes.' Nina had never heard the word *kishkes* before and the sound of it made her laugh so hard, her milk bubbled up in her mouth and her eyes watered. Cee Cee loved the way the kid was starting to learn to be silly, giddy, childlike. And as odd as it seemed, so was Cee Cee for the first time in her life. Neither of them, in the years before their union, had ever learned much about playing or really letting go. Nina because most of her life had been filled with grown-up problems, and Cee Cee because her own childhood had been so focused on the pursuit of a career.

'I'm getting this mother thing down to a science,' she told Hal one day. 'For example, I already know that you can't go to the playground in three-inch pumps. The goddamned heels stick in the grass and the next thing you know, *you're* still walking, but the shoes are a half a mile back! After I figured *that* out, all was well until yesterday when my tiny little ass fell right through the humongous hole in the tire swing. In fact it took two very attractive single fathers to pull me out. Did I mention that the park is a veritable treasure trove of parents without partners?'

This morning Nina was down the road at the home of one of her new friends and Cee Cee scrunched down a little lower in the lounge chair wondering how she'd been crazy enough to put herself so deeply in debt by impulsively buying this big expensive house on the beach. At first when her business manager grumbled about it being more than she could afford, she used the excuse that she was buying it because of Nina. That she wanted the child to feel at home after living near water all her life in Sarasota.

Then she said it was because the house was on a street protected by a guard gate and that would keep the paparazzi out. Which it did, for a while, though an army of them seemed somehow to know where she was going at all times and managed to show up everywhere, snapping and flashing away at her and at Nina, immediately selling the pictures to the tabloids, which printed them constantly. But her real reason for buying the house was much more selfish than any of those.

She had come back to Hollywood feeling like an alien. Realizing, though nothing there had changed, that after her months in Carmel she was seeing it all through new eyes. A perspective that had been changed by the lesson of those bleak and endless days and nights of sitting at Bertie's bedside where under fire she had learned about how fragile the line was between life and death. And the time with nothing to do but care for someone else had given her the opportunity to think about the unimportant attitudes and ridiculous posturing that got in the way of most people's living their lives.

So when the painful vigil was over and she came home and looked at the years stretching before her, her first impulse was to goddamn enjoy them in a big way, to live it up. There were no men who interested her and vice versa, she knew from past experience that indulging in too much food would be bad for her career, she already had a great car, so she bought a house, a big gorgeous house on the beach for herself and for Nina.

Every day since they'd left Carmel she had taken an emotional tally of how they were doing together, watching and monitoring the ups and downs. Worried because there had been quite a few little explosions between them. Like the one last week when Nina had given her some of that haughty more-elegant-than-thou shit at which she was an expert and which could always start some sparks flying. There was no getting away from the fact that this kid had been so well trained by Bertie, she could go to lunch with the Queen of England and know what to do, and just like her mother, she didn't hesitate to make a point of telling Cee Cee what *she* was doing wrong.

'Did you send a thank-you note for those flowers?' she asked Cee Cee the other day. That was what started it.

'A what?'

'The world doesn't owe you a living, Cee Cee. Your agent didn't *have* to send those roses just to welcome you back.'

'Do you have any idea how much money I made for that agency last year? Believe me, my agent *had* to send the roses. He ought to send *me* a thank-you note for the privilege of sending them.'

'I don't agree. My mother taught me that when someone takes the time and effort to send you something –'

'He had his *secretary* send them,' Cee Cee had said, her voice rising, astonished at how much the kid's getting on her case like that really bugged her.

'But the thought was *his*,' Nina replied in a tone calm enough to make Cee Cee's flaring temper feel stupid.

'I already had a mother,' Cee Cee said, steaming.

'Well, she must have forgotten to mention thank-you notes.'

Hah! That time Cee Cee had burst out laughing, because the idea of Leona mentioning thank-you notes was pretty funny. 'The only person Leona ever thanked was the doctor who told her after I was born that she probably wouldn't have any more babies.' Of course the truth was Nina was right about a lot of things. Especially the goddamned thank-you note. It took exactly three minutes for Cee Cee to dash off this really full-of-it thank-you note, and the other day when she stopped by Larry Gold's office, she nearly fainted. The little twirp had framed the goddamned thing and it was hanging on his office wall.

Then there was the constant battle about clothes. Cee Cee remembered how the saleslady at Saks had just about bust a gut overhearing *that* conversation.

'Why?' Cee Cee asked looking at Nina's choices for school clothes, 'does an eight-year-old kid want to dress like a forty-year-old woman?'

'And vice versa?' Nina had asked looking Cee Cee right in the eye, and when she did, Cee Cee glanced over her head at herself in the three-way mirror and realized she was wearing an off-the-shoulder sweatshirt, bicycle pants, lace tights, and high-topped basketball shoes.

'Good point,' she said, and the subject was closed.

And naturally, since Nina was Bertie's daughter there had to be the whole discussion about language, just like the ones Cee Cee used to have with Bertie all the time. In fact sometimes when Nina opened that mouth of hers, it was so spookily like talking to Bertie, Cee Cee had to look around to make sure it was the kid.

'I'd like to ask you if you'd kindly stop saying F-U-C-K in front of me,' Nina said one night at the dinner table, pronouncing the letters of the word as carefully as if she were a finalist in a spelling bee.

'I didn't realize I ever *did* say it in front of you.'

'That's because it's a bad habit.'

'Huh?'

'You say it automatically at least ten times a day.'

'Me? Get the fuck outta here.'

'Just like that.'

'Ten times a day is impossible.'

'Well, if you think it's impossible, what if I fine you for every time you say it, and I get to keep the money?'

'How much?'

'A dollar.'

'A nickel.'

'A quarter.'

'You're on.'

Okay, so by the end of the first week she owed Nina six bucks. But last week it was only a buck seventy-five, which was a big improvement. And now they had made it through six weeks. Six weeks of settling in, getting that this was forever. Figuring out what they were going to do next. Six whole weeks since the day the people came and carried Bertie out of the house in Carmel shoved into a body bag, so just the fact that it was still that fresh, and she and the pip-squeak had already survived tons of little battles and the big one of moving out of one house and into another, meant they were doing all right.

Consider what happens when we are learning any new skill, whether it is playing bridge, playing golf, riding a motorcycle, playing the piano or anything else. We learn by making literally thousands of mistakes. Why should learning the complex skills of raising a child be an exception to the rule? We should take it for granted that we will make mistakes and not berate ourselves or feel guilty about it.

Cee Cee had closed the over-the-counter child psychology book after reading those words and said, 'Yeah!' out loud. This was new to her, but eventually she'd get the hang of it and be great. Now she needed to get back into the swing of things in the business. Needed to call people and tell them she was back, needed to get a real good job to pay for this big fucking house. Frigging house. Fancy house. Some days she would call her agent five times in a row with ideas about how to get her career back on track, but other days she would sit incapacitated, numbly staring at the ocean for hours, not knowing or caring what time or even what day it was.

And most important of all she had to find a school for Nina. In the last few days, after talking to everyone she could think of who had a child, she compiled a list of all the recommended private schools within a reasonable distance of the beach house, then she phoned the admitting offices of those schools and set a time to visit. This afternoon the two of them dressed, and as usual looked one another's outfits over with patent disapproval, then headed off to the Buena Vista School, which had been recommended highly by Larry Gold, whose three kids were all registered there. While Nina was escorted on a tour of the place, Cee Cee sat talking with the headmaster. She had a list of questions a mile long, and after he had answered all of them, he took a long deep breath and launched into what, she could tell by the way he delivered it, had to be an often-repeated sales pitch.

'Cee Cee, listen to me, our school caters specifically to the special needs of the children of people like yourself. Let's face it. We all put our kids into schools where *we're* comfortable, right? Of course I mean by that where the policies of the school are the same ones we live by at home. But also where we ourselves fit in with the parent body, if you know what I mean.' He waited for Cee Cee to nod and let him know she knew what he meant, then he went on. 'Now it's pretty hard for me to believe *you'd* be more comfortable than in a school like ours where you're surrounded by your colleagues.' He handed her the school's roster. 'Go ahead,' he said, 'feel free to look through it. We've got more stars than the Milky Way. And the reason for that,' he added, 'is because we're cognizant of the needs of these families for privacy.'

Cee Cee wanted to ask this guy if the school had such a great respect for privacy, why he was letting *her*, an outsider, look at the list of the names of people who were registered there. But instead she just shuffled through it, and had to agree that a lot of well-known people's kids were registered in that school.

'This child has had a few tough breaks,' she said, looking into his eyes.

'Oh, I know.' The headmaster's name was Jason, and the more Cee Cee looked at him, the more she thought he looked too young to even be a teacher, let alone a headmaster. 'I read about it in the paper,' he said, nodding, and Cee Cee wondered if he meant the *Enquirer*. 'But she'll be in understanding company here, because there are many kids from unusual situations, multiple stepfamilies, cohabiting parents who have never married one another, single parents whose spouses aren't around anymore, or single parents who never had spouses in the first place. In fact in *this* school it's the nuclear families who are unusual.' When his smiling eyes met Cee Cee's concerned ones, he shrugged, laughed a little laugh, and said, 'That's show biz.'

Cee Cee looked around his large office. There were a lot of pictures of this guy on every wall, eight-by-ten framed pictures of him standing among small groups of people. Now Cee Cee looked more closely and saw that one of the groups was Sylvester Stallone and one of his kids, and in another he was with Lesley Ann Warren and her son, then there was another of Jason with Goldie Hawn and her kids.

'Well, we'll give it a lot of thought,' Cee Cee said, standing, relieved that at that moment, through the floor-to-ceiling window that faced the school's back lawn with a wide-angle view of the ocean, she could see Nina on her way back toward the administration building. Cee Cee shook the young headmaster's out-stretched hand and thanked him.

'So what are you working on now?' he asked, walking out the door of his office with her, and the question felt like a blow to her stomach. Larry Gold was trying to get a meeting for her with the network people she had walked out on when she went to Carmel all those months ago, but so far they were refusing even to listen to her apology. Trouble, she was known in the industry as trouble, her agent told her bluntly, but he was trying to smooth things over.

'I've got a lot of stuff cooking,' she said, trying to sound even.

'Well, that's good,' the headmaster said, 'because I'm a big fan.'

Now Nina was standing next to her. When the headmaster put out his hand for the girl to shake, she gave him a look-in-the-eye-firm-grip Cee Cee knew Bertie must have insisted on, said, 'Thank you so much for your time,' and she and Cee Cee were off down the hall.

'So, what do you think?' Cee Cee asked her when they got into the car.

'I think I should go to the public school in our neighborhood,' she answered. 'I don't want to go to a school for weird kids from weird families. I want to feel like I'm with real kids. And anyway, all they did on the tour was drop names and ask me what *you* were like.'

'Neen, your life is special now and your circumstances are too.'

'I'm not special, *you* are.'

'Well, the public school in our neighborhood won't work,' Cee Cee said.

'And Buena Vista won't either,' Nina snapped.

Cee Cee drove silently for a few blocks, their mutual frustration hanging in the air.

More stars than the Milky Way. The kid's right, Cee Cee thought. That's not the place for her. But somehow she had to find a school that offered some degree of safety and privacy to a child whose family profile was so high, one that would give Nina the feeling of normalcy her homelife with Cee Cee would never provide. Someplace where she could see that another lifestyle was possible, and where she would be among lots of families, whole ones, the kind she might want to have herself someday. 'Don't worry. We'll find the right place,' she said, not sure if she was talking to herself or Nina. It would have to be a good school too, because this kid was one smart little cookie, very intense, with an overanalytical mind that never quit. At bedtime she and Cee Cee would take turns reading to one another, and Nina always had a million serious questions about even the most frivolous storybooks.

'*At Piglet's house the water was coming in through the window. He had just written a note which read "HELP, PIGLET, ME." Piglet put the note in a bottle which floated out of the window and out of sight. And then Piglet floated out of the window and out of sight.*' Nina had stopped after reading that paragraph aloud to Cee Cee and asked, 'Do you think Piglet wrote "Help Piglet" and then signed the note "Me"? Or do you think he wrote "Help" at the top and "Me" at the bottom and then only had room in the middle to sign it "Piglet"? Or do you think he wrote "Help Piglet" and then thought he should explain that the note was written about himself so he wrote "Me" in the middle of the page?' Cee Cee couldn't believe the worried expression on the little girl's face while she waited for the answer to those questions. And that was the way her compulsive little mind worked all the time.

'Honey, I think,' Cee Cee had said, putting an arm around her, 'that when the water's too deep, we just blurt out the message and don't stop to think how it comes out.' That seemed to satisfy Nina for the moment, and as they read on, Cee Cee thought about her own life. Like Piglet *she* was in too deep. When Larry Gold called and said Peter Flaherty at the network had finally agreed to 'take a meeting' with her, she knew she was supposed to be happy, but instead she felt afraid, because she was so desperate for it to work out.

'Tell them I have a child now, Larry. Tell them I'm the new Nixon. Say I need to work more than ever. One of those people must have kids, somebody there should understand that.' She couldn't believe his response.

'Trust me, you're gonna have to kiss a few asses to pull this one off. Cee Cee, you *know* what the numbers were. You cost them a million five by walking out and going to be with your sick friend. And don't get me wrong, because I understand that kind of stuff, I cry at the drop of a hat, but you're nuts if you think Peter Flaherty gives a shit. Remember the joke about the guy who needed the heart transplant, and he couldn't find a donor? And finally they brought in Denton Cooley, the specialist, who looked the patient over and said, "I recommend giving him Peter Flaherty's heart. After all, *he* never uses it." I promise you, Cee, the network only cares about people who are dying if there's a Movie of the Week in it.'

The next morning on the way over to the meeting in Larry's Jaguar XJS convertible with the top down, the wheel of which he was barely tall enough to see over, he said, 'It's pretty amazing that even after the article on the front page of the Calendar section, Flaherty is still in that job. I mean, you know every word of it was true.'

Cee Cee wondered as she looked at Larry Gold's tiny hands clutching the wheel of the Jaguar, then at his serious little face, if when he drove the car and there was no one in the passenger seat, whether people who were driving behind him thought his car was a runaway vehicle. The idea of that made her smile.

'Yeah, pretty funny, wasn't it?' Larry said, taking her smile as a response to his question.

'Wasn't what?' She hadn't heard a word.

'That article in the *Times*. Oh maybe you were in Carmel when it came out. About Flaherty and the psychic?'

Cee Cee had no idea what he was talking about, and she could see that Larry Gold warmed to the telling of the gossip the way the old women on her front stoop in the Bronx always did, just after some neighbor passed by whom they were eager to trash.

'Flaherty actually had some girl on the network payroll, with a three-year contract, and the girl was a psychic who told him which shows to pick up and which to cancel and where to slot them in the lineup.'

'Didn't seem to do him any good,' Cee Cee said, pulling down the visor in front of her and looking at herself in the mirror. 'His network is still number four out of a possible three.'

'Which is why after two years of bad predictions, Flaherty dumped the girl, who was not too happy about it.'

'If she was any kind of a psychic, she'd have seen it coming,' Cee Cee said, and she and Larry both laughed.

'So instead of just saying, "I had a nice ride for a couple of years on the network's dough," the psychic . . .'

'Calls the *L.A. Times* and tells them the story,' Cee Cee interrupted.

'Yeah. How did *you* know?' Larry asked driving up Highland Avenue toward the freeway.

'I'm psychic,' Cee Cee said.

'Everyone went crazy while it was in the papers. Even Johnny Carson was doing jokes about it, but I guess it passed.'

Cee Cee's hair blew wildly around her face as they

sailed along the Hollywood Freeway. She hadn't had a haircut or hair color in more than three months, hadn't done anything for herself the entire time she was in Carmel, and then this morning in anticipation of the network meeting she'd spent hours trying to get her hair not to look like a bad imitation of Harpo Marx. But after this ride there was no hope. She hated that she felt nervous, and that she couldn't even seem to calm herself with the news that she was on her way to meet with a man who was so insecure himself he had to hire a psychic to tell him what to do.

'Hey, these people were ready to sue you,' Larry told her as he pulled into the parking lot at the network, gave a friendly wave to the guard, and found a spot next to what Cee Cee recognized as Peter Flaherty's Ferrari, 'but I parlez-voused a little, and I think now they get the idea that when you walked out on the show, you had no choice. I mean, that's what I told them. I said to them ... "People, this girl is not difficult, this girl is not Judy Garland. She doesn't even touch drugs anymore."'

'Did you *say* that?'

'No! Are you crazy?' Larry Gold laughed. 'I'm kidding you. It's like that joke. "When did you stop beating your wife?" No, what I said to Flaherty and that girl who works for him, Michelle, I said, "Do yourself a favor, let Cee Cee come in, we'll sit, she'll explain it, you'll hear her side of the story and we'll get the whole thing back together in no time."'

Peter Flaherty's office was furnished with white sofas, white chairs, and glass tables on chrome bases so that the sun pouring in through the floor-to-ceiling windows bounced off the reflecting surfaces, making Cee Cee want to put on her dark glasses, but she didn't because she was afraid that would make her look too Hollywood, and for this meeting she had to look down-to-earth and sincere.

Flaherty was wearing a tailor-made shirt and an expensive tie and gray suit pants. The jacket was hung neatly on the back of his desk chair. He had a slim, boyish body, a fair complexion with freckles, and perfectly coiffed strawberry blond hair. There was no doubt the guy was great looking. Cee Cee knew that in television circles he was known as a cocksman and was sometimes referred to as 'The Red Fox.' Probably, Cee Cee thought, he had given that name to himself, then hired a press agent to pass it around. As she watched him chatting with Larry Gold, she remembered one night at a party at Jerry Weintraub's house when Flaherty had pulled her into the powder room and made a pass at her. He was the president of the network. The girl, as Larry Gold had called her, was Michelle Kleier, the executive vice-president of programming. She was bouncy and cute with short blond hair and big brown eyes, and she was very obviously pregnant. Her greeting to Cee Cee was a little warmer than Flaherty's, but there was a strain in her smile that made Cee Cee know this wasn't going to be a welcome home party.

The third henchman was Tim Weiss, vice-president of specials. He was young and handsome, with dark wavy hair and horn-rimmed glasses, and he looked as if he had just walked straight out of some magazine ad for men's cologne. Cee Cee remembered him from last summer, when he was the executive assigned to her special, as being wide-eyed and idealistic. This morning he looked at her with the helpless look people give to the mourners at funerals.

When everyone had greeted one another, Peter Flaherty announced to his secretary that he would stop taking phone calls, the door to the outer office was closed and everyone was seated, and then there was a long cold silence during which everyone looked at Cee Cee, making it obvious that she was the one who was supposed to talk first. She had made a big expensive mistake, and now they were waiting for her to explain why and to apologize humbly. All of their faces blurred in front of her, and she was sure she would never remember what it was she had rehearsed and then promised Larry she would say, but she started talking anyway, hoping it would come to her, and it did.

'Larry and I both thought it would be a good idea if I came in and told you why I walked out on the show. I'm sorry if it seemed irresponsible to you, and I understand why you'd be angry, but something very emotional happened to me and at the time I felt as if I had no choice but to do what I did.' Dumb, she thought to herself as she said it. I sound like a fourth-grader, apologizing for cutting school.

'Yes,' Peter Flaherty said, 'we heard there was a death in your family, and that kind of threw you for a while.'

'It was my best friend. She called me one day when I was in rehearsal for the show and said she needed to see me right away. So I rushed out and went up to Carmel, thinking I'd just stay the night and be back at rehearsal in the morning. But when I got there she told me she'd invited me because she wanted to let me know that she was dying and to say goodbye, and she wanted to do that in person in order to let me know she was okay about it.

'And she *was* okay. Brave and tough, with all her papers in order and ready to hit the road. Only the thing was that *I* wasn't okay about it because she was the first real friend I ever had in my life, and also the only really close one I ever had, and I wasn't ready to let her go. So I never stopped to figure out what it was going to cost anybody down here if I stayed with her until she died, because all of a sudden, all I could think about was that I couldn't let her be escorted out of this life by people who might do a good job of keeping her sickroom clean and getting her fed, but who had already written her off as dead when there was still enough life left in her that she could be enjoying.

'So I stayed. I didn't take the time to come down here and work out how and when to reschedule everything, because there wasn't any time to take, and I guess I knew if I called to discuss it with Larry or my business manager, Wayne, they'd try to convince me to come back, and I *couldn't* come back. Because, my plan was to escort her out laughing, since that was how she and I always handled everything bad in our lives. We laughed about them and made them okay. So when she was feeling low because she probably wouldn't make it till Christmas, I got a tree and we had Christmas in July, and I sent for her daughter and got her to come out from Florida and be with us, and we all sat out on the beach and laughed and argued and did dumb jokes about dying. We really enjoyed the time until finally my friend had nothing left ... and I had to let her go.'

That was the end of what she had to say, and the minute she spoke those last words, she knew there was something irreverent and wrong about making the speech in the first place. Because now she understood that what Larry Gold told her was true. These people would never understand in a lifetime how much it had meant to her to be able to spend those months with Bertie.

'Look, I apologize for screwing up the show by walking out, because when I finally took time to think about it I realized *that* part was wrong, very wrong, but I also know that staying with my friend in Carmel was right. The rightest thing I've ever done.'

The two men didn't react at all, and the woman lowered her eyes and looked down at the floor.

'And now I'm okay,' Cee Cee said, knowing it was a dirty lie, because she wasn't anywhere close to okay. She still woke up in the middle of the night feeling around for Bertie's medication, sometimes jumping up out of bed to go to her, and some nights getting as far as her own bedroom door before she realized where she was and that Bertie was dead. But she needed these people to think she was okay so they'd give her back her show, and then she *would* be. She'd take off the extra weight she'd put on while she was in Carmel, work any hours she had to. Do whatever it would take to get the old show happening again.

'I'm ready to go back to work. In fact I need to work. To do something that'll keep me busier than hell,' and while she was talking, hearing her own voice ring through the room, she could tell that though they might be listening they weren't really hearing her. She was looking now at Michelle and Tim, and out of the corner of her eye she saw Peter Flaherty push the edge of his cuff up surreptitiously to take a peek at his watch, and she wondered how much time he had allotted in his day for this meeting. How did somebody figure those things out? Amount of time it takes for out-of-line former big star to beg forgiveness. Two minutes? Five? Ten?

She was losing them. In fact they all looked so uncomfortable they probably couldn't wait for her to get out of there. This was a lot worse than the flop sweat she felt onstage when her jokes weren't working, because at least in those cases she knew she could rewrite the jokes and try them again the next night. But if these network people wouldn't put her on the air because she'd been trouble, they would tell everybody in the industry the reason why – that Cee Cee Bloom was a flake, difficult, unpredictable – and then she wouldn't be able to get work anywhere.

'Well, you're great to come in, Cee Cee,' Peter Flaherty said.

'You're great,' Michelle Kleier echoed.

'Great.' The word made Cee Cee cringe. It always reminded her of that character Warren Beatty played in *Shampoo*, the hairdresser who went from woman to woman telling each one of them, 'You're great, baby. Great.'

'Thank you,' Cee Cee said. She had to keep talking. Had to get Flaherty to say he would give her another chance.

'Please, take a shot with me,' she said, trying to catch his eye, because it always seemed as if he was looking just a little bit past her, as if that was a way he had learned to look at people to throw them off balance, and she was off balance all right, but still in there pitching. 'You know if you put this show on, I'm gonna bring in a big audience share. This is the first time I've done television in years. People will be tuning in left and right to see me. You'll make your money back. I'll even do the show for free.' That sounded like a valiant thing to say, and she meant it, but she heard an intake of air from Larry Gold as he moved forward in his chair, and she suspected if she looked at him he would make some gesture for her to shut up.

'It would be nice if we could resurrect something, Cee Cee,' Peter Flaherty said, his brow furrowed, 'because you know we've always believed in your talent, but frankly I'd have a hard time recommending it. Even with your promise, how could I ever be sure some other whim might not just take you off the set again, and that for some other reason which felt urgent to you at the moment you might not do the same thing again?'

Cee Cee sat back in her chair with an acidy ache in her stomach. A whim. Peter Fucking Flaherty didn't give a shit about what she'd lived through. Wouldn't give a shit if the story she had just told him had been about his own mother, and that made an anger rise in her like hot lava, so that she had to hold on to the arm of the chair to keep from getting up and walking out.

Okay, he was right she'd been irresponsible to leave the show the way she had, but to characterize it as a whim was cold and wrong. She thought about what Hal always said to her when they were on the road if she got upset by a bad audience or a rotten review, 'It's just a show. It ain't life and death.' Well, spending those months with Bertie *had* been life and death, not just another television show people forgot the day after it aired.

Flaherty's eyebrows were raised, and his lips were pursed together as if he was expecting an answer from her. 'I mean how would I know?' he repeated the question, like a teacher waiting for a student to respond.

Cee Cee's blood boiled, her face was hot, and she knew with a kind of drunken headiness that she was about to lose it and say what was on her mind. Later she would replay this scene in her mind and wonder how she'd let that rage take her over so completely at that moment to make her mouth shoot off at the president of the network.

'Maybe,' she answered, 'you could ask your psychic.'

Flaherty went pale. There was a split second when he seemed to be thinking about how to react, when it could have gone either way, maybe he would even take it as a joke, but then Cee Cee saw in his eyes the decision that there was no way he was going to accept this kind of abuse from some former superstar prima donna who should be sucking up to him and begging for her show back. Who in the hell did she think she was? Now he stood, signaling that the meeting was over.

'Thanks for stopping by,' he said, his jaw clenched, his eyes completely drained of expression. Then he walked to the door and opened it. His lieutenants stood too. Cee Cee couldn't look at Larry Gold, because she knew he was probably on the verge of a full-out stroke, that he would go apeshit over this, tell her what he always did, what Bertie always used to, that you didn't always have to say the first smart-ass thing that comes into your head . . . but she didn't care. These unfeeling schmucks would never know, never understand why she did what she did, and if that meant she was drummed out of the business, that would have to be the way it was. When she got to the doorway where Flaherty stood, she looked up at him, and said to his indifferent face, 'It's a good thing you've got *crystal* balls, honey, 'cause you sure don't have the other kind.' And she stormed out, with Larry Gold rushing down the hall of the network building after her.

All the way back out to her house in Malibu, neither of them said a word, and Cee Cee feared with a sick feeling that probably she had made a big mistake taking Nina out of that boarding school so fast. Up until now there had been a shred of hope that things could fall into some state of normalcy, but for certain now her life would be a rat's nest. She'd be traveling around, doing concerts, hoping for a good script with a breakout part to come along in a movie that could shoot God knows where.

She shuddered when she thought back to what the concert tours had always been like, and some of the animals she had had to deal with. Not to mention the scrungy hotels and horrible hours. That was a lifestyle she wouldn't wish on her worst enemy. Finally, when Larry Gold pulled up outside her house, he stopped the car and turned his small body in the seat so he could face her.

'You were wrong, Cee Cee. You should have been humble. What'd you *get* out of it? One second of making Flaherty uncomfortable versus getting your show back on the air.'

'They knew they weren't gonna do another show with me before we walked in there, Larry, believe me,' she said, getting out of the car. But the truth was he was right, and she knew it.

'What do you want me to do?' he called after her. She turned around and looked at his helpless expression. She had behaved like a dumb headstrong jackass who didn't know better, and if there had ever been a prayer to get the show back, she had blown it.

'Get me a job,' she answered, then turned and put her key in the front door, realizing how glad she was to be able to come home to Nina.

Hal's high-pitched singing voice was the first sound she heard as she pushed the door open. He was belting out some old silly song he had written about a frog prince, and Nina was singing along, laughing at all of the funny lyrics.

'Well, what'd they say?' Hal asked, stopping the music as Cee Cee walked in.

'Wait. I've gotta clean the rug burns off my knees from where I was down on them begging their forgiveness.'

'And?'

'And after that I succeeded in big-mouthing my way right out of the business.'

'How'd you do that?'

'Never mind how. I'm ruined, I'm cold potatoes, dead meat. They don't care why I left the show, and they'll probably see that I'll never work again. I'll be back playing the High Sign Café in North Hollywood. Remember that place, Harold? With the mice? And I can promise you they were not the ones from the cast of *Cinderella*. They didn't make me *one* dress. In fact, you may recall I stood on a chair most nights when I sang just to avoid coming face to face with the little rodents.' She turned to head for the kitchen. 'I'd better go call the real estate broker and put the house on the market.'

'Hey, Cee,' Hal said.

'Yeah?' She turned back.

'If I were you, I'd get off the cross. You'll probably need the wood for fuel.'

Cee Cee couldn't help but laugh. And when she did, Nina did too.

'Flaherty is one network. There are two others. There's cable, there's theater, there're other studios who would kill for you. You'll have a gig in no time,' Hal said.

'You think so?' Cee Cee's eyes tested his for the possibility of a lie.

'I do,' Hal said. 'And I don't say "I do" to just any girl.'

But no one was calling for her, the phone in the Malibu house was stubbornly quiet when they were at home, and the answering machine light didn't blink with waiting messages when she and Nina came home from their visits to the various schools. For weeks they'd tried to find just the right one, but they were getting more and more discouraged.

'Today we saw "the free to be me school," where they wore Spandex pants, streaks of green hair, and everything visible that was piercible contained a cubic zirconia.'

'They let the kids walk around looking like that?' Hal asked her.

'I haven't gotten to describing the kids yet. Those were the teachers. And did I mention the hoity-toity one where they asked if I'd like to build a gymnasium in memory of Nina's mother? Or the very regimented one where the headmaster asked if I believed corporal punishment was ever warranted, and when my answer was "Only during foreplay," he had me removed from his office. It's getting exhausting, Harold.'

The next school they looked at was Elmhurst. On the way, Nina asked again, 'Why can't I go to our neighborhood public school? My friend Kevin goes there and he –'

'Neen, listen carefully. Those other kids, the ones you're meeting on our road. Their homes aren't listed on "Maps to the Stars' Homes" that any kidnapper can buy on the corner of Sunset and Doheny for five bucks.'

'What does *that* have to do with school?'

'Your needs are special now, kiddo. Because as Cher once said to Sonny, "You've got me, babe."'

'That was way before my time,' Nina said. 'But I think what she really said was, "I've got you, babe."'

'Yeah? Well, what she meant was stuck is stuck.'

The physical plant of Elmhurst was shoddy, a group of ramshackle buildings sitting on a lot in Topanga Canyon that could hardly be called a campus, but the cheery mural of a playground painted by the children, which covered the side of one of the buildings, brightened up the look of the place. This morning Sandy Lowe, the director of the school, a tall heavy woman with long straight gray hair that she wore pushed back from her face with a plastic pink headband showed Cee Cee and Nina around the tiny campus, and she talked to both of them in the tone and cadence of somebody who spent most of her time with young children.

'Those are our little buddies, the mice and snakes and hamsters and rabbits, and Fred and Wilma over there are our baby rats. They're very tame and the children get to take them out of the cages to feed them and hold them,' she said as they stood in the makeshift science lab where Nina wandered over to the animal cages.

'No!' Cee Cee said, surprised. 'I spent years tryin' to get out of my old neighborhood so I wouldn't have to get anywhere *near* a rat. Now I've got to pay ten grand so my kid can hold one? You gotta be kidding.'

The director smiled, a very slight smile. Nina walked over by the far wall where there was a display of the children's work.

'The school is a family corporation. Many of our activities are completely parent run. The parents care for the school building, as well as sit on the board that governs the corporation. And the parents work regularly with their children on the various projects. For example, what Nina is looking at right now is a parent-student science project about weather. Precipitation. Why it snows. How to make it rain.'

'I know the answer to that!' Cee Cee said in a loud voice. 'I just go and get my car washed.' No reaction.

Dumb joke, Cee Cee thought. Dumb friggin' joke, just like when I was a kid. Make a joke to cover how stupid I really am. I was afraid the director was gonna ask me to tell her how rain actually does get made, and Nina would see how dumb I am because I don't know.

'Calm down, Cee Cee,' Nina said softly to her when they were a distance away from the director, following her back to the office. 'It's me who's trying to get into the school. Not you. This is the best one so far, so don't mess it up.'

'Why doesn't Nina stay with me for a little while so we can talk some more?' Sandy Lowe said, coming over and patting Cee Cee on the arm. 'And you can go over to the development office and talk with Barbara Gilbert. She's the head of the parent organization and she'll be able to tell you better than I can about what, if Nina is accepted at Elmhurst, they'll expect from you.'

'Great,' Cee Cee said. Nina walked away with Sandy Lowe, looking particularly tiny next to the tall wide woman, and Cee Cee thought before she turned away that the little girl had had a look on her face that said she was relieved to get away from her. She liked this place. So did Cee Cee. Settled. This was it. The school for her. Cee Cee's step felt lighter now.

The development office had two desks, both of which were piled high with papers. A small brown-haired woman with a blunt-cut bob that accentuated her large nose sat behind one of the desks, talking on the phone. She was holding a Diet Coke in her free hand, and when Cee Cee stood in the doorway, the woman tucked the phone under her chin and waved Cee Cee in with her now free hand.

Cee Cee took a seat in a chair on the other side of the desk, and after a while when the woman continued to talk on the phone, she felt awkward sitting there listening, so she opened her purse and rifled through it, just to have something to do. I'm so relieved we found the school for us, she thought. After she had yanked Nina out of that school in Santa Cruz, and would really get shit from Bertie's lawyers once they discovered she had, she'd better get the kid's education on the ball already. This school seemed to be the best choice so far.

Barbara Gilbert laughed a nervous laugh in response to the person on the phone then said, 'I have to hop, Katie. I have a parent interview. Talk to you later.'

A parent interview. Cee Cee sat up straighter. She thought she was stopping by to get some information and say hello but clearly this was an audition.

'I'm Barbara Gilbert.'

'I'm Cee Cee Bl –'

'Oh, believe me, I know who you are.'

'Well, Nina and I really like the school,' Cee Cee said.

'Isn't that nice?' Barbara Gilbert said. 'And you met Sandy Lowe? She's a love.' Cee Cee forced a smile. 'We couldn't survive without her. The kids love her, and she's so guileless and unthreatening and childlike herself.'

Oh brother, Cee Cee thought. I may not know how you make rain, but I've been around long enough to already know by the way she said that, that this broad has it in for the director and isn't too sure about me in the bargain.

'Cee Cee. How can I put this in a way that won't insult you?'

What did I tell you? Cee Cee said to herself. 'Gee,'

she said out loud, 'when you start like that, I can hardly wait to hear the rest. Insult away.' Barbara Gilbert laughed a shrill laugh. She was edgy and tense, as if she'd just had a lot of caffeine. More than you get in just one Diet Coke.

'I personally feel that you're not the kind of mother who will be happy in our parent program.'

Cee Cee felt weak. This didn't sound so hot. It was definitely a rejection. Not now, after all the schools they'd looked at, and finally they'd found this one, the one she thought felt right and Nina seemed to like too, this woman was saying no.

'How can you possibly know what kind of mother I am? I just walked in here. Not to mention the fact that I've only been a mother for less than a month to begin with, so *I* don't even know what kind of mother I am,' Cee Cee said, her anger all over her face.

'I mean you work, Cee Cee, and even though many of our mothers do, they work in jobs which give them the freedom to come here regularly and get deeply involved in our program, because that's what we require.'

'Well, at the moment I'm out of work,' Cee Cee said, in a voice she hoped didn't sound like it was begging. 'So I have tons of time, and besides I *want* to be involved. I'm interested in this school because I've looked at others and I knew that if Nina went to school here I'd have to take a few hours out of my week to be around as if I was . . .' She stopped herself from saying the words *a real mother*.

Barbara Gilbert had a little smile on her face, which looked more like a smirk. 'Let's be realistic,' she said. 'You're a famous star with a schedule I'm sure isn't going to leave you the kind of time Elmhurst demands from its families.' No, she was telling Cee Cee no.

Because Cee Cee wasn't the right type, they were going to reject Nina.

'Have you looked at Buena Vista?' she asked.

'We have,' Cee Cee said, and the sinking feeling in her stomach felt familiar. She was amazed that her hands were as clammy now as they had been in the network meeting the other day. 'And we didn't think it was right for us. It would be so good for Nina to come here,' she said, trying to keep her voice sounding even. 'I want to do this for her, because she needs to be in a place where there are a lot of family things going on. So she can see how real families operate and support one another. She never had a father, and her mother . . .'

'I *know* the story,' Barbara Gilbert said, cutting her off. 'I read it on your admissions application, not to mention in all the newspapers. But frankly, I don't think you have any idea what it is you'd be getting into. The families in our school run the school. And that means work. We have a mothers' committee that comes in twice a week and makes hot lunches. Certain mothers come in and straighten up every day. Every other Friday morning all the mothers and some of the fathers come in and we clean the building ourselves, we repair things that go wrong on our own, we do all the dirty work, if you will, and we do it ourselves.' Her face was tense with self-righteousness. 'We've had some families with working mothers who have asked if they could send their housekeepers in to do the work for them, but that is not allowed. It's missing the point of why we exist at all.'

'Yeah? So?' Cee Cee said, 'I understand, and Friday mornings are good for me. Hey, believe me, I can clean as good as anybody else. I wasn't born a star, you know. I grew up in the South Bronx in a sixth-floor walk-up. When my father's dry cleaning store was in trouble, I had to teach tap dancing to little kids so I could get my own lessons free. And after I practiced my tap on the linoleum kitchen floor, my mother used to make me scrub it with a toothbrush. Don't be prejudiced against me 'cause I'm famous. I swear I'll work ten times as hard as anybody.'

Barbara Gilbert looked down with a sigh. This was not what she wanted to hear. Clearly, she had hoped to scare Cee Cee off. Was sure that by now she'd be seeing her to the door, sorry she'd ever thought of putting the little girl in a co-op. When she looked Cee Cee in the eye now, it was with an expression which meant, Now I'm going to drive my point all the way home.

'Besides our group responsibilities, each family has to have a job. Cleaning the animal cages, scrubbing the floors, buying supplies in bulk, delivering them to the school and putting them away, fund-raising, organizing and refurbishing the library.' She rattled off the list with raised eyebrows then asked, 'Which job in those I listed do you think you would want to do?' as if it was a trick question.

Cee Cee's mind raced. She was afraid if she gave the wrong answer Barbara Gilbert would suddenly pull a lever that would release the floor beneath her feet and she'd find herself standing outside in the parking lot. 'How about fund-raising?' she tried. 'I've got lots of good ideas for that. I could maybe get donations from the studios, or how about after I do my next picture we could have a special premiere of it and charge a high ticket price and every cent could go to the school. I could probably help the school make some dough. So much, that maybe you could afford to hire a janitor!'

Barbara Gilbert looked up sharply.

'A joke,' Cee Cee said apologetically. Very apologetically. 'That was just a joke.'

Barbara Gilbert thought about it for a while, then Cee Cee saw the moment when it turned, saw in her face that she realized maybe the idea of having Cee Cee Bloom at the school might not be as terrible as she'd imagined. There was something to be said for the ability of someone like Cee Cee to help bring in some badly needed money.

'Look, I'll be frank with you,' she said, 'there are many schools in Los Angeles which cater to children of people in show business, allowing the students to go off on locations with their parents at any time and that sort of thing. We're not one of them. Also there's no doubt in my mind that you are not co-op material. But since you're so insistent and I feel very sorry about the child's situation, let me speak to the others and get back to you.'

Relief. Cee Cee wanted to pinch Barbara Gilbert's little birdlike face. She was right in a way. The old Cee Cee wouldn't have been co-op material. She was obsessed with her work, fixated on her career, had let too many important things fall by the wayside because of her work. But that was not who she was now, or at least who she wanted to be. She wanted to have her priorities in order, and Nina was at the top of her list. Now Barbara Gilbert pursed her lips and Cee Cee thought of Margaret Hamilton in *The Wizard of Oz* saying, 'I'll get you, dearie, and your little dog, too,' only instead she was saying, 'I'll let you know.'

'Maybe I won't send her to school,' Cee Cee said to Hal that night. 'Maybe I'll just keep her home and teach her everything I know.'

'That sounds great,' he said, 'but what's she going to do the *next* day?'

'Funny,' she said, poking him in the side as she sat down next to him on the piano bench.

'Why don't you just put her into the neighborhood public school?' he asked.

'Now you sound like her,' Cee Cee said. 'Because her life situation is special and she needs a special place. And I picked a co-op so I could be around her a lot and we could bond.'

'Yeah, right. I know that's the big word in child-raising these days. Bond. When I was growing up it's what everyone gave you as a gift for your bar mitzvah. When did *your* mother ever come to school?'

That was a funny thought. Cee Cee knew Leona only cared about her show business career, and didn't ever give a damn about what was going on with her in school. Once when she was a teenager, she and some other kids had cut school and gone into town to see a Vincent Price movie, and when she got home at dinner-time to eat with Leona because as usual Nathan was working late, Leona asked her, 'So what did you learn today?' Cee Cee, who knew her mother wasn't listening anyway, had answered, 'I learned that if you're gonna have your molecules teleported, you better make sure there's not a fly in the other booth, 'cause if there *is*, you're gonna come out looking very weird and so is the fly.' And without skipping a beat, Leona had said back, 'Well, isn't that interesting?' Then pushed a bowl filled with a mountain of buttered mashed pota-toes in front of Cee Cee, spooned half the mountain on Cee Cee's plate, and it wasn't the first time she got the message that her mother never listened to a word she said. No, she would never be that kind of parent. The co-op would be the perfect place for Nina and for her.

But days went by and Barbara Gilbert didn't return any of Cee Cee's many calls to her, and neither for that matter did Larry Gold, and every time Cee Cee called his office the secretary told her he was in a meeting or on the other line or in New York or still at lunch, and he wasn't rushing to call her back either. One day she got past his secretary and as far as his agent-in-training, Mel.

'Oh yeah. Hiya, Cee Cee. Listen, it's a zoo here, and Larry's been really snowed under, so is there something *I* can handle for you?'

You've got to be kidding, she thought. I'm not only getting the cold shoulder from this asshole, but now he's passing me down to the kindergarten? 'Yeah, there's something you can do. Tell my agent I want to know what's going on in my career.' I should hang up. I'm talking to a twelve-year-old here, she thought.

'Oh, hey. Not to worry. Because I know he's got a whole long list on you right here. And you're up for tons of stuff.'

'Like what?' The lying little cuff-snapping sack of shit.

'Let's see, let me look. Ummm . . .'

She felt belittled and stupid. Here she was, waiting like a hungry dog for some kid, fresh from the mail room, to throw her a bone.

'There's an offer out for you to do "Zone."'

Zone. A movie. An offer to do a movie. Real interesting. The title sounded as if it was science fiction.

'What's that?' she asked.

'A feminine hygiene product,' Mel said, and Cee Cee laughed out loud, but while she was laughing she realized he wasn't kidding. 'But I think Larry told them you don't do commercials. And then there's a possible *Love Boat*, and they want you to be a presenter at the Daytime Emmys, and there's a possible running part on *Dallas* . . . but I think they may be going a little younger.'

Without saying another word she hung up. At eight o'clock that night Larry Gold called her.

'Cee Cee . . . don't get crazy. The kid made a mistake,' he said after she had shouted at him so angrily it threw her into a coughing fit. 'He got mixed up. He's a young kid. He's Garry Marshall's nephew, so I gave him a break. He must have gotten you confused with Juliet Prowse and read you *her* list. Big deal. Believe me. You're not up for any commercials.'

'What *do* you have for me?' she asked.

'I'm working on it,' he told her. 'I'm working on it,' which in agent language means I hope you have some dough stashed away, because there isn't a job in sight. And she'd better go back to her list of schools because the bitch from Elmhurst wasn't exactly busting her ass to call her back either.

Ironically, for someone who couldn't get a job, she was still in the tabloids all the time – 'Who's the father of Cee Cee's love child?' 'Cee Cee begs judge, "Don't take my kid away"' – and the paparazzi continued to lurk everywhere she and Nina went. The nosy snooping sons-of-bitches snapped their cameras in her face and Nina's while they called out to Nina by name to try to get her to look at them. But within weeks Nina had learned how to affect the glazed-over look-right-through-them expression Cee Cee always assumed when she spotted them. Sometimes they would even be so brazen as to camp outside the gates to the Malibu Colony waiting for Cee Cee's car to emerge. And they always seemed to be waiting at the front door of a restaurant when Cee Cee, Nina, and sometimes Hal with them, made their exit. Finally one evening Cee Cee decided they should just stay in, and she ordered out for a pizza.

She didn't count on the photographer who stopped the pizza delivery boy before he turned the corner at Webb Way heading toward the Malibu Colony gates, and offered him fifty bucks to reveal where he was going and another hundred bucks to let the photographer stand in and deliver the pizza. And when the photographer with the pizza got into the house, acting deferential and delivery-boyish in a way he couldn't wait to describe to his colleagues, while the unknowing Cee Cee and Nina searched for cash to pay for the pizza in their purses on the hall table, he quietly took the opportunity to snap a few pictures of them in their pajamas with a tiny camera they didn't notice. Within a few days those pictures were all over the tabloids. The sleazoids.

The day Cee Cee stopped at the Colony Market to pick up a few groceries and spotted the issue of the *Enquirer*, she felt as if she'd been slapped, wanted to call an attorney and sue those lousy sneaky low-lifes, in fact she was about to pick up the phone and call her lawyer to see if there was anything they could do to avoid that kind of invasion of privacy when the phone rang. It was Barbara Gilbert.

'Cee Cee,' she said, 'I apologize for taking so long to get back to you but I had to present the idea of you and Nina to our board, and I'm so sorry to say, they don't feel your family will work in our school community. But thanks for thinking of us, and I wish you luck.'

Cee Cee put the phone down and went back to get her list of private schools. Nina was in the kitchen reading *Weekly Variety*.

'Boy, if this is the schedule of shows that are coming

86

on,' she said without looking up, 'I'd think they'd be begging you to come back and do yours.' Cee Cee had to hold in a snort of surprise at the attitude of expertise that accompanied the comment.

'Thanks,' she said moving nearer as Nina closed the paper because an item on the front page caught her eye. FLAHERTY EXITS WEB FOR INDIE PROD. Her eyes skimmed the column which was written to make it sound as if Peter Flaherty had chosen to resign from the network to become an independent producer, but probably, Cee Cee thought, the psychic scandal had finally caught up with him.

'Neen, they won't take us at Elmhurst . . . but I want you to know it's because of me . . . not because of you . . . so I think we should . . .'

'I don't care,' Nina said. 'I'm glad. I want to go to the public school.'

Cee Cee sighed and looked down at her list. She was not going to let an eight-year-old girl decide what was best for herself. She would continue the search until they found the right school and that was that. 'I'll call Crossroads tomorrow,' she said. Crossroads was another private school in Santa Monica.

'Oh, while you were at the market, Larry Gold called,' Nina remembered. 'It's important too. You're doing *The Tonight Show*.'

Cee Cee had a simultaneous surge of elation and terror.

'When?'

'This afternoon. He said somebody dropped out at the last minute and the talent coordinator wants to see you as soon as you can get there. Can I come and watch?'

'Of course,' Cee Cee said.

*

'Larry Gold's office.'

'It's Cee Cee Bloom for Larry.'

'Hold on.'

Larry Gold clicked on. Cee Cee heard the triumphant note in his voice. 'So, you told me to get you a job. I'm still working on it. In the meantime I got you an appearance on *The Tonight Show*. They're excited to have you.'

'Larry, how can I do *The Tonight Show* with no notice? I'm a wreck here. I haven't sung in months, I look like something the cat dragged in, I have nothing planned to talk about. I'll bomb out there. You know if you don't get big laughs, Johnny gets that bored look on his face and never wants you to come back. I can't even find a writer with this kind of notice.'

'Cee Cee, calm down. There's a hairdresser over there, a good makeup man. I'll drive you over, you'll pitch some ideas with the talent coordinator about what you want to talk about with Johnny. I just put down the phone with Hal, he's going to meet us there with a half a dozen or so songs you've sung a million times. You bring any music you like, and Doc is going to be there to rehearse the music with you. You're not going to bomb.'

'How do you know?'

'I know,' he answered. 'And if you do? You're no worse off than you were a few weeks ago.'

'You mean it isn't too late to say yes to the feminine hygiene commercial?' she asked, but Larry had clicked off.

There was an eerie, dreamlike state that went along with being on *The Tonight Show*. Maybe, Cee Cee thought, it was because the scene of Johnny Carson at his desk and the famous sofa with the hot seat next to

88

him was so familiar after seeing them on TV year after year, that suddenly when they were there, real and three-dimensional and it was *you* sitting next to Johnny in the seat usually occupied by Burt Reynolds or David Steinberg, it was like stepping into a familiar book and becoming part of the story. And it was the *real* you Johnny was talking to, whoever the hell *that* was. Not a character you were playing in a movie.

Or maybe the whole thing was so strange because it was loaded with pressure, since everybody knew that a shot on *The Tonight Show* was always seen by so many people, which meant that scoring could make a nobody into a star or revive a flagging career. So the urgency of having every second count must be just like it was for a batter who stepped up to the plate during the World Series. Cee Cee remembered reading articles about ballplayers who described the moment when the ball was hurtling toward them, as seeming to be slowed in time, when the ball looked huge to them as their expanded consciousness readied them to slam the home run. And it was with her adrenaline pumping and that same kind of altered perception of time during which she heard Johnny set her up for what she planned to say, loud and in quotation marks.

'We haven't seen you around for a long time. How've you been?' he asked, eyes twinkling, after the applause which followed her entrance.

'How have *I* been?' she asked, then held up two tabloid covers she had brought with her from home. Each of them had a full-page color picture of Cee Cee and Nina at home, candid photos of them in their pajamas. 'You'd have to live on Mars not to know how *I* am.'

There was a close-up shot of the pictures. 'That's you at home with your little girl,' Johnny said. 'How do they get pictures like that?' he asked, with his perfect timing.

'Well, in this case, I ordered a pizza and the delivery-man came and asked us, "What did you want on your pizza?" So we said, "Cheese" . . . and he took our picture.'

The audience laughed, and the glorious sound of the laughter sent a flush of triumph through Cee Cee.

'No!' Johnny said, in feigned disbelief, tapping his pencil. Cee Cee nodded.

'Some people get pepperoni with their pizza?' she told him. Beat. Beat. Beat. 'I get paparazzi.'

Another big laugh. Johnny laughed.

'Well, you *too*. Right?' Cee Cee asked him. 'I heard the photographers were hiding on the beach right outside your house in Malibu. In fact, if I'm not mistaken, all America drooled over the picture of the gorgeous creature sitting on the deck in a brief little bathing suit.' Johnny nodded, as Cee Cee added, 'And your *date* wasn't bad either.' Big laugh and then she turned to the audience and just as the laughter was beginning to ebb she asked, 'The old boy still looks pretty good, doesn't he?'

The audience applauded, Johnny pretended to blush, and the rest of the interview sailed along with laughs and approving nods from Johnny and it seemed as if only seconds had gone by and then he asked her to get up and sing. Singing would be the easy part. She'd been vocalizing all afternoon.

'This song is for Nina,' she told Johnny. 'She's in the audience.' Then she turned to the camera and said, 'For those of you who *don't* read the tabloids, her mother was my best friend and she died, and now I'm her guardian, and I'm sorry I lost my friend but I'm glad I have Nina.' The camera got a shot of Nina, dressed up for the occasion, grinning, while Cee Cee walked over to the piano where Hal sat waiting, and as Cee Cee perched on a stool he played the intro and she sang,

> You and me against the world
> Sometimes it feels like you and me against the world
> When all others turn their back and walk away
> You can count on me to stay . . .

It was a Paul Williams song Cee Cee had always loved, and the way things had been going it felt right to sing it to Nina.

> And for all the times we've cried
> I've always felt that God was on our side . . .

When the song was finished, the studio audience, especially Nina, applauded, and even Johnny wiped away what might have been a tear before he pointed the eraser end of his pencil at the camera and said, 'We'll be right back.'

That night when the show aired Cee Cee couldn't bring herself to watch it, and when no one called after it was over she told herself it was because it was too late at night. As she tried to fall asleep, the beats of everything she'd said earlier at the taping of the show played themselves over and over in her head. 'And your *date* wasn't bad either.' In the morning she woke up so early it was barely light and she slipped on a kimono and sat for a long quiet time in the window-seat of her room looking out at the people already on the beach. A man with white hair walked south along the water's edge with a big black dog splashing happily through the surf next to him, and jogging along in the other direction a hot-looking young hunk of a guy, his big chest wet with the effort of the run, his blue-and-white-striped shorts clinging to him. Cee Cee watched him all the way up the beach, thinking she couldn't even remember the last time she'd had a good hard man next to her, on top of her, wanting her.

Of course being at the beach seemed to magnify her lack of a lover because it was such a sexy, oily, half-naked, lusty place, and when the sun set, the balmy evenings seemed to scream for someone to love, hold, be with, and failing that, she laughed to herself, a nice hot little roll around in the sack. But there was no one. This morning she padded downstairs and made herself a pot of coffee in the kitchen which was silent, except for the crashing of the waves outside, then she sat down at the round oak breakfast table to look again at the list of remaining private schools.

What was she doing to this kid? If she didn't get her into a school soon, some truant officer or welfare person was going to come and put Cee Cee in bad-parent prison. No joke, she thought, since there would, in fact, be a hearing coming up about her guardianship and surely they would want to know not only all about Nina's education so far, but whether or not Cee Cee had a job.

Ass in gear, she thought. I've gotta get my ass in gear and find a school today. At eight o'clock she was on the phone to all the private schools left on her list. Some of them had no room in Nina's grade, some said they would be glad to interview the child and put her on a waiting list for next year. By ten o'clock she had found a few private schools on her list with available spots for Nina, so she made two appointments a day for the next three days at those, and then stood to go and tell Nina. She could hear by the laughter in her room that she was in there playing with one of her friends. God, she thought, aren't kids lucky, the way they can just meet another kid and say, 'Wanna play?' and two minutes later they were in business. Too bad that wasn't the way it worked with grown-ups.

'Hi, kids,' Cee Cee said, trying not to trip on all the toys on the floor of Nina's room.

'This is Kevin,' Nina said.

'Yeah, hiya, Kevin,' Cee Cee said, nodding in the boy's direction, then looked down at her list and proceeded to read off the names of the schools they were going to visit and the times of the visits.

'Cee Cee . . .' Nina said when she'd finished. 'I don't want to go to a private school.'

'I know you don't,' Cee Cee said, hoping they weren't going to end up in an argument in front of some kid who had come to play. 'But there's no choice so let's not go through it,' she said, trying to keep her voice even.

'I want to be a real person,' Nina said, her voice sounding suddenly adult. 'Kevin doesn't go to a special school for the same reason. We don't want to be weirdos,' Nina said, standing, and Kevin stood too, and now Cee Cee looked at him for what was really the first time.

His hands were knotted fists, and his arms were raised in a V, upward from his elbows. His head was tossed loosely back as if he needed to look at her from his lower eyes, since heavy and unmoving eyelids covered his upper eyes.

'Don't worry,' he said. 'You didn't have too much to drink. I *always* look like this. I have cerebral palsy.' And then he laughed, a kind of cackle of a laugh, and Nina smiled a big smile.

'He lives on the Old Road just down from here, and he told me his mother *fought* to be able to get him into the public school. She went into the office and hollered at people to let him stay there.'

Kevin wasn't easy to look at. He was only nine or ten, but the struggle he must have already lived was apparent in his wise gaze, and Cee Cee leaned against the bedpost of Nina's canopied bed for support. Dear God, she thought as she got the point loud and clear. If you're unusual, you long for sameness. To be part of the mainstream. The same way she had longed just to go to school and out for a cheeseburger with the other kids instead of going to dancing school to become a funny-faced tap-dancing outcast, the way this kid Kevin must long to be treated every day of his life and Nina too. Maybe, she thought, I have to let this one go.

'Let me think about it,' she said folding the paper with the private school names on it, and folding it again and again and one more time, then slipping it into the pocket of her kimono. Later that day she called Webster Elementary School, the public school in her neighborhood, to tell them that tomorrow she would bring Nina by to register.

'There's a to-die-for part in a picture at Universal,' Larry Gold told her a few days later.

'Thank God,' she said.

'But they want you to test for it.'

'Test for it? Come on.'

'Big people are testing. Not just you.'

'You mean a lot of people are being considered for the part besides me?'

'I mean you're on a list, Cee. I'm not gonna lie to you.'

'I'm doing a screen test? Like an unknown?'

'Teri Garr is testing. Madeline Kahn is testing.'

'So it's a second banana part.'

'Well it's the part of –'

'The friend. The star's zany but loyal friend. That's who those people play.'

'Yeah . . . but it's a major –'

'I'm not testing. I'm not testing against those people. I don't do good on tests. Every time the guy got into my car at the Department of Motor Vehicles, I forgot which was the gas and which was the brake, and I failed, even though before the guy opened the car door, I was Andy Granatelli. No tests.'

'Then how am I gonna get you a job?'

'Larry, that's why God made William Morris, so you guys could figure it out.'

'Cee?' It was her business manager, Wayne. 'Can you come in here next week so we can talk? I'd like to do a tax projection and I need to know what you have coming up so we can figure this out together.'

'I don't *know* what's coming up,' she said. 'It's a little slow for me right now.'

There was a silence and then he asked, 'Well, what are you going to do for money?'

'Don't I have any?' she asked.

'Not a whole hell of a lot,' he told her. 'With a monthly nut like you've got, I think you ought to be trying to get some steady work if you can, and failing that, start doing some guest shots, commercials. That kind of stuff ever occur to you?'

'Yeah, sure. It has, but –'

'It would probably make sense for you to take some work like that just to pull in some bucks until something big happens. You know what I'm saying?'

'Sure. Sure. I know.'

'Look, why don't we schedule a meeting for tomorrow or the next day and in the meantime you can sleep on it.'

Sleep on it. Whoever invented that catchy little phrase sure as hell didn't have her in mind. Every night for the last few weeks when she put her head on the pillow her brain moved from one fear to the next the way her car radio once moved from station to station because the SEEK button was broken. No money, no show, no man, too flaky, a kid to raise but how to do it, too fat, *The Love Boat*, too old, a commercial for feminine hygiene, sell the house, Juliet Prowse, and on *Dallas* they're going younger.

Nina had started school at Webster Elementary, and she loved it. Some nights Cee Cee would get out of bed and walk around the house, stopping outside of her room and looking in the open door at the peacefully sleeping child, and when she did she'd think, *I'll do a shot on the goddamned* Love Boat. *That's not too small for me. On any show, whatever it is. And when I get through they'll give me an Emmy for it, because I'll chew a hole right through the scenery.* But when she tried to reach Larry Gold to tell him that, Mel said he was in London for the next few weeks.

One night Hal and Nina were conspiring to cook dinner for Cee Cee, who had just come from a meeting with a producer who wanted her to be in his off-Broadway musical, but wanted her to invest money in it too, when the phone rang and Hal answered it.

'Cee,' he called. 'It's for you. Tim Weiss.'

Tim Weiss. It took Cee Cee a minute or two to figure out who that was. The guy at the network. The one who had worked for Peter Flaherty. Cute young guy.

'Cee Cee,' he said in a very warm voice, 'how are you?'

She felt suspicious. Why the call? 'I'm grand,' she said, no emotion in her own voice. 'And yourself?'

'Well, I'm great because – I don't know if you've heard – Flaherty's gone.'

'I've heard,' Cee Cee said.

'And I've been promoted.'

'Congratulations.'

'I'd like to get together with you, Cee Cee, and talk as soon as possible. Would you be willing to?'

To talk. Flaherty was gone. Maybe things could be turned around.

'Sure.'

'When?'

'What time is it?' she asked him.

'Five o'clock.'

'How's five thirty?'

She could hear Nina and Hal in the kitchen making Hal's mother's roast chicken recipe for dinner, while she sat on her chintz-flowered sofa across from Tim Weiss. He was very attractive looking and smelled of some lime aftershave she recognized as the same scent one of her long-ago lovers had worn but she wasn't sure which one, and his attitude was apologetic and kind.

'Cee Cee, I came here for two reasons. The first is to say that I understand from a very emotional and personal point of view about your leaving the show to be with your dying friend. A few years ago, my own friend was dying too, in Europe, but by the time I had the guts to tell Flaherty that I needed to take some time off so I could get to him, I had missed him, by an hour. I only wish I had had the last few months of his life to do what you did for and with your best friend.'

Cee Cee was stonefaced as Tim went on. 'I also

want you to know that I wish I'd been able to say what I just did in front of Flaherty at our meeting in his office, but frankly, I was afraid. He was volatile and irrational and I would have been fired on the spot. Now he's gone. I don't have his job, Michelle Kleier does, but she and I are very close, and I know she feels as I do that we want to give you a show.'

Cee Cee felt weak with relief and buzzing with joy. Every meeting she'd had with producers had come up dry, and even though there were a few products for which she agreed to do commercials, finally none of the clients wanted her.

'Not just a special, but a series if you'd do it. We'll work out the guarantees with Larry Gold, and your company can produce it. Both Michelle and I saw you a few weeks ago on *The Tonight Show*, and Michelle called me afterwards and said, "There's no one like her." And it's true. But you're so unorthodox it took us a while to sell the concept of a series to the powers that be. Now we've done it and we think we can pull it all together, and that's why I'm here.' He bit the inside of his lower lip now that his speech was over, and sat waiting for a reply.

'I'd want my accompanist Hal Lieberman to be my musical director,' she said quietly, not certain she had better put any belief in this turn of events.

'I know Hal and he's very gifted. I'm sure we can work that out.'

'And I have to have a schedule that's not so killing that I can't spend time with my kid.'

'I understand,' Tim said.

'I'll talk to Larry Gold tonight and we'll call you in the morning,' Cee Cee found the voice to say.

Tim nodded and she walked with him to the front door where she shook his hand. 'I'm sorry about your friend,' she said.

'And I'm sorry about yours,' he said, and when he left, she watched him through the sidelight windows of the front door as he got into his two-seater Mercedes convertible and drove away, then she walked into the kitchen. It was a mess. Garlic and onion and fresh spices and dirty pans and chopped breadcrumbs were everywhere. And then there were the sweet expectant faces of the apron-clad Hal and Nina looking at her.

'I've got good news,' she said. 'I got a job so we won't have to eat the dog.'

'We don't have a dog,' Nina said.

'Well, then, that means it's better news than I thought,' Cee Cee said.

'What kind of job?' Hal asked.

'Nothing much,' she told him, pulling an apron from a hook and tying it around her waist. 'Just my own show. It was a brief but satisfying retirement, but La Bloom is definitely back in la show business,' she said doing a little dance step of joy, carrying the dirty pans to the sink and turning on the hot water.

'Oh, and Harold,' she said as the steam rose around her. 'I forgot to mention that if you want one, you've got a new job too, as my musical director.'

'Ooh, I think I could put up with that,' Hal said. Then he walked over and opened the oven door to look proudly at the crisp, bubbly chicken, whose aroma filled the entire room.

'Now *that*,' he said, 'is what *I* call entertainment.'

March 1984

'Why doesn't somebody bring back the old-fashioned variety show?' That's been the question since we bid a fond adieu to our favorite ones like *Carol Burnett* and *The Smothers Brothers* and *Sonny and Cher*. But it seemed as if the versatile talent who could pull off the jokes, the songs, and the hosting of guests with the sophistication of the eighties didn't seem to be around. In her many years in the business, Cee Cee Bloom has starred on Broadway and in films, recorded hit singles and albums, has survived as many ups and downs as Wylie Coyote. So this year, when to the supreme delight of her fans, she picked up the variety show gauntlet, by not only starring in one of her very own but by producing it as well, all of us crossed our fingers and hoped for the best. Well, good news. Variety is once again the spice of life!

Cee Cee's talented, she's funny, you can't stop looking at her, and somehow, even though we've known her for so long, she's in a package which works for the eighties! In her first season she's done every funny turn imaginable, from Camille to Clarabel the Clown, and as if that wasn't enough, with her newly worked-out and very voluptuous body poured into a sequined dress, she sings so soulfully it can make you cry. In addition to which she has a roster of guests (Michael Jackson, Paul McCartney, Mister T) that would make any rival counterprogrammer shudder.

And as smashing and surprise-filled as the first several shows were, up-and-coming entries promise to be even more exciting (Bruce Springsteen's already on tape).

Isn't it good to know Cee Cee Bloom, who seems to have more lives than any cat we've ever heard of, is back on top again. And so, thank heaven, is variety!

The William Morris Agency
congratulates their client
CEE CEE BLOOM
on her Emmy nominations

Variety, Music, or Comedy Series –
THE CEE CEE BLOOM SHOW

Variety, Music, or Comedy Special –
*THE BEST OF
THE CEE CEE BLOOM SHOW*

Individual Performance –
Variety or Musical Program –
*CEE CEE BLOOM:
THE CEE CEE BLOOM SHOW*

Dear Aunt Neetie,

Cee Cee and I are living in Malibu in a house she told me she is busting her ass to keep. I go out on the beach on the weekends and play with Larry Hagman who is J.R. on *Dallas*. Remember when he got shot? Also I go to school. The first school I went to was in Santa Cruz but I heard Cee Cee tell the headmistress where she could put the five thousand dollars, and we came back here. The co-op school wouldn't take us because of Cee Cee being unacceptibel and now I'm in the school I wanted which is where my best friend goes who is crippled.

I have met lots of people who are famis, like Michael Jackson and also Richard Pryor who set himself on fire once while he was taking drugs, but he's okay now. It's pretty good to live with someone who has her own television show which I guess you know Cee Cee does now, because we get to go everyplace in limosines and the fan magazine guys can't see into the black windows and that's important because last year one of them got into our house and took pictures of us in our pajamas.

It's really lies what they print in those papers. Don Johnson and Cee Cee are not lovers and she did not go with Bruce Willis to Spago. Cee Cee told me those pictures are called paste-ups, a picture of her and one of Don Johnson, and the newspaper puts them together and makes it look like they are what she calls an item, only it's a lot of bull you-know-what. So far it's pretty much okay here, except for how much I miss my mom which is so much that some nights I dream she is alive and wake up crying because she's not.

Love, Nina

Michael Barron
c/o Barron, Malamud and Stern
1600 Golden Triangle Way
Pittsburgh, Pennsylvania 15213

Dear Michael,

  This is a very informal request from me to you just to ask if there might be a chance for you to spend even one hour with your daughter Nina. I will fly her to you anywhere in the world if you'll just say you'll meet her and say hello.

Thank you,
Cee Cee

Los Angeles, California

August 1990

From the back of a limousine parked at the airport curb, Cee Cee sat looking out of the black-tinted windows watching the people hurry in and out of the automatic doors. The couples, the families, the business types, some of them squinting hard when they looked at her car windows curiously, as if squinting would help them penetrate the one-way glass to see who was inside. When she saw Richie Charles emerge through the doors surrounded by his usual entourage of bodyguards, moving with that famous swagger of his toward his waiting limo, which was parked in front of hers, she threw her door open and called out to him.

'Richieee.' She hoped he would hear her over the bus that was pulling away with a smelly gray puff of exhaust. When Richie turned in her direction, he was wearing a patronizing look she'd seen him give to fans. His new late-night talk show was such a hit, the press was calling him 'the black Johnny Carson.' Now when he realized the person who had called out to him was Cee Cee, the stiff smile changed to his real one, and he moved toward her, his arms out to embrace her.

'Gimme one of them big titty hugs,' he said and pulled her close. He was lean and muscular and smelled of some exotic men's cologne. When she backed up to take a better look, she had to smile at the Armani suit and the sockless Italian loafers he now wore as a testament to his success.

'I wasn't sure if you'd make it,' she said.

'Get outta here. And miss this? Who are you talking

to? I've got to stop at my office and then I'll see you on over there.'

'Thank you, Richie. Thank you from the bottom of my heart,' Cee Cee said. Richie held her close again and she knew the façade had slipped and he was straining to hold back emotions he liked to pretend he didn't have. Dozens of airport passersby hurried along the sidewalk, and every now and then one of them, noticing suddenly who they were seeing there, stopped for a moment to gawk.

'Cee Cee,' Richie whispered into her hair after they'd been clinging on to one another for a long time, 'I just realized I'd better get out of here fast.'

'Why is that?' she asked, looking concerned.

'Because darlin' . . . you and I are standing in the White Zone.'

Cee Cee chuckled as Richie squeezed her hand and gave her his reassurance that he'd see her in a matter of hours, then fell easily into his waiting limousine, which pulled away from the curb and moved slowly into the Los Angeles day.

ATLANTIC CITY, NEW JERSEY

1985

'On the Boardwalk in Atlantic City, we will walk in a dream. On the boardwalk in Atlantic City, life will be peaches and cream.' Leona used to start singing that song the minute the bus pulled out of the Port Authority, and keep singing it all the way onto the Garden State Parkway until Cee Cee, who always felt sick on buses anyway, wanted to scream at her to stop. And if Leona's singing and the stinky odor of the bus fuel weren't bad enough, those Hebrew National salami sandwiches Leona always packed for the trip and unwrapped and devoured, and occasionally pushed into her daughter's face to offer her a bite, would eventually make Cee Cee green with nausea.

This time she was in Atlantic City to play Caesars Palace. Not exactly Carnegie Hall, but the money was great and after her business manager heard how high the offer was, he told her to grab it.

'You want me to take a nightclub act to Atlantic City? Now? When my show's a big hit? Wayne, it's my time off and I'm going to go sit on a beach somewhere.'

'Atlantic City *is* a beach somewhere. During the day when you're not onstage, you'll sit on it. Take the kid, she'll love it there.'

'No shot.'

'Cee Cee, you people in your business,' he began, and she knew he was about to launch into his voice-of-doom speech, 'you make a mistake when you live your lives and plan the rest of your lives based on how much you make in your best year. And the truth is, if you live like that even with a hit show, you'll run out of money.'

No matter how much money Cee Cee had, and she was never sure exactly how much that was, she always worried about it. She had never been able to forget the scenes from her childhood of Leona sitting over a dining-room table covered with bills every month, frantically trying to decide which ones she could get away with not paying for a little while longer, all the while muttering, 'The poorhouse. Pretty soon they'll be sending my mail to the poorhouse.'

And all those times in Wayne's office when Cee Cee sat across the desk from the furrowed-browed 'accountant who got lucky' as Hal called him and Wayne tried to explain why she had to incorporate and become a production company, or whatever the hell else he told her, like what he was going to do about her tax problems, she didn't understand a word of it. Sometimes he sounded as if he was talking to a two-year-old, and finally, still in the dark but wanting to end the dizzying confrontation with the sheets of numbers, she would say, 'Look, here's our deal, I'll *make* the money, you take care of it.'

Bertie used to tell her she was being infantile by evading the issue of her own finances and that an artist had to be a businesswoman too, and Cee Cee knew that was probably true. Because when you put your money into somebody else's hands, you ran a risk they could lose it or steal it or, as the song went, 'run Venezuela,' but she decided she'd take that chance instead of clogging up her brain with the problems.

'Cee Cee,' Wayne urged, and when he urged he always made it sound as if it was for her good and never his commission, 'do yourself a favor. For a lousy two weeks in New Jersey, you'll make a shitload of dough, and then if your television show gets canned, you'll have a cushion.' Mister Tact.

'My show is number three in the country. Why would it get canceled?' she asked, hearing the panic in her voice because she immediately suspected he knew something she didn't.

'Hey, no reason. I'm just saying that plenty of people in your position who started out as big stars died without a pot to piss in.'

'*There's* a happy thought.'

That night she had walked from room to room trying to decide how much of a comedown it would be when people in the business found out she was playing Atlantic City, the armpit by the sea. Why would she *do* that to herself? She didn't even like playing the place when she was a kid and she had no other choice. At the moment she was a big television star, and eventually she'd make movies again. Or maybe not. Maybe she'd die without a pot to piss in.

Probably it was hearing that her two allies at the network, Tim Weiss and Michelle Kleier, were both leaving their jobs that finally made her call Larry Gold and tell him she was willing to do the gig in Atlantic City. Michelle was leaving the network job because she was pregnant again and this time she didn't want to have to leave a baby and rush back to work, and Cee Cee hadn't heard anything about where Tim was planning to go, but he was definitely out of there, and he had been her strongest champion.

She could remember so many of the people at the networks and the studios whose names had reverberated through the show-business community at one point or another because of their power positions, and who were now nowhere to be seen or heard from again. The turnover was almost comical. And of course, the new people liked to come up with new projects of their own and not inherit shows from somebody else's regime. Cee Cee had known from the start how both Tim and Michelle fought to get her show on the air, then defensively changed the format, the time slot, the promotion techniques to keep it on top. And each time the show would do great and their belief in her would be lauded. But if neither of them were there, she wasn't sure what would happen.

The day after she talked with Larry she sat down at the kitchen table and on the long thin pad the house-keeper used to make shopping lists, she made a list of the best writers of special material and jokes, choreo-graphers and boy dancers, lighting and costume design-ers, and then started worrying again so she called Hal in New York. After two seasons as the musical director of her show, he had taken his original musical to a small theater off-Broadway. Now a move to Broadway was in the works, and he was up to his ears trying to make the show bigger to fit the bigger venue.

'I have to put an act together to take to Caesars Palace in Atlantic City,' she told him.

'Why? Who'd you murder?'

'Funny. But Wayne says the offer's too big to turn down. And there's always the threat my series may get canceled, so I may as well have an act ready to take on the road.'

Hal sighed. 'The timing couldn't be worse for me. I'm overwhelmed with work,' he told her in an apolo-getic voice, and she knew he didn't have a minute to spare to help her with some nightclub act.

'I understand,' she said.

'But I'll send you some ideas, and I'll call some people I think you can use, and come to think of it, I do have an idea or two in my trunk you may like.'

'Thank you, Harold,' she said gratefully. She was about to go on and tell him who she'd put on her own list to call when he said, 'Cee Cee?'

'Yeah?'

'I'll fly in for a couple of days and help get you started.'

Within ten days of Hal's arrival in Los Angeles, the act was complete. Between his contacts in the creative community and Cee Cee's, they put together a team of unbeatable talent, and rehearsals began. There were ballads and blues and soft shoe numbers and funky getdown rock numbers, and Cee Cee's tribute to the saucy sexy ladies, Belle Barth, Mae West, Totie Fields, was funny and original. The act was drop-dead great and showed a versatile Cee Cee no small screen production overseen by a Standards and Practices censor could ever possibly produce.

But even after the long flight from L.A. to Kennedy Airport and the limo ride from New York, she couldn't sleep at all. At first she thought it was because she was nervous about the opening tomorrow night. But that was impossible. She knew the act backward and inside out, to the point where every gag sounded like an ad-lib and every haughty toss of the head was a guaranteed laugh. No, the fact that the opening was hours away wasn't what had kept her awake. It was knowing that for the first time in almost thirty-five years, she was back in Atlantic City, New Jersey, and she was feeling an unexpected tug of sentimentality about the old days she'd spent here.

This was the place where all of it had started for her. Onstage at the Steel Pier in the Jerry Grey Kiddie Show, a show in which she had first appeared when she was five years old, and from which she had retired at age ten. And it was in those shows where suddenly she had felt her power as a performer and had known that if nothing else in the world ever worked for her, when she stood on a stage and sang a song, even in the light of a bare lightbulb, for that moment people loved her, or thought they did anyway, and for years that brand of love had almost made up for the fact that she wasn't pretty, and her mother was fat, and boys didn't exactly fall all over her. Atlantic City was where she had first met Bertie. Bertie who was already gone for two whole years. How could it be?

And just forty miles north of Atlantic City on Long Beach Island was the place where she had met and married the only husband she would probably ever have. John Perry. She had been nineteen and he was thirty-one, the owner of the theater where she was working. The one who had predicted the eventuality of the success she was having now. And one night, aching with a girlish crush on him, she'd gone to his house on the beach, wanting him, begging him to make love to her, and instead he told her she was fabulous and brilliant and how famous she would be some day, then patted her on the ass and sent her on her way.

Of course later that summer, almost as a vote of confidence in her future fame, he had asked her to marry him, swept her off her feet, managed her career until she started actually to approach the fame he'd predicted, and then he left her. Not because he didn't love her, but because he said he couldn't handle what he knew would become her superstardom. Told her one heartbreaking night, the memory of which still hurt, that he wanted a woman, needed a woman who would bask in *his* glory.

Now it was six-fifteen in the morning of her opening night at Caesars, and she knew she ought to turn over and try to catch at least a few hours of sleep or tonight on stage she'd be a dishrag, but she was too wide awake, thinking about the old days, and soon she was on her feet, padding around trying to find some sweat clothes to throw on so she could go out for a little walk on the boardwalk. Last night, by the time she and Nina had arrived it was late and they were both too tired from the trip to feel like going out to explore. They had ordered dinner to be sent up to the suite, and when Richie Charles called to say he had arrived that afternoon, they invited him to join them. Richie was in Atlantic City to be Cee Cee's opening act, and Nina had taken an immediate liking to the funny black man, who after dinner taught the kid three new card games before Cee Cee told them to break it up, and sent Nina to bed.

For a minute Cee Cee thought it might be a bad idea to let Nina and Richie become friends, because the comic's outrageous, X-rated, foulmouthed behavior was well known, but then she decided it was mostly the character he played onstage who was whacky and not so much the quiet, lonely, brilliant comic she had known for years as they both had worked their way up. Onstage Richie did a lot of jokes about using drugs and getting laid. He had even been reputed to drop his pants and 'moon' the audience, or unzip his fly, as the women in the audience shrieked and he did some material about 'the truth about black men.' But the offstage Richie was gentle and thoughtful and as child-like as Nina herself.

This morning as Cee Cee opened the door from her bedroom and stepped into the living room of the garish suite, she remembered that she didn't have to tiptoe out, because last night Nina and Richie had made a plan to wake up early, rent bikes, and go for a long ride on the boardwalk at sunrise, and Nina had probably met Richie in the lobby before six so that by now the two of them were well on their way.

The jangling sounds of the casino jarred the early-morning hum in Cee Cee's brain, and she passed through quickly, amazed as she'd always been in Las Vegas that even at this hour there were rows of white-haired ladies holding plastic cups filled with coins, and pulling at the slot machine handles. Some of them even sat on folding lawn chairs they'd brought from home and parked in front of a favorite slot machine. Now she was out the door onto the boardwalk, where she stopped for a long nostalgic time to breathe in the salty fishy smell and watch the sun coming up over the ocean and the waves rolling in to an empty beach.

For an instant she closed her eyes to take herself back, to pretend that no time had passed at all since the days she'd spent there as a kid, sure that she could still smell the unchanging carnival smell that must be wafting from Fralinger's Salt Water Taffy, down a few blocks, which someone in New York had promised her was one of the institutions still standing.

I can't believe I'm actually getting a thrill out of being in Atlantic City, New Jersey, she thought, and turned left because some vague memory told her it was in that direction where everything would be that she wanted to see. A group of bike riders moved breezily past her and set a flock of pigeons fluttering, and she was excited to be on the boardwalk, passing chintzy little souvenir shops crowded with schlocky merchandise, where she used to rush every summer just before she went back to the Bronx so that she could buy her father a tin ashtray. She remembered how painstaking the decision was over which ashtray it should be, and how she would carefully count out the change Leona had given her with the warning not to spend it on 'chazerai,' nothing junky or worthless, which was why she bought ashtrays, because they were useful.

The city's new look was disorienting to her. The marquees of the casinos jarred her, and in the store windows she noticed the featured T-shirts, which used to say on them FUTURE MISS AMERICA, now said I LOST MY ASS IN ATLANTIC CITY. There had always been a kind of low, carnival atmosphere about the place which she'd recognized even as a kid, but in those days it was a high camp, ricky-ticky kind of cheapness, now it felt tawdry and overdone. She started walking faster, knowing now exactly where she was going, and when she finally saw what used to be the Steel Pier in the distance jutting out into the water, she felt as if someone had kicked her.

Even from that distance she could see what was now a closed-up and deserted building surrounded by a wooden construction fence. The pilings were still up and a geodesic dome that must have once housed a theater or ballroom after Cee Cee's time stuck out over the water, but there was nothing left of the life of the place Cee Cee had once believed was the epitome of the entertainment world. With the star-filled stage shows. And elegant movie theaters, and the famous diving horses and the Auto Show, with all of the tall gorgeous show-room models standing on the revolving platforms next to blindingly shiny cars that looked as if they had just landed from outer space.

She continued to walk toward the remains of the pier, passing pizza parlors and submarine sandwich shops and frozen custard stands, but now she moved more slowly because the closer she came to it the more obvious it was how desolate the spot was where the dazzling showbusiness center had once stood. And probably, she decided, the closer she got the more painful it would be, so she stopped and for a while, with the squawcking of sea gulls over her head, she stood and looked over the railing above some steps leading to the beach.

It wasn't until she was about to turn and go back to the hotel that she looked down and realized with a warm feeling and misty eyes that she knew those steps as if she'd just walked down them yesterday, because it was beneath this very spot under the boardwalk where she'd been asleep in 1951 and a little girl's crying had awakened her. The little girl was Bertie, and that was when the two of them had their first conversation.

The memories of that morning bubbled up around her and she stayed holding on to the railing remembering it so vividly she could even see the bathing suit Bertie wore, and how she'd felt when she'd snuck away from the snoring Leona that morning to come down to the beach, where real kids went. Kids whose lives weren't devoted to show business, who didn't feel more worn out than a kid ever should from the late show she'd appeared in the night before. It was the way she always remembered feeling, because from the time she was five she was already living some grown-up show-business life. And that was why she'd been so wiped out that when she finally did get to the beach, she'd fallen asleep under the boardwalk, until Bertie's sobs woke her.

Of course the beach had been different then. Not littered with soda cans and newspapers and cigarette butts the way it was today. Now remembering how it was, superimposing a mental picture of those days on the empty beach, filled her with a glowing nostalgia as she walked slowly down, and stopped holding the bannister halfway to the bottom. In the distance near the shoreline she could see an old woman wearing a big straw hat and carrying something that looked like a Geiger counter, sweeping it across the beach, probably searching for lost coins. A cool morning breeze moved over her and she felt a chill she wasn't sure if she should attribute to that or to the fact that she was reliving a moment which, in retrospect, had changed her life.

Never in the five summers she had spent here working the kiddie shows, with all of the late-night performances, had she been awake early enough to see the beach as empty as it was now. In those days, by the time she had a chance to be outside, the sand was always covered with families playing ball and playing cards and buying ice cream from the wandering ice cream men who walked up and down shouting, 'Hey, ice cream! Getcher ice cream.' Cee Cee's favorite ice cream had always been Dixie Cups, which she dug at and ate with a little flat wooden spoon. Now she looked up at the white clouds looking like bubble bath against the blue sky and hoped Nina would like it here.

That little girl was getting better every day, Cee Cee thought to herself. Loosening up the way Cee Cee had hoped and prayed she would. She was ten now and filled with imagination and ideas. At school last semester she'd been the director of her class play, which was *Peter Pan*. She had long ago grown tired of Barbie dolls and was passionate about her dance classes, and told Cee Cee that someday she was going to marry Baryshnikov, and kept the autographed picture of him, which Cee Cee had been able to get her, framed over her bed.

They were close, and for Cee Cee who hadn't had a

real relationship with a man in years, and whose only real friend was gone forever, it was probably the closest relationship she was destined to have. Sometimes that thought made her feel depressed and empty, but most of the time she figured what the hell, having Nina and having her career was so much more than almost anyone else she knew had, she was infinitely blessed.

When she got to the bottom step and was about to duck under the boardwalk to her spot, she stopped short and her heart pounded, because there where she'd first laid eyes on Bertie, as cracks of the morning sun came through making stripes of light all around, slept a bearded scruffy man probably in his sixties. He was wearing an old, dirty plaid flannel shirt, and worn shoes, and lay on top of a sleeping bag, with a tattered backpack hooked onto his back.

Her first instinct was to turn and run up the steps, before the man woke up and pulled a gun from his bag and tried to rob her, or maybe unzipped his pants and tried to flash her. But the poor guy looked a little too old and weary to be dangerous, and maybe that was why she wasn't running, even moved a step closer for a second wanting to wake him and tell him this was her spot and that he was ruining what was supposed to be a sentimental moment. But she didn't wake him. Instead she pulled her wallet out of the pocket of her sweat pants, removed five one-hundred-dollar bills from her wad of spending money, walked over to the man and slid the bills into the pocket of his shirt, and walked back to the hotel to do a sound check for her opening night.

'Atlantic City, what a place! Every year a bevy of hopeful young beauties come here and parade in bathing suits and evening gowns displaying their looks and their talents, vying against one another to be the one chosen to serve. And *those* are just the hookers.' Gotta work on some better Miss America stuff.

Before Cee Cee's show every night Nina would have room service deliver her dinner to the suite at Caesars Palace. After the waiter left, she would take her plate of food out from underneath the silver cover, and her glass of milk out of the ice-filled holder, put them on the floor next to the sunken Jacuzzi, turn on the power, and modestly slip out of her robe at the same time she slid into the steaming water. Then she would eat her dinner with the water bubbling wildly around her.

'Now *that's* got to be bad for the digestion,' Cee Cee would always say, walking through the suite pushing the buttons to close all of the floor-to-ceiling drapes as she vocalized to get ready for her show.

During the day Nina would sit out by the pool ordering ginger ales, which she charged to Cee Cee's tab and sipped while she sat in the sun playing gin rummy for money with a former show girl named Donna who was now a change girl at Caesars.

In the late afternoon while Cee Cee had a massage or rehearsed or shopped, Nina would go with Richie Charles to Tivoli Pier, or to Margate City to see Lucy the Elephant, or take a ride in a rolling chair, or just sit on the beach with him and build sand castles. Some afternoons she lolled around in the air-conditioned suite on the big round bed, reading or talking long distance to Kevin back in Los Angeles. Kevin loved to be filled in on which shows Nina had seen, which stars she'd met when they stopped backstage to congratulate Cee Cee, and which dirty jokes she remembered from the various comics, jokes she wrote down and then read to him over the phone so he could explain them to her.

'A guy is sitting in a bar and a beautiful woman at the other end of the bar says to him . . . wait a second, I think I heard Cee Cee walk in . . . hold on, Kev,' she said, then put the phone down and ran to the bedroom door to peek into the living room and check.

'Nope, she's still at rehearsal. Where was I?'

'A beautiful woman at the other end of the bar says . . .' Kevin reminded her in his halting voice.

'Right . . . the beautiful woman at the bar says to the guy, "I will do anything you want, fulfill your wildest dreams, and all *you* have to do is be able to ask me for whatever it is you want in three words."'

Kevin giggled, a silly giggle on the other end of the phone. 'Yeah?' he said.

'So the guy looks at the woman and says, "Paint my house."' Nina paused, waiting for an explanation of why in the world that was funny.

'Tell you in two years why that's funny.'

'Hey, you're only twelve.'

'That's two years older than you.'

Kevin laughed for a long time, and when he finally stopped, she asked him, 'Well? Why is it funny?'

Kevin was still giggling. 'Because the woman thought the man was going to ask her to do something sexy.'

'Yes? *And?*'

'And he didn't.'

'So?'

'Neen, let's talk about this in a few years.'

'Paint my house. Paint my house. I don't get it. And I'm never telling you any more jokes.'

'Are you still hanging around with Richie Charles? I saw him on his comedy show on HBO. My God, he's raunchy.'

'He's my best friend here,' Nina said in a voice

serious enough to let Kevin know that to say anything negative about Richie would be a violation. 'Of course, Cee Cee won't let me watch his act. He opens for her and she doesn't let me leave the dressing room until she walks out to go on. She turns down the volume on the speaker so it doesn't pump into her dressing room, and I can't hear it. After *she* does *her* version of Mae West, how much worse could he be?'

'Worse.'

Every night she sat in Cee Cee's lavish dressing room, perched on a tall director's chair near the makeup table, telling Cee Cee all the events of her Atlantic City day. And when Richie came offstage and the stage manager knocked, Nina would hold Cee Cee's hand, feeling the sweatiness of her palms which never went away no matter how many times she did the show, and walk out to the wings with her. Then she would give Cee Cee a good-luck hug, smelling the thick pancake makeup and feeling Cee Cee trembling slightly with her pre-entrance jitters.

'Ladies and gentlemen, Cee Cee Bloooooooom!!!!!' And off Cee Cee went, doing her little strut of a walk as the crowd went wild, and Nina, who had seen the act so many times she knew it by heart, went back to sit in the dressing room with Richie, who was teaching her everything he knew about cards, which was considerable.

'Okay, now you got it? Never hit fifteen, seldom hit fourteen, think about hitting thirteen, and take a look at what the other players have before hitting twelve. If there are a lot of face cards, then *maybe* you hit twelve because then you think there's a good shot another face card isn't coming up.'

'Got it,' she said as he dealt.

'You sure?'

'Yes. It's about quick adding and figuring out all the possibilities fast,' she told him matter-of-factly.

'Are you a kid?' Richie asked squinting at her. 'Or are you actually a dwarf pretending to be a kid?' Now Nina had two cards and so did he.

'Hit me,' was her reply.

'I like Atlantic City. Some people say it's low class. But I don't notice that. Probably because I live in Los Angeles where *their* idea of culture is frozen yoghurt.'

The jokes. Cee Cee decided she'd better call Bernie Adelman in Los Angeles and ask him to do a little work on the jokes. Like the frozen yoghurt joke. That wasn't working so great because this audience didn't know what culture had to do with yoghurt. Or maybe even what yoghurt was. And maybe she ought to change the order of some of the songs. For the first few minutes after she made her last exit, Cee Cee's head would always spin while she tried to come down from the pounding adrenaline-high she had to produce every night in order to do her demanding act.

Covering every inch of that huge stage and never dropping her vivacious, outrageous character for sixty-three minutes was a killer, with only two brief breaks when she rushed into the wings to change costumes while the boy dancers did their interlude. Probably, she thought, this was what it was like to be an Olympic athlete.

Her body had to be stretched out and limber for the dancing, her voice had to be warmed up and loose for the singing, and the energy behind every move and every sound had to be bigger than anything she put out for films and television. Grand enough to fill the Circus Maximus so that each person who paid their money to see Cee Cee Bloom that night felt that she had been there just for them.

Once, years ago in New York, she had gone to see a matinee of *Mame*, and during the curtain call, Angela Lansbury had looked down into the front section where Cee Cee sat looking up at her with awe, and Angela Lansbury winked. In spite of all the sophistication Cee Cee had about the theater, she still remembered believing on her way home that day that Angela Lansbury had winked specifically at her, Cee Cee Bloom, and it was that kind of intimacy she now wanted to make every person in her audience remember when they went home from her show.

Wanted them to remember all of the jokes and songs, her 'Saucy Sassy Ladies' segment where she brought the house down in a clingy dress, singing as Mae West,

A guy what takes his time
I'll go for any time
I'm a fast movin' gal that likes 'em slow.
Got no use for fancy drivin'
Want to see a guy arrivin' in low.
I'd be satisfied
Electrified
You know
With a guy what takes his time.

And every night she fine-tuned the moments, never happy unless it all worked perfectly. Sure it was only Atlantic City, but if you were going to do it, you might as well goddamn do it right. Some performers came offstage and didn't want even to think about their work until it was time to go on again, but Cee Cee was already making mental notes during the encore and the curtain call, pushing herself to make her show its best.

The few minutes immediately after her final bow was usually the best time to do the postmortem, because everything was still fresh in her head. She stood sweating in the wings, wiping her face with a cool towel handed to her by her dresser, who placed another larger towel around her shoulders, and a big plastic Evian bottle in her hand, and Cee Cee caught her breath and drank the water, rerunning her performance in her head.

'Great show,' she told the dancers as they passed her with a sweaty grab of the hand or a pat while she waited for the band to finish their final notes, and for Artie Butler, her musical director and conductor, to come offstage, so they could rehash the show together. Where did it feel rushed? Slow? When did the audience seem restless? What needed to be cut? Added? Revamped?

So much had changed since Cee Cee's days of performing live. Now light cues were all computerized so there could be no making changes at the last second when it would be too late for the lighting designer to reprogram the timing. Cee Cee remembered wistfully those days of playing small clubs with Hal, and how she used to be able to stand offstage about to do her encore, and peek through the curtain, trying to psych out the mood of the audience by their faces, and to figure out if they'd prefer 'Knock Me a Kiss' or 'Guess Who I Saw Today.' A nod to Hal was all he used to need, and a nod from him was the cue to the lighting man who stood in the back.

'I notice that Atlantic City seems to draw a much older crowd than Vegas. I just saw a waitress ask a man who finished dinner at that table if she could take his plates, and the man handed her his teeth.'

Dumb. Dumb. It gets a laugh, but that joke always sounded to her like one that Milton Berle stole from Henny Youngman who borrowed it from Fat Jack Leonard. Tonight, as she and Artie talked, they walked toward several well-wishers who had found their way backstage to congratulate her. Every night of the run there was a group of people who had either come to the show from New York, or were working on the boardwalk themselves and were about to open in a few days. Tonight she gave a hug to Merv Griffin, remembering her first shots on his television talk show years before, and how kind he'd been to her when she was nervous, assuring her every time his show broke for a commercial, 'You're doing great.'

Behind Merv there were several other people Cee Cee didn't know, who had somehow managed to get backstage to meet her, and she shook their hands and said her thank-yous to their compliments and then was glad to see Steve Lawrence and Eydie Gorme waiting to say hello too. Steve and Eydie were opening next week. They were raving about Cee Cee's show, and when Cee Cee happened to look at the man who was waiting to talk to her standing behind Steve and Eydie, her heart stopped and she didn't hear another word Steve or Eydie said, because the man behind them was John Perry, her ex-husband, who was smiling now, knowing she had seen him.

Steve and Eydie's lips were moving and Cee Cee was nodding to them and saying an automatic 'thank you' every now and then, hoping they thought she was listening, because she couldn't be rude but, dear God, she prayed, let them hurry up and finish what they're saying and go. And finally they squeezed her hands and said goodbye and congratulations a few more times, and when they were gone she was standing in the cool darkness of backstage, face-to-face with the only real love she'd ever had in her life.

Neither of them spoke, and after a minute of sizing him up, still slim, no paunch, gray temples, hardly a wrinkle, eyes still as big and blue as ever, Cee Cee counted on her fingers behind her back, trying to figure out how old he had to be by now. Let's see. They were married in 1960, broke up in '70. Now it was what? 1985. So she hadn't even seen him in fifteen years, which meant that he was . . . had to be . . . holy shit, the man was fifty-six years old, and goddammit, did he look great.

'I know you,' she said to his smiling face.

'And I know you.'

'Boy, do you look good!' she said. His skin, the springy rosy way it looked, his big chest and muscular arms, and his wonderful brown curly hair, which now except for a little bit of gray in it was the same as she remembered. The son-of-a-bitch still had looks that could break your heart. And best of all was that expression on his face she knew so well, the one of abject appreciation when he took her in, his eyes seeming so grateful to look at her, as if no one else in the world existed and nothing else could distract him, as if a bomb could go off right next to him and he wouldn't notice because he was so rapt looking at her. How she had missed feeling the warmth of that look.

'And you, Cecilia, not only look great, but apparently are still tearing the world apart with your extraordinary talent.' There was a long silence as their eyes searched one another's, but Cee Cee broke it.

'So let's fuck,' she said. Then she howled with laughter at her own joke and he did too, and they fell into one another's arms, alternately holding one another tight for long warm hard hugs, then at arm's length to look at one another and rejoice, and then hug again.

'Where in the hell have you been? In Ohio, for Christ's sake? Who stays in Ohio all these years and doesn't surface once in a while and call a person?'

'Well, *I* was lucky,' he said. 'I had the distinct advantage of being able to see you whenever I felt the need. All I had to do was turn on the television or pick up a newspaper or a magazine or drive by a billboard.'

'Yeah. I do have a tendency to be rather high-profile, don't I?'

'You *are*, shall we say, visible.'

'J.P., I can't believe I'm actually looking at your face. I was always kind of figuring I'd just never see you again. I knew you got married. You wrote me that years ago. But I didn't know if you . . .'

He nodded. 'I've got three kids. Two boys and a girl. All in various stages of trying to be in show business. And they'll be envious as hell when I tell them I stopped in to see you. After me, they're your biggest fans.'

'Where *are* they?'

'In Ohio with Katie. Their mother. I'm here, believe it or not, on business.'

'What kind of business?'

Now he flushed, and for the first time she noticed a little sweat on his brow, even though there was a draft of air so cool in the wings where they were standing that it made Cee Cee need to pull the towel she wore tighter around her shoulders.

'It's nothing. It's silly. Look why don't you go and do whatever you're doing and I'll call you tomorrow if that's all right. Maybe we can get together and just talk?'

Tomorrow. How could she wait to talk to him until

tomorrow? She wanted to take his hand and drag him into her dressing room and have him fill her in on what he'd done every second since they'd been apart. And okay, maybe she did feel an urge to hold him close and see how it felt to kiss him again, touch him again, find out if he still had any feelings for her besides admiration for her stardom. Liar, she thought, you could drag him into bed this minute with the rush of feeling you're having. Crazy and wrong as she knew that was, she was afraid that was what she would do if it wasn't for . . . Nina. My God. Wait until John saw Nina. He would know the instant he saw her that she was Bertie's daughter. The first time he ever met Bertie she was sixteen. Not so many years older than Nina was now. Cee Cee remembered telling Nina about those days only recently.

'You never knew John Perry,' she had said, feeling melted the way she usually did when she thought about him. 'We split up long before you were born. I met him when I worked in his funny little theater in Beach Haven. He was someone out of this world. Your mother thought so too. She was an apprentice at the theater and I was a singer.'

'For a while my mother was in love with him too,' Nina had said, and hearing that truth come from her surprised Cee Cee.

'Did *she* tell you that?'

'My mother wasn't like you, Cee Cee. She never told me anything. But I didn't have to hear the words. It was just the way she always talked about meeting him when you two were young, and how handsome he was, and then she would say, "And all the girls were crazy for him," with this look in her eyes, and then she'd say, "But he married Cee Cee."'

'Funny,' Cee Cee had said, liking the story because

it made her sound so triumphant over every other woman in the world, until Nina added, 'I think she was trying to tell me that you don't have to be pretty for someone good to fall in love with you. To say that it's what's inside that counts. You know?'

'I *do* know,' Cee Cee had said, hurt with the kind of a wound she now understood a daughter could give to a mother under the guise of being matter-of-fact.

'How *is* Bertie?' John asked. He beamed as he waited for the answer.

'She's gone,' Cee Cee said, then saw right away that he hadn't understood what she meant by gone, because the smile was still on his face. 'I have her daughter because Bertie died. Two years ago.'

Cee Cee tried to identify what came into his eyes next. From the minute she had seen him watch Bertie walk across a room that summer in Beach Haven in 1960, before she'd admitted to Bertie or even to herself that she loved John Perry, Cee Cee had been afraid that it would be John and Bertie who would get together. Both of them were so beautiful, so confident, and part of some cool Christian world a person like her would never understand or be able to enter. And somewhere in a sick, niggling little place in her chest she'd always held the fear that it was only a matter of time before the two of them fell in love. She could still recall every detail of that night in 1960 at the Sunshine, the theater John once owned.

It was after the cast party for *Damn Yankees*, in which Cee Cee had starred as Lola. She and Bertie had taken a walk on the beach. There were tiki torches blazing everywhere, making the night seem romantic, and Cee Cee had felt confident and important and strong about her future as a performer. And as the two friends walked Cee Cee had searched her mind for a way to talk to Bertie about how much she loved John. To tell the only person in whom she had ever confided how much she wanted to make love to this man, and how she was living on the secret fantasy that someday he would be hers, and before she could get the words out, to her horror, Bertie confessed to her instead that only the night before John had taken her virginity.

After that, even when Bertie was far away and Cee Cee and John were married and Bertie was safely married to Michael, Cee Cee hated herself for wondering, every time Bertie asked about John in a letter, or John casually asked, 'When did you hear from Bert last?' if the two of them weren't secretly longing to be with one another.

'My God. I remember now reading that you'd become the guardian of a friend's child, but I had no idea it was Bertie's. What happened?' John asked. The look on his face was pure sorrow.

'She had ovarian cancer. She moved away from Florida where she had been raising Nina because she wanted to die alone in peace and quiet.'

'And?'

'And she made the mistake of calling me to say goodbye. So I flew up there and took over her care.'

'And God knows, that was certainly the end of the peace and quiet.'

They both grinned.

'You *do* know me, don't you?' she asked.

'Is the child okay?'

Cee Cee nodded. 'Considering the circumstances. And that she's stuck with me.'

'What's she like?'

'You'll meet her. She's like her mother, as raised by me.'

'Now *that's* a combination to be reckoned with.'

'You bet it is,' she said, putting her hand out and reaching for his. 'So come along and start reckoning.'

'You want me to meet her now?'

'Unless you can't. Unless there's someone waiting for you?' Please let there be nobody waiting for him, she thought and almost let out a whoop of joy when he gave her his hand. And the instant she felt its familiarity, she was flooded with a series of flashbacks of their years together. Years of deep love and great fun and very hot sex. The bad part had been the way he had taken over her life where Leona had left off. Pushing her to achieve and then standing back and taking the credit when she did. Living through her success, and on the one hand loving it because it took them to a height and a lifestyle he might never have had without Cee Cee, and on the other hand resenting it mightily because he was completely dependent on her for that high.

For Leona it had been okay, because she had no talent of her own and had always known it would take Cee Cee to get her anywhere. But John had aspirations for himself and a male ego she had tiptoed around for years, stopping herself a million times from telling him his ideas for her were too small, clichéd, wrong. Instead she had tried desperately to please him, to make his ideas work for her, terrified if he ever knew how little she really needed him professionally, he would lose interest in her personally, sexually, completely. And finally, after ten years of his being told, 'Hey, buddy, would you get outta the way,' when he stood in the wings, and after signing endless bar tabs and credit-card slips and hotel charges 'John Perry for Cee Cee Bloom,' he sat depressed and hurt in a dark Miami Beach hotel room one night smoking a cigarette, and told her what she knew he would have to say to her sooner or later which was, 'I want a woman who will bask in *my* glory.'

'You breathe all the air in the room,' Bertie used to tell her. 'And there's no more left for anybody else.' It was funny when Bertie had said it. And it had always been all right with Bertie for Cee Cee to be the one with the big hungry ego. Bertie was content to play the part of the fan. But J.P.'s frail ego had doomed the continued success of their marriage.

When they walked into the dressing room, Nina and Richie were each staring at their respective hands of cards. Nina picked one up from the pile on the table then shrieked a winner's shriek.

'I cleaned you out,' she said giddily, then jumped to her feet and did a little dance.

'The kid's a mechanic,' Richie said, 'I never saw anybody that lucky in my life. I'm taking you out to the casino and getting you a job as a dealer.'

The two of them were oblivious to Cee Cee and John in the doorway.

'Hahhh!' Nina hollered. 'Pay up, pay up.' Then she looked over and said a casual 'hi' to Cee Cee, who introduced John Perry, but there was no recognition from Nina at the name, she just nodded an uninterested hello, then gathered up the cards and shuffled as John watched appreciatively, smiling at the characteristics he immediately recognized in her.

'Looks just like the Bert I remember,' he said.

Hearing that made Nina look up at Cee Cee. 'You mean this is John Perry, your ex-husband?' she asked surprised.

'One and the same.'

Richie looked at John now for the first time too.

'Wow, this is an honor,' John said, reaching to shake Richie's hand.

'John Perry, this is Richie Charles . . .'

But before Cee Cee finished John was already going on about the HBO special of Richie's he had seen a few weeks earlier, remembering some of Richie's jokes and talking about them with a fan's wide-eyed admiration while Richie smiled a half smile, which looked more to Cee Cee as if he was baring his teeth. It was an expression she knew Richie gave to strangers he didn't trust. Silly, she thought. It's just harmless old J.P. And starry-eyed at that over meeting Richie. How the worm turns, she thought, remembering the way she had idolized John the year they met, trying to act as if she had it all under control when all along she could barely sleep at nights for fantasizing about him. And now here he was, looking kind of down at the heels and acting like some fan who just fell off the turnip truck. She could even see an expression on Nina's face as she looked at him as if she was wondering what the big deal had been about this guy.

'I owe you two bucks,' Richie said to Nina. 'I taught you too good.'

'Well now, how's this for an idea? What if I get room service to bring some food up to the suite and we have a little party?' Cee Cee asked.

'Not for me.' Richie stood. 'I'm gonna turn in and lick my wounds after the beating I just took from the hustler over there. Nice to meet you,' he tossed over his shoulder to John as he left.

'I'm tired too,' Nina said, following Richie, 'and I already ate. Goodnight,' she said and was out the door.

'She's gorgeous,' John said, looking after her, and Cee Cee was glad when she felt a surge of pride instead of jealousy.

'I'll change,' she said, and after she took her clothes

down from a hanger in the big mirrored walk-in closet, she stayed in there to change out of the dress she'd worn onstage, thinking it was oddly modest of her since this was someone who had seen her naked every day for more than ten years. But this was a different naked body, she thought, looking down at herself. The aging version, and she didn't want him to look at it and compare it to the way he remembered her. Stop, she thought. Don't get all hot and bothered about this visit. He's married. He's here on business. She emerged wearing a black sweater and black pants, holding her stomach in, trying to decide if she should remove the elaborate stage makeup and risk him seeing the comparison to her own pale skin.

'You've never looked better to me,' he said, and there was that look on his face again. Maybe she'd leave the makeup on.

'It's the first time in my life I can eat anything I want, because I probably sweat off five pounds a night out there,' she said, wondering if she should take him upstairs to the suite and order some champagne. No, that would be seductive and she didn't want to do that. Somewhere in Ohio this man had a family waiting for him to come home. Too bad, she thought, then wondered to herself if maybe fucking your ex-husband shouldn't count as cheating. After all, she'd already done it with him so many times in this lifetime, how could a few more hurt?

'Your act is wonderful,' he said. 'You're better than you've ever been.'

'For an old broad,' she joked.

'Not old to me,' he said.

'True. But then, you *are* a senior citizen.'

'Don't knock it. We're an interesting group. We've lived. We've loved. What's the song from *The Boy Friend* about artists?'

Cee Cee thought, then laughed when she remembered the song and sang, '"The modern painters of today may paint their pictures faster. But when it comes to making love, you can't beat an old master."'

'Precisely,' he said.

A seduction. Was this a seduction? Boy, it felt good. Stop, stop. He's married, she thought, but she couldn't stop the fantasies that danced in her head, and the rush of physical memories her body had of his. He had been one hell of a lover. Of course, at that time in her life she knew no comparison.

'How's your father?' he asked.

'He's okay, just okay. Sick enough lately to have to go back to a nursing home where he sits and grumbles about everything.' Again they looked long at one another.

'I've never stopped loving you,' he said all of a sudden, and those were exactly the words she'd been thinking about him just before he said them, but she was afraid to say them back to him, couldn't say them back to him. He was married. Married.

'My marriage to Kate is over,' he said, as if he'd just been reading her mind.

She tried to see if there was any flicker on his face that might let her know whether or not that was a lie.

'Who asked you?' she said afraid now and turned away to busy herself, packing up a little cosmetics case she carried between the dressing room and her suite upstairs every evening, John's last statement resonating inside her, making her heart beat faster and her face feel hot. What if what he had just said was true and the reason he had come here was not business but to test his feelings for her. To see if now that they both had changed and grown he would finally be capable of handling her success.

'Nobody asked me,' he said gently, 'I was just confiding in an old friend. Maybe just looking for a shoulder to cry on.'

'I'm sorry to hear it's not working out,' she said, but it was a lie. She continued to pack her makeup, but she was rattled now and dropped two of her makeup brushes to the floor, stooped to pick them up. One of them rolled away and after she grabbed to retrieve it, she was about to stand when she felt him close behind her, and as she stood slowly he moved tight against her, and she could feel his hardness pushing against her back and his arms go around her.

'I knew the minute I saw you how much I still love you, Cee Cee,' he said.

When she looked straight ahead she could see the two of them in her giant makeup mirror, and it was an odd picture. Her stage made-up face, grotesque with huge eyes and the thick false lashes it was necessary for her to wear in order for her eyes to be seen from the back of the massive showroom. And in those eyes the confusion she felt having him there behind her, wanting her, saying the things he was saying.

Now he was nuzzling her neck, her ears, her shoulders, calling up sensations she never thought she'd have again.

'J.P.' She turned to face him, and he took her face in his hands, but before he could kiss her she pulled away.

'John, listen to me. I'm not just me now. I'm a family. With that little girl, and believe me when I tell you that both of us have been through the wringer.'

'Cee Cee . . .'

'Wait. I'm just telling you, I'm standing here looking at you, and what I see is not just some guy who happens to look good, although you sure as hell do look divine. But I see my husband, okay? Yeah, my ex-husband, but it doesn't feel that way. It feels to me like "Oh, here's John who went on a little vacation and now he's back."'

'Well, maybe you're right about that.'

'No, I'm not right about that. You married someone else. You must have loved her. You created children with her, children you raised and loved and who would be sick if they thought their father was in Atlantic City right now making a grab for his ex-wife, even if they are my fans. Believe me, J.P., my body remembers everything about yours. I mean, I look at you and I can hardly stand up for wanting to climb all over you and fuck your socks off.' He laughed a little burst of a laugh, but Cee Cee's face was serious. 'Trust me, in the last two minutes I've already gone so far as to figure out if it would be hotter to do it on the sofa or on the cold tile floor. But as sure as I'm standing here, I know if you come back to me now or next year or when we're too old to remember how to do it, it's got to be after you straighten out your other life first. Go home. Work it out with Kate. Sit down and talk to your kids. And if you're going to get out of Ohio, get out for reasons that are about you, not about me. Because if you don't, after all the shit I've already put that kid through, you can bet I won't let you touch me with a ten-foot pole.'

There was no sound in the chilly dressing room until he joked, with a half smile, 'So you *do* remember everything about my body.' That made her laugh.

'Tell me about the business you have in New Jersey,' she said.

'It's silly,' he told her. 'I mean maybe it's really silly. Though part of me loves the idea. The Sunshine Theater is for sale again. It's been through several owners since I gave it up, and the current owner tracked me down to see if I was interested in owning it again. I still know enough people on Long Beach Island who might back me, and I've got some dough of my own I could put in from the sale of the theater I owned in Steubenville. I've been teaching since then, and directing Shakespeare in Chagrin Park in the summers. So I'd just do my summers in Beach Haven instead, the way I did years ago.'

'You were so good at it,' Cee Cee said, feeling herself falling into the familiar old position of massaging his ego.

'Want to be my backer?' he asked, but she was sure he was joking. 'I'll change the name and call it the Cee Cee Bloom Playhouse. Kind of like the Helen Hayes Theater.'

'Thanks anyway,' she said.

'Cee Cee, you're right about me straightening out my life first. You should know though that Kate had a four-year love affair with, of all people, our pediatrician, and we almost broke up over that but –'

'No, I shouldn't know that,' Cee Cee said, shaking her head. But it was information which made her feel a little less guilty for wanting to drag this married man inside the mirrored closet and watch on every side while she peeled away all of his clothing and then worked on him until he exploded. Drive him crazy the way she had during all the years they were together.

'Go home,' she said, 'and let me know how it all works out.'

He gave her a pained smile and hugged her. Then he left, and she wondered as she listened to the sound of him walking to the stage door, opening it, and leaving, if she'd ever hear from him again.

★

The first weeks after their return from Atlantic City were the calmest Nina could ever remember since she'd come to live in Cee Cee's world. At first she thought it was just the comparison of their peaceful Malibu house to the chaos in the hotel in Atlantic City, which had been filled with the constant undercurrent of room service, maid service, laundry service, and the casual way the people from Cee Cee's show felt free after a light knock on the door to wander in and out. Or maybe the calm was the result of Cee Cee's seeming more sure of herself. As if being able to put together an act, and then get the offer of a mammoth five-year contract from Caesars Palace, had given her confidence in her continuing ability to survive no matter what happened to her television show.

But more probably the calm could be attributed to the fact that John was calling every day from Ohio, keeping her up on the progress he was making in straightening out the end of his marriage, making plans with his children, and peace with the wife he was leaving in order to move to Los Angeles. He had already managed, he told Cee Cee and she lightly mentioned to Nina, to find himself a job in L.A., through an old summer stock friend who had become a movie producer. John would be the producer's development executive, which meant he would read scripts that had been submitted to the producer, and then advise the producer as to which of the scripts could be turned into a film that would make a lot of money.

John admitted to Cee Cee that he didn't have a clue what it was that made one film more commercial than another, but he had read William Goldman's book *Adventures in the Screen Trade*, which said that the thing to remember about the movie business was that 'nobody knows anything,' so he figured it might as well be him making money from not knowing anything as anybody else.

'Are you having R.J. Wagner–Natalie Wood fantasies about your ex?' Hal asked Cee Cee. He stopped by to watch her show shooting one afternoon while he was in Los Angeles for negotiations with Universal Studios because they were trying to buy the film rights to *Penny Candy*, his second Broadway musical.

'You mean do I think I'll marry him again?'

'Forget I asked. There's a funny little look in your eyes that tells me you've entertained the thought more than six or seven hundred times.'

'Harold, I don't know what the fuck's going on,' she said, while a makeup lady with a sponge was dabbing more concealer under her eyes. 'Look up, Cee Cee,' the makeup lady said, and Cee Cee tipped her head up a little and kept talking. 'He's available. Lonely even, thinks he wants to be with me, seems to have changed, and now he's coming out here to see if he can find happiness in Tinsel Town. So how do I know what'll happen? I'm a shell-shocked, gun-shy, beaten-up broad who's so short on trust that even when the talking scale in my bathroom tells me how much I weigh every morning, I say, "Bullshit." So who am *I* to tell you how I feel?'

Within weeks John arrived and was living at the Sunset Marquis Hotel. He looked more professorial than Hollywood, Nina thought, wearing corduroy pants no matter how hot the day and a sweater vest over a shirt, and a brown tweed blazer, that same brown tweed blazer he wore so often Nina joked to Cee Cee that pretty soon it might crawl off him and walk on its own to the cleaners. He would show up a few nights a week for dinner, and sit at the kitchen table with them, telling them funny stories about his adventures in show business.

Cee Cee acted relaxed with him, wearing no makeup and her hair in that funny way it looked after she took off the wigs she wore on her show, or pulled out the hairpins and just let it fly everywhere, and the three of them would eat and talk and most of all laugh at the stories, which came with John's fresh point of view about the Hollywood whackos and their habits. About the crazy producer who invited him to the racetrack, where John watched the guy lose fifty thousand dollars on one race. The friend of the producer John worked for who had a portable bathroom in the back of his Mercedes limousine. 'Hello? Yes this is his car phone, but he can't talk to you now. He's in his car men's room,' John said. Nina was starting to like him, even starting to understand what it was about him that made both Cee Cee and her mother think he was attractive. And she also liked that he called his children in Ohio every day. Sometimes she overheard him say things like, 'I love you too, and can't wait to have you come here to be with me.'

> When you do find a man with whom you develop a deep relationship that is leading toward marriage, you will discover that your children will have mixed feelings toward your husband-to-be. Your children will want a father surrogate in their lives, but on the other hand, they have had you to themselves and will be hesitant to give that up.

After Cee Cee read that in one of her books, she tried to include Nina as much as she possibly could so the kid wouldn't feel left out.

One night she brought out a pile of very old photographs she had found. One was taken on the day she and John were married. Cee Cee was wearing the weirdest white dress, and looking really goo-goo-eyed.

And while they looked at it they argued for ten minutes about who had taken the picture, the judge or one of those bizarre witnesses they had dragged in off the street because having the wedding had been such a last-minute decision they hadn't invited anyone. One of the pictures was inside a little red plastic viewer that Nina put against her eye and held up to the light to see. It was taken at the pool of some hotel in Miami Beach, and in it both Cee Cee and John wore annoyed expressions as if they weren't too happy that the picture was being taken at all. 'That was the week we broke up,' Cee Cee remembered to John, and then told Nina. 'And the week your mother and I made up after a long fight we had.'

'About what?' Nina asked her.

Cee Cee took another turn looking at the picture in the viewer. 'I don't remember,' she said.

Nina's favorite picture was one she'd seen before, which John looked at now. It was of Cee Cee and John and Bertie in Hawaii. Cee Cee was so skinny it was amazing, and they all looked so happy and young. John shook his head the way people do when they're about to say, 'Where does the time go?' But he didn't say that, he just looked at Cee Cee and said, 'You haven't changed a bit.' And she said, 'Neither have you. You're still as full of shit as you always were,' and gave him a little punch on the arm.

It felt good to be so comfortable with a man, and the odd part was that she wasn't sleeping with him. Particularly odd since everything below her waist fluttered every time he walked into the room. But for once in her life, instead of being led by the underpants she was trying to behave like a grown woman, to reserve judgment, to see what happened.

The first thing that happened was that John's producer friend was offered a power job at an agency, which he took, so he no longer needed John, which meant that John was out looking for a job every day. Cee Cee called some of her friends at the studios, who said they would look out for something for him, and she asked Larry Gold to try to get some producers he knew to try to find something for John, but after some time passed and he couldn't find any job at all and didn't even have a job interview in sight, he started hanging around at the studio on Fridays when Cee Cee's show was taping.

Nobody seemed to mind him being at the tapings, everyone was friendly to him. He chatted with all of the people on the staff of the show. Sometimes after they'd repeated the same sketch again and again, and he was tired of watching it, he would walk down and sit in the commissary to have a cup of coffee and read the trade papers, and soon people who ate there regularly knew him by name and knew that he had something to do with Cee Cee, probably he was her boy friend. Seemed like a decent guy.

Then he started coming to the rehearsals during the week too, sitting in the back on a folding chair with a little spiral notebook in which every now and then he'd scratch some notes. Later, when Cee Cee was taking a break, he'd come into the dressing room and when everyone was gone but the two of them, he would take out the spiral notebook and say things to her like, 'You know that spot in the hospital sketch where you're the doctor giving the patient the reflex test? Well whoever that day player is, he's mugging so much it upstages everything you're doing.'

'He's not a day player. He's part of the company of people who do the sketches with me.'

'Well, the director is doing you a major disservice if he keeps letting him get away with that behind you.'

'I'll look into it,' she said. There were more notes like that. They were good notes. Good for Cee Cee, from someone who seemed to care more about her than about the general welfare of the show. It was much more personal care than she'd ever had from Larry Gold. And it felt familiar, because it was the way John had advised her when she was a young struggling singer, and the way Leona had focused on her, from the phrasing of each line she sang to the color of the mascara she wore. But she liked it for another reason too. Because John was telling it to her like it really was and, with very few exceptions, she was already up to her ears in yes-men. People who always said, 'You were brilliant, Cee Cee,' even when she knew she wasn't.

'That sketch is completely tasteless,' John would tell her after watching the rehearsal. 'Beneath you and the show. Don't do it.'

'Are you sure?'

'Think about what it says. Is that the kind of statement you want to make?'

This man directs Shakespeare, she would think. He must have class. I do hooker jokes. What do *I* know? 'I'll have them cut it,' she would say after reading it again through newly educated eyes, and go out to face the producer and the head writer to tell them to cut the sketch, knowing they would exchange looks and tell her she was being difficult, but she didn't care what they did. John was right, and she was starting to feel very tied to him again. The man she had been the most intimate with in her life.

How odd that she had been continuing to fend off their sexual intimacy. Hadn't let him lay a finger on her all this time, though they joked about it and it was always in the air between them. But she had to admit she was starting to feel so hooked into him that she didn't want to think of what adding sex to what they had now could mean to them emotionally.

It didn't take people long to start thinking of John as a good way to get to Cee Cee. If the network wanted her to do some promotions or get her to come and perform at the affiliates convention, something she hated, they would start the conversations with John to feel out how he liked their ideas, or to have him help them determine what was the best way to approach her. One afternoon at the commissary a successful television producer named Jay Green put his coffee cup on the table across from where John was sitting, and when John looked up, Jay Green smiled and introduced himself. After they'd talked for a while, he told John he'd like to give him a script to read that was a potential mini-series with a part in it that was perfect for Cee Cee.

'She won't do a mini-series. We think she should only do features,' John told him.

The television producer's eyes smiled at that statement, but the rest of his face was serious as he said something about how he was sure John would change his mind when he read the script he had in mind and also, he dropped, it might be something John would be interested in co-producing with him. So John took the script and read it several times, making notes about things in the story he thought should be changed and parts of what the lead character did that wouldn't be suitable for Cee Cee, and over the next two weeks he took several meetings with Jay Green before even mentioning the project to Cee Cee.

The night he did mention it to her, her mind was in a million different places, and later when she thought back to it, all she remembered was John saying he had a chance to produce some television show, and she had thought, Thank God, he's going to have a job, and she said 'Great.' So when Larry Gold called her at home and said he needed to talk to her without anybody else around, she couldn't imagine what was such a big deal and a secret, but she took the call in her bedroom and closed the door.

'Look, forgive me,' he started out. 'But you and I have been together for a lot of years. Okay? And I'm hoping we'll continue to be for a lot more years, so I'll be straight with you. Are you shtupping that guy Perry? I mean is that why he thinks he can take meetings on projects and make promises to people that you're gonna do the projects without even checking in with me?'

'What?'

'Jay Green thinks that I should be opening negotiations on your behalf for some piece of dreck miniseries I don't think you would spit on. And he says he knows you're available to do it because Perry's his partner, and that's what *Perry's* saying. Cee Cee, what's the haps here? I thought we decided no miniseries and no Movies of the Week.'

Cee Cee searched her mind trying to think if she had said yes to something and forgotten about it, or led John to believe she wanted to do a mini-series. To begin with she hadn't even read whatever script Larry was talking about. But she didn't want to tell that to Larry. It would make John look ridiculous, so instead she said, 'Well, we did discuss the fact that it was a terrific part.'

'You've got to be kidding!' Larry said. 'With a page-one rewrite by Alvin Sargent, maybe it's a good part. But other than that, this thing belongs in the trash masher. Cee Cee, I'm always the first one to tell you how brilliant you are. But, in this case . . . reconsider.'

Reconsider. Reconsider what? John had committed her to something and she wasn't even certain what the something was.

'Not really committed. How could I commit you without you seeing it? Don't be crazy,' he told her that night. Antonia, the housekeeper, was off, Nina was at Kevin's, and John had brought take-out Chinese from the Mandarin for dinner for the two of them. 'Look, I have to admit the script is not one hundred percent. But Jay says once we get the network to say yes, we can afford to bring in a new writer and I'll supervise the writing. That way we'll know from day to day exactly what we're getting. I'll tell you what. On Saturday morning, let's drive up to Santa Barbara. You can read the script in a bungalow at the Biltmore, and we can get away from all the tensions here. I know you're going to see the potential in this, and drop your prejudices about mini-series.'

Cee Cee watched him while he said all that, opening all of the little white cartons of Chinese food, as the steam rose from each one, not looking at her while he talked. For a long time she'd recognized that to be in her position was to be a target for every person who thought she could help to get them something they needed or somewhere they wanted to go, and though that had probably been true for years and years, this was the time when she prayed it wasn't the case. Figured that John, since he had loved her when she had been nowhere and nobody, would be exempt from needing her that way. And on Saturday night in the bungalow at the Santa Barbara Biltmore she let him make love to her for the first time in fifteen years, hoping the act of sex would not only ease her worries but rekindle some deeply rooted passions from years before.

Every man she'd been with since him, no matter how hot and sexy, took a while to psych her out, and of course the reverse was true, too. To know exactly where and when to touch one another, how hard to press here, how gently to rub there, which moans meant go on and which meant stop. But within seconds the two of them had one another going the way they always had during their ten-year marriage. He was holding her face in his two hands, telling her how he'd never stopped loving her, knowing how she always needed to hear the words, how protestations of love were more erotic to her than any touch. She was holding his great ass and pulling his pelvis toward her, while he promised her they were going to be together forever, telling her how much he wanted her, how he'd lived his life just waiting to come back to her this way, then pulling her to him hungrily and kissing her with a long searching kiss, during which he moved his hands under her sweater, easily in one move unfastening the front clasp on her bra, then finding her nipples and taking them between his thumb and forefinger the way he remembered she loved it and playing with them first softly, then squeezing until she moaned, and then if only from the long absence of sex in her life she was filled with heat, the aching needy place inside her that had to have him there to fill it, and she felt her knees getting weak.

Again with the agility he'd always had, which she used to think was almost sleight of hand and be jealous of every woman he had been with, since it was obviously a result of years and years of practice, he unbuttoned the top button on her slacks, then unzipped them and gentled them down to the floor by rubbing

his own body against hers until the pants moved to her thighs, then to her knees, and when they were piled around her ankles, before she could step out of them he slid his fingers under the lace on the thigh of her panties and pressed them into the swollen throbbing folds longing to be caressed.

Oh, yes, she wanted it, and she pressed her pelvis hard against his fingers so he could feel the urgency in her, and he lifted her and carried her to the bed, quickly removing his own clothes, then the rest of hers, while she somehow managed to find an instant of presence of mind to grab for her purse on the floor and fish around inside it for one of the condoms she'd shoved in there just before she left her house.

But by the time she found it, he was moving astride her, and she helped him on with the balloonlike piece of rubber, afraid one of her nails might tear it, then looked at his very familiar body and his very familiar cock, and his face contorted with a passion she remembered so long ago could make her wild with desire for him, and realized with a sudden discomforting wave of sobriety she never had during sex, as he entered her with a first thrust, that it was only the lubrication of the condom that made his slide inside of her anything but unyielding, because she felt nothing. Then he thrust harder and this time she was wetter as her body responded to the sex, any sex because it had been so long, but she knew as she began to relax into the physical feelings, that this moment she had hoped for was nothing more than what she'd heard people call a mercy fuck. Because all she felt for him now was sorry.

Sorry he was pushing sixty and still trying to find himself, sorry he had left his family instead of hanging in and working on his relationships with them because

he had some fantasy that being with Cee Cee could fix his life, and that she had been a party to the fantasy because she'd needed it so badly herself. And now she knew that the security she had begun to feel about leaning on him had been a result of her bottomless need, and also a result of the front he'd developed to get her to depend on him so that he could manipulate her, and the truth was that she couldn't go back again and find solace in him and security and a mind she respected the way she had when they were just starting out their life together. She had come too far to ever go back.

John was lost now in that other world of sexual heat, eyes closed, moving inside her against her to his own rhythm, and Cee Cee beneath him felt as detached as if she was watching from the back row of a movie theater. 'Baby, we're so close, we're one person, how did I ever leave you, baby? Oh God, you feel so good to me, you're mine, you're still mine, aren't you, baby? Oh, Cee Cee, oh yes.' It *did* feel good having a naked man against her own nakedness, it had been much too long and even in her removed watching-from-a-distance place she had to admit that. But each time she opened her eyes and saw John there on top of her, so filled with the passion she was lacking for him, she knew that though it might be sad to feel anger or hatred about someone you once loved so much, what was much more heart-breaking was to feel pity.

After that night in Santa Barbara things started to slide badly. Cee Cee turned down the mini-series, John went out for a brief spurt of job hunting, and the tension between the two of them became palpable. Once Cee Cee snapped at him and overheard somebody on the crew joke, 'Uh oh, trouble in paradise.' One

Friday night Nina had stayed up late, but shortly after she'd fallen asleep she was awakened by the sound of Cee Cee and John having a fight downstairs. They were probably sitting at the dining-room table, which was directly under her room, so she could hear every word rising from their heated quarrel.

'Hey, nothing personal, but you and I both know television is simply a lot of mindless bullshit for morons, which is why your show has been so successful for so long. Because it has no substance.'

'Is that right?' Cee Cee said. She had never thought her show was fodder for PBS, but bullshit for morons was a little low. 'If television is such shit, then I'd like to know why you've been kissing up to so many people trying to worm your way into it.'

'Oh, now that's funny. Who in the hell have I been kissing up to?'

'Everyone I introduce you to. Everyone I *don't* introduce you to. Everyone in the business.'

'You couldn't be more wrong. Of course with your upbringing you wouldn't know the difference between someone with charm and someone who is, to use your classy phrase, "kissing up."'

'Oh, honey, let me tell you something,' Cee Cee said in a tone Nina recognized as her haul-off-and-let-one-go voice. 'You have been *so* charming to *so* many people out here, rumor has it that *your* nose is browner than George Hamilton's.'

Nina wasn't sure what *that* line meant, but the giddy triumph she heard in Cee Cee's delivery meant she'd probably been rehearsing it for a while. Then it was quiet and Nina figured maybe they were both sorry for being so mean to one another and had probably made up and were kissing or something, but then she heard John say, 'Cee Cee, I've been talking to my wife on the phone every night, and the truth is I really miss her. I love her, and I never should have left her for some unrealistic fantasy I had about what you could be for me, or what we could have together, because you were never right for me and you still aren't.'

Nina felt sick when she heard that, because so many times over the last few months she had seen a girlish look on Cee Cee's face when she referred to John as a joke, as her 'once and future husband,' that made Nina know she wasn't joking, and now she wished she could rush downstairs and put her arms around Cee Cee, who had to feel after that news as if John had punched her in the stomach.

'When did you start talking to her every night?' Cee Cee asked with the same hurt Nina had heard from her on the first Mother's Day they had spent together, when Nina had flared at her, 'Don't keep hinting around that it's Mother's Day. You're not my mother and I'm not getting you any gift.' 'Oh, I understand,' Cee Cee had said in that voice which had hit a chord so deep in Nina she'd walked immediately over to the Malibu pharmacy and spent ten dollars on a silver compact and another dollar fifty on a card that said MOTHER'S DAY GREETINGS TO SOMEONE SPECIAL. But apparently that voice didn't have the same effect on John, because now he went on to say, 'I'm going home. It's almost the holidays and I want my family back. My flight leaves tomorrow morning.'

There was no response, and Nina leaned over the edge of her bed to get her face closer to the floor so she could hear the next.

'You talked to her every night? Even when we were in Santa Barbara?'

'Even when we were in Santa Barbara.'

'When? You were with me every minute.'

'When you were in the shower.'

'You filthy rotten lowlife.'

'Likewise I'm sure,' he said, and then Nina heard nothing until the sound of the front door slamming shook the house, and it took Nina a long time after that to fall asleep.

In the morning when she went downstairs she could smell coffee, and when she walked into the kitchen, Cee Cee was there, red-eyed and edgy and fighting to be cheerful. 'I think you, me, and Kevin ought to go to the movies tonight,' she said. 'Let's find out what's playing at the Malibu Cinema.' She was wearing a silk kimono and her face looked as if she hadn't taken off her makeup properly the night before, still smudged around the eyes, and there was a little red spot on her cheek.

'John went back to Ohio?' Nina asked her as Cee Cee absently bit into a piece of toast that was black around the edges.

'Yeah,' Cee Cee said. 'How do you know? Did you hear us fighting last night?'

'Uh-huh. He was really mean to you.'

'Yeah, that was pretty bad. And as if he hadn't hurt me enough, I, like a schmuck, followed him out to the car and stood there crying while he was putting his things in the trunk. It was like I was saying, I didn't have enough. Give me more shit. Can you believe it? So he did. He told me I had a star complex, that I take myself too seriously, and that I've lost my sense of humor. I was so hurt by that, I forgot to mention that only six months ago the *New York Times* called me the comedy star of the decade.' She giggled a ripple of a giggle at that, then looked at Nina with a pained grin that had toast crumbs all around it.

'Well, why didn't you?'

'Well, I would have but at that moment, I didn't remember.'

'What do you mean?'

Cee Cee put her elbows on the table now and rested her face in her two hands. 'I mean I lost it. He was rejecting me so I totally lost it, forgot that every day for the last two weeks I woke up with a speech in my head I was planning to make to him, about how you can't go backward in life, and how even though it felt good to see him and be with him, and how I'd be willing, even glad to help his career in any way I could if he wanted my help, I couldn't keep allowing him to take over my life the way he was trying to, and the way he did when I was a kid.'

'Good speech,' Nina said, putting a piece of bread in the toaster for herself.

'Isn't it?' Cee Cee said. 'Too bad it's on the cutting room floor. I was even gonna say that he ought to start to meet some other women and date them because I didn't want to go back to a romance with him, and certainly not a marriage. And all of a sudden when I heard him saying he was on his way back to Ohio, all my plans to be rational went right out the French doors. I mean, I panicked because all I could think was "He's leaving me. How can he leave me?" And I looked at the same man I couldn't wait to get rid of two weeks before and thought, "How am I going to live without him?"

'So I said, and this is the part I hate myself for, in this real dramatic voice I said, "John . . . don't go to her. Stay here and we'll try to work it out." I still can't believe I was so crazed I was asking him to stay and I didn't even want him to. And then, as if it wasn't bad enough, he said something that really got me. He said that after all this time, he'd better confess the truth, which was that when he showed up in Atlantic City, he was really coming to ask me to be an investor in the Sunshine . . . you know, that theater he used to own? Not to renew anything, not because he cared about me, but then when he saw me onstage that night he got tangled up in the web of his feelings for me. Do you love that phony bullshit? The web of his feelings? Like I was the spider and he was the fly, and that it took him till now to realize it was all just him reacting to the bad way his wife had treated him a few years back and trying to get back at her was childish and that he wanted to go home. "Of course, you do," I told him. "Maybe *she* can bask in your glory. But as far as I can see, you don't even need any sunscreen to bask in *that* goddamned glory.'"

Cee Cee wiped her mouth with a napkin. Her eyes were full and her face was red, and she stood and walked away toward the sink for no apparent reason except to hide that fact from Nina. For a while she stared out the window at the ocean, then finally she asked Nina, 'Can I fix you anything?'

'No thanks,' Nina told her, 'I'll just have my toast.' Then she walked over to the sink and put an arm around Cee Cee as the day filled with sunshine and a couple wearing matching white sweat suits jogged north along the beach outside the window.

Dear Cecilia,

First I'll start by saying don't get excited, it's not a big deal because if it was I would call you up instead of writing it in this letter, but I'm not so hot in the ticker department if you know what I mean.

Believe me, you have got enough on your mind with a television show and somebody else's daughter to worry about without having to think about me. So all I'm doing is writing to say 'hello' and thanks for all the money you send me from some guy named Wayne Gordon's office whoever he may be.

Time goes by so fast, it's hard to believe your mother, may she rest in peace, is already gone so many years. If she was alive she would be calling you every day saying why don't you come and visit once in a while, but I don't believe in telling children what to do.

You know that old expression 'all I know is what I read in the paper'? That's what I should say, since down the street at the news-stand I see your picture in the paper all the time.

Everyone here thinks you're some big deal, and when I tell them you're my daughter, they think I am too.

Your father,
Nathan Bloom

MIAMI BEACH, FLORIDA

1986

In Miami Beach the light of the day is so soft and flattering, Cee Cee decided, as her taxi drove down Collins Avenue, the reason why so many old people moved there had to be because the light made them look younger. Her father had lived in an apartment in Miami Beach off and on for years in which it had cost her a fortune to keep him, and now he was dying there in a Jewish convalescent home where it was costing her even more. She had been summoned by his doctor two days ago, who told her Nathan was having chest pains and trouble breathing but that he refused to go into a hospital, and maybe her input would change his mind.

The call made Cee Cee want to pick up the phone, call Nathan, and shout, 'Daddy, get your ass into the hospital,' but a lifetime of guilt for ignoring him prompted her to call off a few days of production meetings for her show and ask her travel agent to book her to Miami (God's waiting room) Beach.

'Can I come too?' Nina asked. She was a skinny beanpole now, with long curly fly-away hair that was always in her eyes and a close-lipped smile she used, to try to cover the mouthful of braces on her teeth.

'Of course you can, but why would you want to?' Cee Cee asked.

'While you're seeing your dad, I could visit my aunt.'

Bertie's Aunt Neetie. Cee Cee's first impulse was to say, 'No way, José,' and close the issue because she couldn't bear the thought of Nina spending even one minute with the Miami Bitch, which was how she thought of Neetie. Aside from Michael Barron, Neetie was Nina's only living blood relative, and she was always hovering out there with something shitty to say about Cee Cee in her letters or phone calls to Nina, or something snide to say about everyone in show business in general as if she knew them all personally, and she was an expert at constantly making the point to Nina that Bertie, if she was alive, would have done everything pertaining to Nina so much better than Cee Cee did. So that when Nina openly and candidly read the poison missives out loud to Cee Cee, it was all Cee Cee could do not to call the old witch in Florida and tell her to fuck off, but she didn't. Instead she took a deep breath and tried to explain away the things Neetie had written, and though there was no doubt in her mind that Nina's spending a few days with Neetie would cost a lot of deep breaths and a lot of explaining, she still answered, 'Sure, honey. I'll help you pack.'

Things had been a little rough with her and Nina recently, and late at night when Nina was long asleep, Cee Cee turned to the now dog-eared child-raising books looking for answers. This time to read about what they called pre-adolescence. A time when confusion reigned because at eleven they were no longer children and not quite adolescents.

> This stage usually hits parents with a wallop. Your stable, reasonable and well-behaved child seems suddenly to have taken an overdose of obnoxious pills.

Nina seemed to fade in and out of surliness. She was a classic case of being neither here nor there, still sleeping with teddy bears but blushing and flirting when one of the crew members on Cee Cee's show kidded with her. And when Cee Cee saw that, she wished like hell there had been a healthy relationship Nina could have witnessed somewhere along the line, a man she could have had some time with, since she had lived her whole life without a father. A man.

Men. Now there was a joke. Each time a new one came into Cee Cee's life, she was amazed to see that no matter how bad the departure of the last one had been, the kid was still ready and willing to pin her hopes on the new one. Once Cee Cee read a quote somewhere that said a woman without a man couldn't meet a man of any age without thinking, even for a second, maybe this is *the* man. And she could see by the way Nina closely observed each man who showed any interest in Cee Cee, the way she asked him telling questions about himself, that she too was trying to test the potential each one had to be the man in their household.

But none had worked out. Some of the men who found their way to their door were too interested in Cee Cee's stardom, wanted to use her power for their own purposes or to be able to say they were involved with a star. Others were intimidated by her lifestyle, and she had to admit it wasn't exactly easy. After all, there was no dating her in a conventional way. Everywhere she went she was swamped with autograph seekers, besieged by photographers, and stared at by everyone else. So the men who stepped forward, as she described it, 'bearing bouquets of flowers and cocks that didn't fall to half-mast as they approached my famous and exquisite bod,' were rare and unusual.

And even when they did, eventually some interior buzzer of hers buzzed, like the rasping end-bell on a game show telling the contestant the answer was wrong, and Cee Cee would know it was over with this one too, so she would try to explain nicely, then turn down his requests to come over, and eventually stop taking his calls at all, and soon another would be phased out.

'No more Dan?' Nina would ask (or Chad or Mark or Roger).

'Not for me,' Cee Cee would answer, knowing she would have to face the disappointment in Nina's eyes again.

Perhaps there is an in-law or a relative, a grandfather or an uncle who can play an active male role with your children. In rare cases a male friend can do this. This person can be invited over to dinner or picnics. He can take the children to movies, take them fishing or camping, take them to sports events, go swimming or sailing with them.

Yeah, sure. There was no one in their lives to fit that bill, except for Hal, but he lived and worked in New York, and these days only came in on occasional visits. Cee Cee's father, who had never been a force in her life, was another story. As soon as she'd started making money she had helped him to move out of an old folks home in New York to an apartment in Miami Beach. Bought him stock, MCA, Warners, enough to give him a reason to get up in the morning, to call his broker and check on his money.

Over the years she had extended vague invitations to him to come to Los Angeles to visit, never sure what she would do with him if he said yes and showed up, but Nathan Bloom had always declined. Now he was ailing and not long for this world, and the illness had dictated that he move back into a convalescent home, the one toward which her taxi now moved through the bright, sunny Miami Beach day.

'Why don't I take this cab to Neetie's and you take

that one to see your dad? You don't need to come with me to see Neetie,' Nina had said to her at the Miami airport.

'You mean because she loathes and despises me and that makes you uncomfortable?'

'Yes,' Nina answered.

'You got it.' Cee Cee felt remiss agreeing to take separate taxis, but she couldn't bring herself to have to see Neetie and her pinched, judgmental face waiting for Nina's cab to drive up outside her building, so she agreed to let Nina get there alone. At the cabstand she gave her enough money to last for several days, exchanged phone numbers with her, and hugged her goodbye, regretting her decision the second the cab pulled away, and she tried hard to fight back the fear that Nina would see Neetie after so many years and love her so much she would beg her aunt and uncle to keep her in Miami Beach.

Even at its worst the L.A. heat didn't have the kind of dense humidity Miami Beach did. By the time Cee Cee had paid her cabdriver and carried her overnight bag to the door of the Beth Shalom Convalescent Home, she was soaked with sweat, and her black silk sweater stuck to her in several wet places. As she pushed the glass doors to the lobby open, she tried to steel herself for what it would be like seeing Nathan after so long. Nathan, who had been a silent figure behind a newspaper for most of her childhood. Cowering from that cow Leona. 'Let the kid sleep late, for chrissake, Leona,' he would offer now and then on a Saturday morning as Leona hollered for a tired Cee Cee to 'Getyertapshuzon.' And when he did, Leona would turn on him and yell, 'And you mindyerowngoddamnbizness,' and he always did. Occasionally there would be a burst of humor from him, a moment when he could ease the overbearing Leona into an uncharacteristic grin or a sudden girlish giggle. Like when the two of them sang together.

'I'm the sheik of Araby,' Leona would sing, and Nathan with a sexy little twinkle in his eye would follow every line with the words, 'Without a pair of pants.'

'And your love belongs to me.'

'Without a pair of pants.'

'At night when you're asleep.'

'Without a pair of pants.'

'Into your tent I'll creep.'

'Without a pair of pants.'

'This is where you got your talent, Cecilia,' Nathan would tell her pointing to himself.

'Oh yeah?' Leona would say. 'I guarantee ya, Eddie Cantor ain't losing any sleep over you, Bloom.' Sometimes by the end of the song he would be wearing a kitchen towel around his little bald head as his costume for the sheik of Araby. Remembering him that way now as she walked up to the desk at the convalescent home made Cee Cee regret all the years she had stayed away from him, and wish she could have them back.

When she asked the nurse at the front desk where 4C was, she answered, 'Ahhh, you're Nate's daughter. He's a prince of a man,' then gave her directions to her father's room. As she moved down the carpeted hall, Cee Cee looked at the old people who sat slumped and staring in wheelchairs posted outside the doors to their rooms, probably because they didn't want to stay inside the rooms all day but only had the physical wherewithal to get as far as the door jamb.

Now and then the eyes of one of them would meet hers and she would see a glimmer that probably meant, 'Look! A young person!' But that was all the contact most of them seemed able to make. On the cardboard plaque outside of room 4C there was a sign which indicated that inside the room there were two occupants. MARTY ELMAN AND NATHAN BLOOM it said, and there was a photograph of each man's face next to his name. Cee Cee looked long at the picture of her father. It was an old one from long ago, in fact it was half of one in which the other half had been her mother standing next to him. Cee Cee knew because somewhere in a box of pictures at home she had the original, and now she wondered if Nathan had used that particular picture because since then no one else had taken another one of him. That thought made her so sad she reached up and put her fingers on the picture.

'They all have them now,' someone said, and Cee Cee turned to see a small round blond nurse holding a pile of what looked like sheets. 'Originally we started putting pictures up so our Alzheimer's patients could find their way back to their rooms. Then everybody wanted them.'

Cee Cee nodded a numb nod in reply.

'I'm your father's nurse, Cee Cee. I would know you even if I never saw you in the movies or on TV, which I did, because he has a million pictures of you in his drawer.'

'He does?' Cee Cee wasn't sure why that surprised her.

'He's asleep now, I just checked him,' the nurse told her, shaking her head sadly. 'Not good. On the first floor alone we lost three this week. They wear out. The human body unfortunately was only designed to last sixty-some years. You take perfect care, you last more. Not such good care, you last less. Your father, he's in his eighties, so it's his time.'

'I'll go see him.'

'Don't mind the roommate, Elman. He's a pain in the *tochas*. You know what a *tochas* is?'

Cee Cee nodded.

'Anyways, how's that little girl of yours?'

'She's fine,' Cee Cee said. 'Thanks for asking.'

The room was divided by a panel of curtains, and Cee Cee wondered why, with all the money she was paying, Nathan only had a semiprivate room instead of a private one. She made a mental note to ask somebody in charge after she spent some time with her father, whose head was thrown back and his mouth was open in a snore, as he twitched in the throes of a dream.

Overlaid on the disinfectant odor in the room, she breathed in a familiar Nathan scent from her childhood she recognized as Old Spice cologne, and the smell of it brought back the old apartment of her childhood, and the memory of Nathan standing with only a towel wrapped around his waist, his hairless pink chest and fat little arms, leaning over a sink of hot water trying to shave, while Leona hollered at him so much it was a miracle he didn't cut his face to ribbons.

'Hiya, Sheik,' Cee Cee said softly now to the soundly sleeping old man. 'Long time, no see.'

Aunt Neetie looked as if there might be tears in her eyes when she walked out of the lobby of her building to greet Nina's taxi. She was a slim woman with hair dyed too black, and skin that was a kind of muddy brown and very wrinkled from the sun.

'Well, aren't *you* a big girl!' she said. Nina thought by the way she walked toward the taxi with her hand in her pocket that maybe she was about to pull out money and pay the cabdriver, but when she made no move to, Nina opened her pink plastic 'Hello Kitty' wallet, took out some of the money Cee Cee had given her, and remembered to add a tip before she handed it to the driver.

As the cab pulled away Neetie explained away her watery eyes. 'I'm allergic to hibiscus,' she said. 'And it's all around now.' Nina's suitcase sat on the front step of the building where the cabdriver had dropped it. 'Can you manage that bag all by yourself or shall I get Uncle Herb to come down? The Cuban doorman is off today. He says one of his kids is in the hospital. The little spic has so damn many kids there's always an excuse,' she said, and then laughed a forced throaty laugh.

Nina picked up the heavy suitcase and dragged it toward the front door of the building.

'You're the picture of your mother,' Neetie said, opening one of the glass doors into the foyer of the building to let her in and holding it open. The air-conditioning brought goose bumps to Nina's little arms.

'Thank you,' Nina said, pulling the suitcase over the threshold and across the marble-floored lobby toward the elevator. The building smelled of onions cooking and the odor made Nina, who hadn't eaten anything on the flight from Los Angeles, feel hungry and queasy at the same time. The elevator was so small, Neetie and Nina and the suitcase just fit inside. There was a notice taped to the elevator wall, listing a schedule of events which Nina read to herself as she and Neetie took the ride up.

MONDAY NIGHT – SEVEN P.M. BINGO
(REC ROOM SEVEN O'CLOCK)
REFRESHMENTS WILL BE SERVED.
WEDNESDAY NIGHT – BOOK DISCUSSION –
THIS MONTH *AIRPORT*.

The elevator doors opened and Nina pushed her body against the suitcase and shoved it into the hall. 'It's the third door on the right,' Neetie said, walking ahead of her with a kind of stoop-shouldered walk. 'Your Uncle Herb is watching television as usual. Herbieee,' she yelled out, opening the door to her apartment, 'Roberta's daughter is here.'

Nina stood in the doorway of the apartment. Neetie, who had obviously been unable to part with the furniture from her larger home, had managed to cram it into the small apartment rooms. After a minute a skinny little man with white hair, wearing trousers and a white sleeveless undershirt that revealed his white armpit hair, opened a door to a back room through which Nina could hear a television show blasting. The man nodded and made a few noises that sounded oddly like burps, and then instead of a voice, out came croaking noises that sounded as if they might have been, 'Nice to see you.' Nina took a step back. Something was wrong.

'A couple of years ago he had a laryngectomy. Cancer of the voice box. Had to have it removed,' Neetie said as if she was talking about a lamp or a chair instead of Uncle Herbie, who nodded in Nina's direction during the narration, watching her reaction carefully. 'Now he speaks through a hole in his throat,' Neetie said. 'I never mentioned it in my letters because I didn't want to worry you.' Then she asked with amusement in her voice, 'What's the matter, did he scare you?'

Nina looked at her uncle's neck where she saw the hole and then into his eyes where she could see that her answer was important to him, so she lied. 'Oh, no,' she said, then thought, *I'm going to vomit*.

'Isn't she big, Herbie?'

'Burp, burp, she sure is,' is what it sounded like he said.

Nina's sick feeling must have filled her face, because Neetie said, 'Don't worry, you can't catch it. It's from smoking too many cigarettes. You don't smoke, do you?' She was making what Nina could tell by the strange little smile on her face was her idea of a joke.

'Burp, burp. Leave the kid alone, Anita. Here, I'll take you to your room,' Uncle Herbie said, walking over and picking up Nina's suitcase, and with a wag of his head to the side invited her to follow. Now she had to be alone with him. Obligingly she followed him down a narrow hallway and into the guest bedroom, the door to which, when he opened it, bumped into one of two beds with headboards that matched a large dresser with mirrors over it, two night tables, and a chair. On one of the tables there was a small framed photograph of two women and a little girl of about seven or eight years old. Uncle Herbie saw Nina look-ing at it.

'Burp, burp, it's your mother and your grandmother and my wife. On the beach in Atlantic City,' she thought he said.

Nina wondered if the picture was taken the year her mother first met Cee Cee there. Uncle Herb put her suitcase on one of the beds. 'Burp, burp, bathroom's just down the hall,' he said. Now she would unpack, and then they would eat dinner. She wondered if when Uncle Herbie ate, some of the food fell out of the little hole, and that thought made her feel really sick. Uncle Herb burped some more and said some more words as he pointed out the closet, the chest of drawers, the clock radio, and Nina tried to be polite and not look at the hole, and nod, and hope he'd leave the room. When he finally did and closed the door behind him, she lay face-down on the bed trying to pull herself together, but the pain of disappointment rushed to her eyes. This was certainly not the Aunt Neetie and Uncle Herb she had conjured up in those moments when she thought about escaping from Cee Cee, times when Cee Cee embarrassed her so horribly, like when she was dating some really awful guy who was too young for her with hair down to his shoulders, or that one who wore the gold jewelry and smoked eight cigars a day. Or those times she came for parent-teacher meetings to school wearing those Halloweeny thrift shop outfits that made her look like a cartoon character.

Nina would pacify herself on those days by writing and mailing letters to the couple she liked to think of as her 'real family.' An elegant older couple, living in a building she knew from their return address was called the Versailles, which she had always pictured to be like the Plaza Hotel, where she and Cee Cee had stayed last year when Cee Cee had to go to New York for meetings. Surely there would be a dining room with chandeliers and a violinist who played during tea in the lobby. And the aunt and uncle would take her in, clucking their tongues with understanding at what an ordeal it must have been these last few years for her to put up with all the craziness in Cee Cee's life.

Of course after she mailed the feverishly written letters and sent them off to the Versailles, the tide at home would turn because Cee Cee would eventually either dump or get dumped by the guy, or do something marvelous just for Nina like having the Muppets as guests on her show and inviting Nina's entire class to be her guests at the taping, and things would be all right between them again for a while, but soon they'd fall apart again and when they did, Nina would get through it by picturing what her life would eventually be like when she came to live with her real family at the Versailles.

There was a tap at the door, and Aunt Neetie came in smiling. 'Well, you must be worn out from all that traveling,' she said to Nina as she walked over to the suitcase, opened it, and removed the clothing piece by piece, moving back and forth to the chest of drawers to put them away. 'I guess Miss Cee Cee didn't want to come over here *with* you because she couldn't stand to look me in the eye because of what she did to me, and I'm sure you know the story.'

Nina knew which story Neetie meant, since over the years Neetie had told her various versions of it in her letters. All this time had gone by since Bertie's death, and still she wouldn't let 'the story' go. Somehow she always managed to get some dig in about how Cee Cee had tricked Bertie into giving the care of Nina to her and taking it away from Neetie.

'My ass,' Cee Cee had flared furiously when Nina had mentioned it the first time. 'Nobody tricked anyone. Your mother knew I was the right one and that's why she let me have you.'

'You know, of course you're getting to be the age when you can decide you don't want to be with her anymore. And when you do, you can march right into that courtroom and say, "Judge, get me the hell out of that nuthouse." And frankly, honey, I hope you do. And that me and your Uncle Herb will still be around to take you. Maybe move up to the fifth floor to a three-bedroom.'

Nina just nodded.

'And I suppose she's raising you as a Jew?' Neetie asked now. Nina looked at her curiously, wondering why there was a sneer on her lips, and Neetie took her look to mean yes.

'I thought so. Well, don't worry, I'm used to Jews. You live in Miami Beach all your life the way I have, all you see are wall-to-wall kikes. And the joke is they think *I'm* one of them because I have black hair. Sometimes they do jokes to me in Yiddish, can you imagine? Well, I'm not here for the company, honey, I'm here for the climate.' Now she was putting Nina's pink sundress on a hanger. 'I never knew what the hell your gorgeous classy mother ever saw in Cee Cee Bloom. I tell you, every time I saw your picture in one of those scandal papers – not that I buy them, but they're all over the beauty parlor I go to – I wanted to cry. Anyway, let's talk about happier things. You and I and Herbie are going to have a grand old time. Right?'

Nina didn't say anything, but when Neetie left the room to check on dinner she opened her little purse, took out the wallet inside and looked at the telephone number Cee Cee had left with her, and considered calling it and begging Cee Cee to come and get her.

'Cecilia,' Nathan said, opening his eyes. 'Is it really you?'

'It's me, Daddy,' she said, looking at the old man in the bed who only bore the slightest resemblance to her memory of her father. And Cecilia, the name he called her. Who was that? The little girl inside of her only he remembered who wasn't Cee Cee Bloom the star. The ordinary person who had long ago created the character of Cee Cee Bloom. Made up her walk, made up her flashiness, made the choice that she would be tart-tongued and bawdy, outrageous and sexy, while Cecilia, Nathan Bloom's daughter, watched all of that from the inside, like the puppeteer watches the puppet.

Nathan's eyes flickered with joy and she took his hand gently. 'I'm dying?' he asked her. 'That's why you came because I'm dying?'

How should she answer a question like that?

'I just came to see you.'

'You're doing a show in town here?' he asked her, and she realized he was saying he knew it could only be his imminent death that would bring her to his side, or business, and she hated that he was right.

'I needed to come and talk to you,' she said.

'No kidding?' he said, and then winced with pain as he moved himself a little higher on the bed. 'I'm not so good, kiddo. I had some prostate trouble, a little hip trouble, now I got chest pains.'

'I know. The doctor wants you to go into the hospital.'

'Forget about it.'

'Daddy, it could save your life. Give you years and years.'

'Who wants more years?' he asked, making a face that was so familiar because she made it all the time, too. 'I had enough years. Your mother, God rest her soul, got a flucky. You know that story?' Cee Cee couldn't believe it. He was going to tell her a joke. 'A guy goes to a whore. Everybody else goes to the whore gets VD. The doctor tells this guy he didn't get VD, instead he got a flucky. The guy is scared, because he never heard of such a thing. Then he realizes the doctor meant he 'got off lucky.' Your mother got a flucky because she never had to get old. Come to mention it, maybe that's why I'm still here. Leona would have noodged me into an early grave,' he said.

'Daddy, they think you might have a leaky heart valve. If that's true, they can replace it and you'll feel good.'

'Leaky, sure. Why *wouldn't* it be leaky at my age?

You're old, you're sick, you die, that's life.' Cee Cee shook her head and there was silence.

'So since I saw you last you're a mother?' he said and asked at the same time.

'That's right. My best friend left her daughter in my care and I'm raising her.'

'Why you?'

'It was the best choice.'

'Oy vay,' he said and smiled.

'What does *that* mean?' Cee Cee asked, annoyed that he had been awake less than three minutes and was already aggravating her.

'I beg your pardon. I was the one who retrieved your turtle from the toilet and sat shivah for all your goldfish. In my mind you're not a mother.'

Cee Cee flared. 'So who *was* a mother? Leona who drove both of us crazy from morning until night? Grandma who made you walk her from room to room in her house so she could say goodbye to the furniture, and then had the nerve to live so you'd have to do it again the next day and the next for years?'

'Don't get excited. I'm entitled to an opinion.'

'Hey, you know what?' Cee Cee said.

'Yeah?'

'Why don't you come out to Los Angeles and see for yourself what kind of a mother I am.'

'I'll read about it in the paper,' he said.

The nurse Cee Cee had met in the hall came into the room carrying a small metal tray.

'So, Nate. Your famous daughter schlepped here a long way. You think maybe you'll go for a little walk down the hall with her today?'

'No walking noplace. I walked farther in my lifetime than both of you put together ever will, so that's enough walking.'

'Nate, it improves the efficiency of your circulation,' the nurse told him, and when she put the thermometer in his mouth and held his wrist, while she looked at her watch to get a pulse rate, with the hand she wasn't holding he gave her the finger. Cee Cee had to bite her lip to keep from laughing out loud.

For someone who didn't like Cee Cee, Aunt Neetie sure made a big thing out of the fact that she not only knew her but that her great-niece Nina lived with her in Hollywood. It was something she had obviously talked about to her neighbors who sat by the pool at the Versailles.

'Is that her?' everyone asked, looking hard at Nina. Older people, mostly ladies wearing beach hats and bathing suits and jewelry, were lying on lounge chairs or sitting around tables playing cards.

'That's the little doll,' Neetie said, spreading orange-and-blue-striped beach towels across two lounge chairs. Then she made the introductions.

'Say hi to my beloved Mrs Altschuler and Mrs Haber.'

'This is the one who lives with Cee Cee Bloom?'

'This is the one,' Neetie said, gesturing toward Nina as if she were selling her.

'Oh, that Cee Cee! I'm her biggest fan,' said one of the ladies, whose giant saggy breasts were falling like too much pleated fabric over the top of her bathing suit as she leaned forward to Nina to make her point. 'You tell her Mrs Altschuler, formerly from Cleveland, never missed any of her shows or any of her movies.'

'That goes for me too,' an unintroduced woman who was clearly not one of Neetie's beloveds announced. She was tiny, with short gray hair and a smear of pink ointment covering her nose and cheeks.

'I'll mention it,' Nina said.

'Is she in town here?' the woman with the falling breasts asked.

'She is,' Neetie answered. 'She's visiting her sick father in a home on Bay Road. But she'll probably stop by here,' and she smiled a knowing smile as if to say that she knew a lot about Cee Cee's schedule.

The women squealed at the idea. 'No! Come here? Anita, you have to call us. My daughter would kill me if Cee Cee Bloom was here and I didn't talk to her.'

'Well, you know,' Neetie said, 'people like Cee Cee are funny about their privacy . . . but of course I'll call you.'

When the women had drifted away and Neetie and Nina were alone, Neetie said to her, 'Those two are widows, rolling in dough. Altschuler's husband was a lawyer and the other one's husband was in louvered doors. When they get dolled up at night you could go blind from the glare of the jewelry.' Neetie reached into the straw basket purse where she kept the suntan lotion and pulled out a pack of cigarettes. When she saw Nina's surprise as she held her hand up to shield the match she was lighting from the wind, she said, 'Don't tell Herbie or he'll kill me,' then she inhaled and blew out a big puff of smoke. 'Believe me, I don't envy them. I mean what in the hell is jewelry if you don't have a man, kiddo. Right? Jewelry can't keep you warm at night.' Nina tried not to picture Uncle Herbie keeping Aunt Neetie, who was puffing away on the cigarette and unbuttoning her white gauze coverup, warm at night. Underneath she wore a black bathing suit and had a very skinny, sagging brown body.

'My husband left me a couple of times. He was even in the pokey more than once, before you were born, when your mother was a kid. For illegal gambling activities. But you want to know what? I got him back every time. And I stashed away plenty of cash during the good years, and had a beautiful house where your grandmother, my sister Rosie, could come and visit, and now this condominium. I got the world on a string, honey.' She puffed away a series of puffs on the cigarette until there was smoke all around her face.

'What was my grandmother like?'

'A doll. A beauty, just like your mother. A widow at a young age, but she never wanted to remarry.' Neetie shook her head when she told Nina that. 'Personally I think that's what killed her, killed your mother too. The doctors can call it cancer or stroke or whatever you like. I say a woman without a man dries up and dies.' She took a long puff on the cigarette, creating dozens of tiny lines around her mouth as she puckered, then blew out the smoke, and asked, 'So what about Cee Cee Bloom? Who's *her* latest boyfriend?'

'She doesn't have one at the moment.'

'With that face it's no wonder,' Neetie said and laughed. 'Of course men don't care so much about the face, do they? Just the neck down.' She laughed at that, then lay back, the cigarette now burning between her two fingers as she drank in the sun's rays. 'Tonight we'll go to dinner to a cafeteria. Won't that be fun?'

Nathan held Cee Cee's arm as he moved haltingly down the hall. He was wearing a paisley bathrobe Cee Cee was sure he'd had when she was a little girl. Earlier she had tried to get him to eat a meal.

'Don't give me any more of those lousy potatoes without salt.'

'You're not *allowed* to have salt, Daddy.'

'I'm gonna be dead in a little while, who's gonna know if I had salt?'

'Pretend there's salt on them.'

'You pretend I'm eating them.'

'You need your energy.'

'Why? I'm not going disco dancing. I'm lying here waiting to die. For that I don't need energy.'

After that the nurse came in to bathe him, and Cee Cee stood in the hall outside talking to the doctor, who looked just the way Cee Cee pictured him when she spoke to him on the phone from Los Angeles. Small and slim with horn-rimmed glasses and wispy gray hair. 'As I told you the other day, he has a negative attitude about intervention of any kind, says he's too old. The symptoms he has indicate that he has the mechanical problem of a leaking heart valve, and if it's replaced he could do well for quite a while.'

'Then why is there a doubt?'

'He says he's lived enough.'

That night, after Nathan fell asleep, Cee Cee checked into the Doral Beach Hotel to a suite that felt as large as an entire floor of the convalescent home, where she took a long bath, got into the big double bed and turned out the light, and couldn't sleep. For hours she paced the floor of the too-lavish room, wanting to blame her sleeplessness on the fact that she could hear *Nightline* on the television in the suite next door, but long after the people next door had turned the television off and there was nothing to be heard but silence, she was still wide awake.

She thought about how hateful and selfish she'd been, never being available to Nathan, then she worried about the possibility that Nina and Neetie were having a terrible time together, then she worried about the possibility that they were having a great time together. She ordered up a sandwich from the twenty-four-hour room service, and even though she wasn't hungry she sat eating it and every last potato chip they sent with it, thinking about the fact that it was in a hotel suite in Miami Beach a lot less grand than this one where the breakup of her marriage had happened, a lifetime ago. And how in the lobby of the same hotel from which John had made his exit, after a long, bitter estrangement she and Bertie had been reunited.

And what a reunion. Cee Cee was playing the showroom at the Carillon, and Bertie arrived in Miami Beach to sit by the bedside of her dying mother. It was one of those bizarre twists of fate that Cee Cee was certain was part of a predestined plot written on the day of everyone's birth, and she remembered how when she first walked into the lobby of the Carillon that day with those dogs she used to have yapping at her heels, and saw Bertie standing there after not seeing her for so long, she thought she was hallucinating.

'I forgive you,' Bertie had said to her, and just remembering that haughty look Bert always got on her face when she thought she was so right about something, Cee Cee bristled. 'Yeah, well thanks a whole fuckin' lot, Bert,' she had said, 'but I *don't* forgive you, and I never will.' Of course that night she'd felt like a total schmuck for walking away from her, so in her usual fashion of overdoing it, she had gone to the hotel kitchen and picked up a bunch of dinners, then schlepped them over to the intensive care unit to feed all the relatives of the sick and the dying. Saint Cee Cee. Yeah, sure. Mother Teresa wasn't losing any sleep over the competition.

Anyway, Bertie did forgive her and they had gone on. Started sending their letters to one another again. And it was a few weeks later when Bertie sent her a poem in the mail. Cee Cee couldn't remember now who had written it.

Friendship is the comfort
The inexpressible comfort
Of feeling safe with a person
Having neither to weigh thoughts nor measure
    words
But pouring all right out
Just as they are, chaff and grain together,
Certain that a friendly faithful hand
Will take and sift them
Keep what is worth keeping
And with a breath of comfort
Blow the rest away.

The poem had stayed in her mind forever. After all, pouring it all out was definitely her M.O., and for all their lives Bertie had managed to sift them out. Yeah, she thought now, it's good that Nina's visiting Neetie. The frostily air-conditioned living room of the suite was getting colder every minute, and she wished she remembered what the bellman told her about how to turn the air off. Even if Cee Cee personally hated that old bitch Neetie, it didn't matter because it was good for Nina to make a connection with somebody who gave her a sense of her own history, let her know that she had one, that once there was her grandmother Rosie who loved her daughter Bertie and that she was beautiful and fun and called her daughter 'Puss' the same way Bertie did with Nina.

And it was good that Cee Cee was here in Miami for the same reason. To connect with her father and the part of herself that had come from him, a man who could make someone laugh by putting a dishtowel on his head and singing the words 'Without a pair of pants' had definitely to be related to her by blood. And that was worth a lot. Finally after taking the room service tray out into the deserted hotel corridor, she fell asleep on the sofa in the living room of the suite, dreaming some vague dream about her mother, and eventually she woke with a pounding headache, dressed, and called down to the front desk and asked if the bellman would please get her a taxi, and soon she was back walking down the corridor of the convalescent home.

Nathan was arguing with a nurse about his breakfast.

'Daddy,' Cee Cee said, 'you're going into the hospital. Today. So put on your paisley robe or whatever you have to put on because I'm taking you over there now.'

'Like hell you are,' Nathan said.

'Doctor Feiffer told me you won't go to the hospital because you think you've lived enough. Well, you know what? You may have lived enough for you, but you haven't lived enough for me. I made a mistake, I stayed away from you for too long, and now I want you to stick around for a while so I can get to know you. Purely selfish, I'll admit, but I want to make up for some of those years, so Nina can get to know you, and I want to hear stories about my grandparents and what Leona was like when you were dating, and what you said the night you asked her to marry you.'

'*She* asked *me*.'

'Well, I want to hear about that too. And about what I looked like the first time you saw me in the hospital nursery.'

'A big mouth just like now.'

She was pulling a little suitcase out of one of the closets, not sure if it was her father's or Marty Elman's, and packing toiletries in it and pajamas and a clean seersucker robe.

'I remember there were a lot of stories I used to ignore like about how smart I was and what my first words were, stories nobody else knows about me but you.'

'I can tell you all that stuff in one day and you can go home,' Nathan said, but he was turning on the bed now and putting his feet on the floor.

'I'm not going home until I get a date from you of when you're coming to Los Angeles to visit.'

Nathan gave her a dismissing wave and a grunt, but he walked across the room to the bathroom unassisted.

Nina had never eaten in a cafeteria and the food looked great. The plates piled with squares of red Jell-O on lettuce, the pineapple rings on beds of cottage cheese, with a little strawberry half on the top. 'Live it up,' Neetie told her. 'Have the Jell-O and the cottage cheese and a cream puff too. There are cream puffs at the end of the line.'

While Uncle Herb stayed home, 'the two girls,' as Neetie called them, had gone to the movies to see *Hannah and Her Sisters* and then for an early dinner, and they got dressed up to do it. Neetie wore a white-and-yellow-flowered dress that made her dark skin look even darker, and Nina, whose hours in the sun had brought out every freckle on her face, wore a dress Cee Cee bought her, which was a pale yellow pinafore.

Cee Cee had called her from the hospital. She sounded nervous, and she told Nina that it was good that they were in Florida to be with their respective families and that even though she may not have acted like it sometimes, she thought people should be good to their families and try to take those relationships to their hearts. The things she said were really corny like from a greeting card, and probably she was feeling sentimental because she was calling from a hospital where she told Nina her father was going to have surgery immediately, which meant she and Nina might have to stay a day or two longer.

Nina said that was okay with her, and it was. She was getting used to the *burp burp* of Uncle Herbie, who was kind and smiled at her a lot and knew how to play twenty-one and gin rummy too. She had been relieved to find out that his surgery had removed his larynx, where he spoke, not his esophagus, where he ate, so no food fell out of the little hole. He also explained to her that though some others who had the same surgery sometimes used an amplifying device, he had chosen to learn, from another man who had the surgery years earlier, how to speak with his breath. Nina admired that.

The only tiresome part of her stay was Neetie's endless tirade against everyone in the world, but that was actually starting to be funny. Nina made a game out of trying to see if Neetie could get through any fifteen-minute period without either talking badly about somebody else or complaining about her own life.

'I never even got a cent out of the deal,' she was saying now, as Nina held a red Jell-O square in her mouth, loving the way it dribbled down her throat as it melted, 'because when my sister Rose died she left everything to your mother. Not that she had a fortune or anything as far as I know, but she didn't leave me so much as an earring. Remember that emerald ring she used to wear? I would have liked that. No, she gave it all to your mother, so then your mother dies and what happens? She leaves everything to you, naturally, and again I'm out in the cold, which is a figure of speech, since I'm living in Miami Beach,' she said and laughed at what she was sure was her own wit. A busboy poured more coffee in her cup when she gestured for him with a snapping finger.

'You mean *this* emerald ring?' Nina asked and reached under the pinafore where the emerald ring, which she only wore when she got very dressed up, was hanging from the chain around her neck, and she held it out toward Neetie.

Neetie leaned forward, raising an eyebrow, reached across and fingered the dangling ring hungrily.

'My sister Rosie's ring,' she said, her eyes full of longing. 'I'll never forget how much she loved it. I can picture it on her hand. God, I miss her. You know, she didn't leave me so much as a bobby pin because she was always so worried about your mother. Of course at the time I was hurt, but now in my old age I got smart. I mean there's no telling why people do things. Right? But that ring.' She was still gazing at it and touching it, and Nina politely leaned forward to make it easier for her. 'I remember when our mother gave it to her,' Neetie said, and then her eyes fogged up as if that thought was an upsetting one. Finally she let go of the ring and dug her fork into the turkey pot pie she had chosen from the hot foods section, as Nina slid another cold square of red Jell-O onto her fork.

'Want to try it on?' she asked, hoping Aunt Neetie would say no but think what a nice girl she was for offering, except she'd barely finished the question when Neetie was standing behind her unclasping the chain, which she pulled away from the ring and placed on the table, and then she slid the ring onto her bony brown hand, and held her arm out stiff in front of her with her hand flexed as she gazed at the gleaming green stone.

'My sister's ring,' she said, and then she wiped her eyes with her paper napkin.

★

As Cee Cee sat in the hospital watching Nathan's condition improve by the hour, measured by the number and volume of his complaints, she realized that the last time she'd been in a hospital was when Nina was born, and while Nathan was asleep she found a pay telephone in the hall and called Neetie's number.

'Hello?'

'Anita, this is Cee Cee Bloom.'

'Oh, hello, Cee Cee.'

Cee Cee knew she should ask about Neetie's husband, or maybe make small talk to be polite, but she couldn't think of any.

'How's Nina?' she asked.

'Why, she's a perfect angel,' Neetie said, and without another word she handed the phone to Nina.

'H'lo?'

'Neen, we can go home tomorrow. I called my office and they made us reservations on Pan Am at two. The car will pick you up at noon.'

'Okay.'

'Neen.'

'Yes?'

'Are you glad to be going home?'

'Um . . . yes.'

Cee Cee had the limousine pick her up first and then to Neetie's to pick up Nina. She'd considered having the car pick Nina up first in order to avoid Neetie completely, but she knew that was wrong and that she had to be adult about this. Now as the long black car pulled up outside the Versailles and she saw Neetie and her husband waiting with Nina, she braced herself for the first meeting with the woman in more years than she wanted to count. Looked at her and remembered seeing her just before Bertie's mother died, in the same hospital where Nathan had just been signed off by his doctor as 'strong as an ox.'

The poor old uncle croaked out a hello to Cee Cee and Nina gave her a welcoming hug, and as the driver opened the trunk of the limousine and put Nina's bag inside, Uncle Herb gave Nina a little pat and excused himself to go upstairs, and Cee Cee stood face-to-face with Neetie on the curb with the Miami Beach sun beating down on them and she could feel Neetie's dark eyes burning a hole right through her face. Stay even, Cee Cee told herself. In two minutes you and Nina will be out of here. If you can pull this one encounter off like a lady for Nina's sake, you'll have moved up in your own eyes and in hers.

'She was very, very well behaved,' Neetie said.

'She always is,' Cee Cee said.

'And your father is okay now?' Nice of her.

'Recovering comfortably from the surgery, thanks for asking.'

'Well, Herb and I enjoyed her. Unfortunately he's under the weather.'

'Sorry to hear it.'

The driver closed the trunk. Almost out of here, Cee Cee said to herself, almost the fuck out of here. Neetie pulled a pack of cigarettes out of her purse and lit one. She's nervous, Cee Cee thought. More nervous about this confrontation than I am. Hah! But when Neetie put the hand holding the cigarette up to her face again, and Cee Cee saw the green flash of light on her hand, her heart lurched and all bets were off.

'Neetie, what are you doing wearing that ring?' She couldn't stop the words from tumbling out, and for a second thinking maybe it was Neetie's own ring and that she'd said something dumb.

'Nina gave it to me,' Neetie answered with her head up just a little too high so as to look defensive, but she looked worried. Cee Cee glanced over at Nina, who nodded to confirm that what Neetie said was true, but the little girl's face told the whole story.

'What did you say to make her give it to you?' Cee Cee asked, straining to keep her voice under control.

'Nina, what did I say?' Neetie asked shrilly.

'Nothing. I wanted her to have it,' Nina said. A lie.

'Why?' Cee Cee demanded.

'Because she doesn't have any memento of her sister.'

'No,' Cee Cee said, able to imagine the coercing that must have taken place over the last few days. 'Neetie, Bertie left that ring to Nina, and I want you to give it back to her.'

'You're nuts,' Neetie said. 'Who in the hell do you think you're talking to? You can't come here and tell me and my flesh and blood what to do about things that don't concern you.'

A well-dressed older couple walked out of the front door of the Versailles. Cee Cee spoke quietly but with great clarity. 'Neetie, give the kid the ring back right now, because if you don't I promise you I'll cause a scene out here in front of the Versailles that'll make Louis the Fourteenth spin in his grave like a chicken on a spit. I know you conned this child out of something her mother wanted her to have forever and she's so goodhearted she gave it to you. She's a soft touch, which is why she came to see you in the first place, but I can tell you as sure as I'm alive that I'm not so soft and she's not leaving here and I'm not either without her mother's ring. Now hand it over.'

There was an expression of hatred on Neetie's face that made Cee Cee's heart race. She could feel her

185

blood moving angrily through her body and she knew she would gladly miss her flight to Los Angeles and the next week's worth of flights if that's what it would take to get the ring back for Nina.

'Very dramatic, Cee Cee,' Neetie said, now trying the soft-voice technique herself. 'Is that little speech from one of your movies?'

Good shot, you nasty cunt, Cee Cee thought, but what she said a little louder this time was, 'You want to see my movies? Tell you what. If you don't give me the ring, I'll get in and drive the limo through the plate-glass window of the building the way I did in the bar scene in *Jilted*.' Out of the corner of her eye Cee Cee looked at Nina, who had a tight-lipped look on her face which after their years together Cee Cee knew very well was holding in a smile. 'Or I'll stand in the street with a bullhorn the way I did in *The Long Walk* when I played the prison guard. Remember that one, Neetie? Only instead of barking orders I'll tell your nice neighbors that you steal from kids.'

Neetie's tan faded and her horrified face was a pasty color of beige now. 'You Hollywood trash,' she said, 'I could have gone to court a hundred times and taken this child away from you and maybe I still will if you don't mind your own business and get your trampy little self out of my –' But before she could finish her sentence, out of the building in a burst of gold lamé and rhinestones came Mrs Altschuler and Mrs Haber, the ladies from the pool.

'It's Cee Cee,' they both squealed, and they were each carrying writing pads and pens, which they proffered in a request for autographs, and Nina watched as Neetie tried to regain her composure and Cee Cee instantly turned into the charming gracious star she always was for her fans. Fussing over the women as much as they fussed over her.

'Hi, girls,' she said. 'Is it hot enough for you? Oh, honey, I love your necklace.'

'Anita keeps us posted on everything you do,' Mrs Haber said. 'We think it's so nice that you and Nina make such an effort to be close to her.'

Cee Cee looked into Neetie's black, angry, frustrated-by-the-intrusion eyes, and saw a flash of embarrassment.

'Oh, don't be silly,' Cee Cee said, 'Neetie is Nina's family, which naturally makes her *my* family. In fact, just as you came out the door, she was about to give Nina a ring that belonged to her sister Rose. Nina's grandmother. Isn't that generous of her?'

'Ooh, let's see. Gorgeous! You're giving *that* to her, Anita?'

As the women waited, Neetie slowly and reluctantly pulled the ring from her finger and placed it into Nina's outstretched hand.

'Thank you, Aunt Neet,' Nina said, giving her a little hug.

'Ahhh,' Mrs Altschuler said. 'That's adorable.'

'Listen,' Mrs Haber said, 'my mother, rest her soul, always told me, "If you don't have your family, who *do* you have?"'

Cee Cee and Nina rode for a long time in the air-conditioned hiss of the limousine, each of them thinking over the last few days, before Nina, who had been looking out the window at the causeway, said quietly, 'I thought you told me we should be nice and loving to our families, but you were pretty mean to Neetie.'

'You know what?' Cee Cee said. 'In her case I'll make an exception.'

They were almost at the airport when Cee Cee looked down at the seat and noticed Nina's hand there, realizing for the first time it was actually big enough to wear the emerald ring. Not quite big enough for it to fit on her ring finger, so she had put it on her index finger. Cee Cee placed her hand over Nina's and patted it gently.

For the next few weeks she spoke with Nathan several times a day. He grumbled and railed about everything from the medication and the nurses to the bad reception on his hospital television. One day when she called him the doctor was in the room, and Nathan put him on the phone. 'Cee Cee,' Doctor Feiffer said, as if he was greeting an old friend, 'he's doing so well, I recommended he take a trip out West. Think you can handle that?'

Cee Cee heard Nathan in the background saying something like, 'Hey! You're the doctor, for chrissake. Don't *ask* her, tell her.' Two weeks later when he arrived in Los Angeles he made it clear, even on the ride from the airport, that he was only staying for a short time because a Harriet Goldstein 'from Philly' was already counting the days until his return to Miami Beach because when he did they were probably going to 'shack up.'

On the first night as he sat at dinner Cee Cee watched him talking with his mouth full and getting so much spaghetti sauce on his face and then his napkin, that when Nina asked to be excused to go to the kitchen to get herself more milk, she gentled the napkin away from him and took it to the kitchen with her to replace it.

'She likes me,' Nathan said, looking at the still-swinging door to the kitchen. 'And it's a good thing too.'

'Why is that?' Cee Cee asked, knowing she was taking the bait.

'Because at this stage of the game, she's my only real chance at being a grandpa.'

Cee Cee smiled, then felt a wistful pang. 'Yeah, I guess I *am* getting a little past the time when I can give you a grandchild.'

'Hey, listen,' Nathan said, 'on the wall of the occupational therapy room at the convalescent home, they had a sign with a quote from Satchell Paige. A colored baseball player, before your time, a great man. It said "How old would you be, if you didn't know how old you was?"'

Cee Cee laughed. 'So what's the answer for you?' she asked.

'Two months ago, eighty-five. Today, twenty-five. How 'bout you?'

'Some mornings twenty-six, other mornings a hundred and twenty-six.'

'So on one of the mornings when you're twenty-six, grab some guy and make a baby,' he said, laughing a funny snorting laugh Cee Cee knew she sometimes used herself. 'I'm a *modern* guy. A free thinker,' he said.

Nina came out of the kitchen with a glass of milk and a fresh white cloth napkin, which she slid onto Nathan's lap with what looked like the expertise of a headwaiter. Nathan smiled a thank-you, then looked at Cee Cee. 'See? What'd I tell you?' he asked.

On the weekend he took Nina to Disneyland. It was the first visit for each of them and when they came home at ten at night, sunburned, exhausted, each wearing mouse ears with their names embroidered on the front, and both of them farther off the ground than the half a dozen Mylar helium balloons they were carrying, Cee Cee, who opened the front door to let them in, wasn't sure which of them she envied more.

Every night Nathan would call his girlfriend in Miami Beach and when she answered, Cee Cee could overhear him open the conversation by saying, 'Hiya, hot stuff.' He had the twinkle of the sheik of Araby every day now, and she felt tied to him, close to him, saw Nina blossom by having his attention, and she felt sad thinking about how overbearing her mother must have been with him to have kept this kind of spirit down.

One night when she got home, Nina and Nathan were throwing a Frisbee back and forth on the beach. It was already dark, so they were playing by the floodlights from the deck of the house. Nathan was showing off and catching the Frisbee behind his back, and Nina was shrieking loudly and diving for the Frisbee onto the sand. Cee Cee just stood on the deck and watched them for a long time before she called out to announce that she was home.

After a few days, Nina was able to tell Cee Cee lots of things she'd discovered about Nathan that Cee Cee had never known or imagined. Things that, when Nina told them to her, made Cee Cee laugh out loud. That Nathan liked his corned beef lean and his women fat. That he did a very funny imitation of a character named Rochester, who he told her used to be on the Jack Benny radio show, and that he loved to sing. Sing! Cee Cee couldn't believe it. The only song she'd ever heard him sing was 'The Sheik of Araby.'

That night while she brushed Nina's hair, a before-bed custom that had started in Carmel, Nina excitedly told her that she and Nathan had a surprise for her. 'Great,' Cee Cee said, tugging at a tangle.

'Ouch.'

'Sorry.'

'And after I get my nightgown on we want you to sit in the living room so we can show it to you. It's a duet, like when I sang "Ballin' the Jack" with you when I was little, except that this one has a little harmony to it, so sometimes I have to hold my ears so I don't get mixed up and sing his part instead of mine.'

'What's the song?' If it's 'The Sheik of Araby,' I'll kill him, Cee Cee thought.

'You'll see,' Nina said, sliding her nightgown on over her head and running down the hall to the guest room to get Nathan.

As Cee Cee sat on the living-room sofa getting ready to be the audience, Nathan came bounding into the living room as excited as a child, followed by Nina who whispered some conspiratorial words into his ear, then hid behind the drapes as Nathan stepped up onto the brick hearth, held his hand up to his face as if he had a microphone, and said, 'And now, direct from the Sands Hotel in Las Vegas, Nevada, that famous singing team of Nathan and Ninotchka.' Ninotchka was his pet name for Nina.

'No, Nina Barron,' came Nina's whispered voice from behind the drapes. Her bare feet were sticking out.

'Excuse me, Nathan Bloom and Nina Barron.'

Nina emerged, blushing and all smiles, the braces on her teeth gleaming as they caught the light from a living-room table lamp, her bangs hanging in her eyes, and she looked nervously at Nathan, who gave her a nod, then she began to sing in some barely recognizable minor key, 'I really can't stay.'

'But, baby, it's cold outside,' Nathan sang, and his voice by contrast was nothing short of great. Right on key, belting out the song as if all the world could hear him.

This is hysterical, Cee Cee thought, and she had to bite her lip to keep from laughing out loud.

'I've got to go 'way.'

'But, baby, it's cold outside.' Nathan was rocking back and forth snapping his fingers as if he was Stubby Kaye in *Guys and Dolls*.

'This evening has been so very nice . . .'

Her father. She had always assumed that her talent had come from Leona, only because she had spent her whole life having no idea who this man was. And he had tried to tell her so long ago that he was the one who carried the musical genes, but Leona had always shut him up.

'My mother will start to worry.'

'Been hoping that you'd drop in . . .'

Her father and Nina each had a faraway look in their eyes, as if they weren't a short fat man and an eleven-year-old girl standing in a living room, but two stars, playing to an audience of thousands, except that Nina was holding her fingers in her ears as promised, in order to block out Nathan's big voice.

'Ahh, but it's coooold outside!!!!' When they were finished they took hands and bowed a deep bow they had obviously rehearsed, and Cee Cee stood to give them a big ovation. Then the two of them hurried over to the sofa where she stood and all three of them hugged. A family hug. Because that's what we are, she thought. A silly little family of three lost souls. And it *was* cold outside.

Nathan's last night in Los Angeles was a night on which Cee Cee had a taping of her show. Nathan and Nina were coming to sit in the front row of the bleachers to watch. The house in Malibu was filled with the scent of Old Spice as Nathan dressed carefully in gray trousers, a light blue shirt, and a madras blazer, and then plastered down the wisps of remaining hair on the top of his head. Later at the studio, after the page led them to their taped-off seats, he lifted the back flaps of the jacket to sit as if he was wearing tails.

After Cee Cee sang her opening number and the audience applauded, while she waited for the next take to be set up, she came down to the bleachers to talk to the studio audience. It was what she did every week, usually asking for questions. Tonight after she sat on the edge of the runway she said, 'Ladies and gentlemen, a very special man is sitting out there with you. If it wasn't for this man, I wouldn't be here tonight. He fed me, he clothed me, and I got my singing voice from him. Please welcome someone who has known me for more years than I'll ever admit, my wonderful daddy, Nathan Bloom.'

The audience cheered, applauded, whistled, stomped, and craned their necks to see Nathan, who stood to greet their welcome with such aplomb it was as if he'd been rehearsing for this moment all his life. He bowed a little bow, nodding his bald head this way and that, and then waved an open-handed wave after which he blew a kiss. And when he did, both Cee Cee and Nina recognized the gesture. It was the one Cee Cee always made when the show was over and she took her last bow to say goodbye for now to her fans.

Harriet Goldstein
and
Nathan Bloom
are pleased to announce
their marriage
in Miami Beach, Florida
October 1st, 1986

Michael,

Just a note to ask if you ever received any of my earlier notes mentioning how I believe it would mean a lot to Nina to know you, even if it was just for a short visit.

Will you let me know?

Cee Cee

Old-fashioned variety shows disappeared for good reason. They were dumb. With skits that wouldn't cut it in the high-school play, awkward cross talk, Muzak-like music, and too many costume changes. The production values of one musical number on MTV have made the smoke-filled special effects, or the Vaseline-covered screen which suddenly appears when a singer performs a love song on network television, look downright silly. The current proliferation of talk shows, and the intimate glimpses they offer into the personal lives of stars, make the banal chitchat on variety TV seem archaic.

Somehow, Cee Cee Bloom has kept her own variety show going and in the top ten, in spite of an abundance of the elements mentioned above. Cee Cee is a dinosaur in that she's one of the few existing comediennes who can really belt out a song as well as dance her feet off, but soon, despite her extraordinary gifts and Herculean effort to keep it all afloat, even the invincible Bloom won't be able to keep the dying form from expiring. Like its predecessor and most traceable influence, vaudeville, the variety show is soon to bid us a fond adieu, and in the future our glimpses of it will pass by us only as a part of those 'Remember When' collections of the good old days.

Not to worry for Cee Cee Bloom, however. A talent like hers will always find greener and more up-to-date pastures.

LOS ANGELES, CALIFORNIA

August 1990

Hal looked better than Cee Cee had ever seen him as he emerged from the baggage-claim area. When he spotted her driver Jake he waved a friendly wave, and when Jake, who had been chatting with an airport security guard, saw Hal walking toward the car, he hurried to relieve him of his luggage.

'Careful,' Hal warned, 'there are lots of goodies in those bags.' When he opened the back door of the car to get in, he was surprised to see Cee Cee waiting for him. 'Hey!!!' he shouted, sliding in close to her in the backseat and giving her a big bear hug. 'You didn't have to make this trip,' he said, but Cee Cee could tell how completely delighted he was that she had.

'Yes I did,' she said, 'because you're not the only one I'm picking up here.' She looked at her watch and then back at Hal. 'Zero minus two hours,' she said.

'You're not going to fall apart on me are you?' he asked.

'Why would I do that? It's only the biggest, most important day of my life.'

The front door of the car opened and Jake stuck his head in. 'Think I ought to go up to the gate and see what's happening?' he asked Cee Cee. 'According to the monitor, the flight's in.'

'Maybe you should,' Cee Cee said, and after a word with the airport security guard about not ticketing the VIP car, Jake was gone through the doors into the terminal.

'Do you think it's too late?' Cee Cee asked Hal. 'Do you think it still means something?'

'I think it means the world,' Hal said as she put her head against his shoulder, 'more than anything you've ever done.'

The airport doors opened again and a stream of people emerged, and at the end of the stream was Jake, and when Cee Cee saw who he had in tow she sat forward, opened the car door, and with a happy welcoming smile got out of the car, knowing that her appearance was causing its usual excitement, but she didn't care. 'Have I got a hug for you,' she said, moving forward with tears in her eyes. 'Thank you for being here.'

Nathan Bloom and Mrs Nathan Bloom, the former Harriet Goldstein, stood arms-around-one-another as smiling and pudgy as Tweedle-Dee and Tweedle-Dum. 'Please,' the little sweet-faced lady said, 'are you kidding? For our children we'll go anywhere. After all, now you're *my* daughter too, right?'

'You bet,' Cee Cee said, wondering what Leona would have thought of this woman, Cee Cee's stepmother. The idea of Nathan in love was too delicious to believe. And he was. She could tell by the glow on his cheeks.

'Listen, for us it's another honeymoon. From here we go on to San Diego,' Nathan said, and Cee Cee recognized that sexy little twinkle in his eyes she had seen there only fleetingly years ago. Jake loaded their bags into the trunk of the limo and Cee Cee made the introductions to Hal.

'Not bad for two old kokkers, right?' Harriet asked Hal as she slid onto one of the rumble seats across from Nathan. 'I hate to say it, but the only time I was in a limousine before this was to my late husband's, may he rest in peace, funeral. Pooh, pooh, pooh. So life is full of surprises.'

'It sure is,' Hal said, sitting close to Cee Cee and patting her on the leg.

Jake got into the driver's seat, pulled the rearview mirror down, and looked at all of them in the backseat.

'All in?' he asked.

'Only one more stop, Jakie,' Cee Cee said.

'You got it,' Jake told her, and they were on their way.

CABO SAN LUCAS

1987

The incident in Cabo San Lucas came right on the heels of Nina's dancing school recital, which was probably what made Cee Cee handle it the way she did. Still, it was inexcusable and it wasn't until she looked back on it that she realized the way she behaved was a page torn from the worst part of her life with Leona. Only this time instead of Leona, it was Cee Cee standing out there during Nina's rehearsal in the auditorium at the Elks Club, mouthing the words of the song and poking her fingers into the corners of her own lips, pushing them up to make a smile so that when Nina glanced out there she would see her and be reminded to smile at the audience. Now *that* was life with Leona to a frigging 'T.'

As if it was yesterday Cee Cee remembered the way her fat, unhappy mother used to sit in a chair by the wall during all of Cee Cee's sweaty tap and ballet and jazz classes. And while the other mothers went outside to have a cigarette and gossip, Leona would listen to every word the dance teacher said to the kids, and write the names of the steps in the dance routine into a little spiral notebook that she would pull out later at home, so she could drill Cee Cee relentlessly. In fact, all these years later when Cee Cee was rehearsing a tap number for her show, in the back of her head she could still hear Leona's voice calling the steps out to her. *Step shuffle ball change, step shuffle ball change, step brush hop, step brush hop.*

Today she had canceled some meetings after Nina asked her to please come to a rehearsal of the recital because, she confided to Cee Cee, she was afraid at the performance she would be so nervous she might 'mess up,' and she wanted Cee Cee to see her dance while she was relatively calm. All year long the dance classes had been closed, so Cee Cee had never been able to come and watch, and now when the girls came running out on the stage to the blasting music, what Cee Cee had imagined would be an amateurish exercise looked surprisingly professional. But the most extraordinary surprise of all was the way Nina, ordinarily so low-key in the presentation of herself, now pushed back her shoulders and held her chin high and danced with a confident presence Cee Cee had never seen in her.

The girls were performing to a recording of Irene Cara singing 'Fame,' and their little voices belted out the lyrics along with the record as they moved across the stage at the Elks Club, as Cee Cee found herself covered with goose bumps while she watched, wondering if it was seeing Nina so transformed or the message of the song that was getting to her.

> I'm gonna live forever
> I'm gonna learn to fly high
> I feel it comin' together
> People will see me and die.

When Nina looked out into the semidarkness at Cee Cee, it was with an expression hungry for approval. Cee Cee knew it instantly and lifted a hand with thumb and forefinger circled as a high sign, the same one Leona had given her at every recital, and when Nina saw the gesture, her pretty little chin rose and her eyes flashed.

> I'm gonna make it to heaven

Light up the sky like a flame
I'm gonna live forever
Baby, remember my name.

The sentiment in those lyrics! How that feeling had
burned in Cee Cee every day of her life, stronger than
any other need, until it compelled her to spend all of
her energy moving toward the single-minded goal of
success in her career. The success she now had. Once,
years ago, during the long hungry times when she was
getting nowhere as a performer, she had walked onto
the location of a film on a New York street where they
were casting extras.

'Please,' she begged the second assistant director,
'just let me walk by in a crowd.'

'We're not casting uglies today, honey,' the guy had
said, and turned away to talk to someone else, and the
rejection had burned into Cee Cee's chest, but still she
pressed him, going after him and tugging on his arm.

'Hey, listen, I'll wear a hat with a veil. Nobody will
see what I look like. Please let me get a movie credit
on my résumé.'

'Get lost,' the son-of-a-bitch, rude with his own
little piece of power, said without even looking at her.

Stung and hot-faced with rage, Cee Cee stood on
that New York street, ringing with unyielding resolve,
and just as the director was about to shoot a scene, in
fact they were already on a bell and rolling, she shouted
at the top of her lungs, 'One of these days you assholes
are gonna be beggin' *me* for a job.' A few people on the
set had laughed, and the irate director had yelled,
'Cut,' and had to get everybody settled down again
while two burly guys on a signal from the A.D. picked
Cee Cee up by the elbows and walked her a block
away.

She had long ago forgotten who that director was and what the picture was they were making on the New York street, but just a few weeks ago a woman who was an extra on Cee Cee's show in the French Café sketch told her she had been in New York working on that shoot and had never forgotten that determined little girl. 'I guess,' the woman, who was a professional extra, said, 'that's the kind of belief you have to have in yourself in order to survive in this fucking business.'

And the woman was right. The day after Nina's recital Cee Cee and Nina would fly down to Cabo San Lucas, where Cee Cee was starring in a new picture. It was her first feature film in years. It had taken all those seasons of slaving away on television to become so hot again that the movie studios finally believed in her renewed potential to sell tickets. She was looking forward to it. Martin Kane, the director, was good at getting strong emotional work out of actors, and she knew he would lean on her to get her best. And she'd managed to wangle the job of unit still photographer for her latest flame, Scott Becker, the young, adorable guy she'd met at Goldie Hawn's party. So he was a few years younger, like seven or eight, maybe nine, but he was a hot little honey, and she needed that now.

Nina's dance teacher was rehearsing the curtain call, and she was having a hard time getting everybody lined up on the stage. The girls fussed and took forever coming from one side of the wings, where they'd been crowded, since the Elks Club wasn't exactly the Hollywood Bowl, waiting for a turn to enter and take an individual bow. Each time the teacher tried to get them out onstage it was an endless struggle with bad timing, giggles, improper spacing, so she'd stop the music and send them off to try their entrances again from the beginning. Cee Cee looked at her watch. It was five o'clock. She was supposed to have a conference call with Martin Kane and the producer of the new film at six. If the rehearsal kept going like this, she'd never make it. Maybe she could help move things along here so they could all go home.

'Excuse me,' she said, walking down to the front row of folding chairs and tapping the dance teacher on the shoulder. The teacher turned quickly and Cee Cee could tell by the woman's expression that she was harassed and tense. She now had the entire cast, thirty girls between the ages of ten and fourteen, up on the stage.

'Yes?' she said to Cee Cee.

'Well, I wanted to tell you that I know a little bit about this kind of thing and maybe if I could just explain how we did . . .'

The teacher's look stopped her. She was a long-necked long-waisted, regal-looking woman in her fifties with white hair pulled back in a severe bun. She was wearing a long-sleeved black leotard under a rehearsal skirt, which made her look like one of those modern dancers in an old Jules Feiffer cartoon who leap and dance to poetry.

'Mothers in the back row, or wait in the car, please,' she said tense-jawed to Cee Cee.

This woman's got to be kidding, Cee Cee thought. She obviously has no idea who she's talking to. 'Hey,' she said, 'I understand you're under pressure, but I've been in a lot of Broadway musicals. I've worked with every choreographer from Jerome Robbins to Jeffrey Hornaday and I'm telling you if you start with half of the girls on one side and the other half on the other, you're going to move them faster and get the feel of a bigger production number.' There, she thought, that ought to do it.

The teacher's face was stone. 'I never have them enter from both sides,' she said in measured tones.

'Yeah, well maybe not, but if you try it you're gonna see that it takes half the time.'

'Will you please sit down?' the teacher said. Obviously she wasn't understanding Cee Cee's point.

'Actually you could have the two groups cross one another. That's how we did it in the revival of *High Button Shoes*.'

Miss Olivia snapped her head away from Cee Cee, looked at the girls on the stage, and said loudly to them, 'All right, one more time. Clear the stage.' Some of the girls straggled slowly in the direction of the wings, a few didn't move. This woman is crazy, Cee Cee thought. Here I am offering her the highest-priced help around for free. About to teach her and the girls Jerome Robbins's choreography, and she's ignoring me? Oh I get it! She probably thinks I'm one of the regular women who come here all the time. Those mothers who have nothing else to do but sit and drive her crazy all year round. She figures I'm one of them. Doesn't know who I am. Of course once I explain, she'll know it's a matter of one professional talking to another.

'Uh . . . Miss Olivia,' Cee Cee said, and the teacher turned to her with narrowed eyes. 'You realize of course who I –'

But before Cee Cee could tell her exactly which credentials she had that gave her the right to interrupt the rehearsal, the teacher leaned toward her and spoke so close into her face Cee Cee could smell the Dynamint she had in her mouth. 'In *this* room,' she said, 'you are Nina's mother.' Without looking, Cee Cee could feel that the girls who had been standing upstage and the ones who had started to walk away were now all in one clump downstage listening to the exchange between the two women.

She could hear the rustling of the net tutus as they brushed against one another and the whirr of the overworked air conditioner while she looked into the huge Keane painting eyes of the stone-faced Miss Olivia and realized there was no getting around the fact that this woman, who had knocked herself out all year to get these girls this far, was ten thousand percent right, and Cee Cee had been a total jackass to intrude.

In fact, not only did she know that, but so did every kid on that stage, including Nina at whom Cee Cee couldn't look, because she was afraid to see one of *those* expressions the kid had been giving her lately, expressions that according to the books were just what to expect from kids her age.

> Children in this stage of their lives crave a lot of attention, but on the other hand they don't want to stand out from the crowd. Nothing is more devastating than to be singled out for punishment or even praise in the classroom, or to be considered different in any way. If mother has the nerve to appear at school, daughter is mortified for days afterwards.

Nina had invited her to the rehearsal, but she hadn't counted on Cee Cee behaving like an egomaniac in front of the entire dancing class. Now Cee Cee felt so dumb she thought that if life was fair, the ceiling would fall in on her head and everyone would feel so sorry for her they'd forget what a schmuck she'd been. And now they all were waiting in this eternity of a moment for her to say something.

'I hear you,' she said to the teacher, 'and I'm sorry.'

'What was that?' Miss Olivia asked, with the clear implication that she wanted Cee Cee to repeat her apology loud enough for the benefit of the girls.

'I said,' Cee Cee said, obligingly louder, 'I'm sorry, Miss Olivia,' and as the rehearsal resumed, she moved to the back row where she sat for a long time trying to calm her feelings of despising herself, and eventually she became so caught up in watching the girls that she forgot all about the conference call she was expecting at home. In fact, by the end of the rehearsal she had to admit grudgingly the finale looked great, and so did every other number in the show.

Nina seemed actually to have talent, and her budding beauty was so mesmerizing that half the battle was won the minute she appeared onstage because you didn't want to look at anyone else. At least Cee Cee didn't. She sat watching her as dopey with admiration as any stage mother alive. So maybe the kid wasn't a fireball, crazed and driven and needy for the audience's love the way Cee Cee had always been, but there was a genuine spark there. Cee Cee wasn't making it up, and it wasn't just because Nina was hers that she thought that either. The kid was really good. Which was why she let what happened in Cabo San Lucas happen, and that was a mistake she wished she could erase.

The night the plane landed bringing the two of them to the Los Cabos location, it was pouring rain. The airplane stood on the field far away from the terminal until finally around the building through the teeming rain came the lights of a car. After the pilot opened an umbrella and walked Cee Cee and Nina down the steps of the studio's private jet and the driver made sure they were safe in the backseat of the limo, Nina settled comfortably into the seat and wanted to know all about the movie Cee Cee was here to make.

Over the last few years she had spent a great deal of time on the set of Cee Cee's television show, but this would be her first time on location for a film, and the idea of spending a few weeks in a pretty place she'd seen in the brochures seemed to please her. They would be staying and shooting at the Palmilla Hotel. As the car moved along on the bumpy dark road toward the hotel, Cee Cee told her the story of the film, which was about a family who was vacationing together as the marriage of the parents was falling apart.

'You mean there're kids in this?' Nina asked.

'Two kids,' Cee Cee told her. 'Stacy and Sammy are the names of the characters, the daughter and the son. Chelsea Bain plays Stacy. You'll like her. She's an amazing little actress.'

In the morning, in the dining room of the hotel, Nina was introduced to dozens of people involved with the production – the hairdresser, the makeup man, the assistant directors – and all of them fussed over her, and then looked at Cee Cee and said things like, 'She's so beautiful,' as if Nina wasn't even sitting there, and Cee Cee would say, 'Thank you,' as if she had something to do with it.

When Chelsea Bain and her mother walked into the beam-ceilinged, tile-floored room and Nina spotted her, her heart pounded and she felt a feeling in her throat she didn't want to admit to herself was jealousy. And when the child actress who had obviously been chosen because of her close resemblance to Cee Cee was introduced to Cee Cee and told her, 'You're my idol,' and Cee Cee answered, 'Aren't you a doll!' Nina wanted to leave the table. And Chelsea was from New York, so she even had that little New York toughness in her speech that Cee Cee had. As the two of them talked about the script for the film, Nina definitely felt wounded, left out, more than she ever did when Cee Cee paid attention to other adults.

While Chelsea's mother took a seat at a distant table and Cee Cee moved to another table to talk to the producer, Chelsea remained, looking Nina over, sizing her up, then said, 'You're her daughter? Are you kidding? I look more like her than you do! Oh, yeah. That's 'cause you're not her *real* daughter. Right?'

Nina didn't answer.

'My mom told me about you and her, and your real mom is dead. Right?'

Nina nodded.

'Tough break,' Chelsea said, only it wasn't at all sympathetic, and then she walked away and Nina hated her. And she hated her even more when Cee Cee came back to the table and after ordering breakfast for them in her version of Spanish, which sounded to Nina like Speedy Gonzalez talking to Daffy Duck, she told Nina, with a gesture toward the table where Chelsea and her mother sat, 'I saw that kid's screen test. She was so good she jumped right off the screen. Wait till you see her work.' She also told Nina for the hundredth time to drink only the bottled water.

The atmosphere on the set was loud and friendly, and Nina couldn't decide which member of the crew was the cutest. All of the men were handsome and flirted with her, and when they were together buzzing around the set, the abundance of maleness made her think of the way she imagined a band of pirates to behave, muscular and sweaty and sexy. But the process of making a movie was so slow and painstaking, that after a few days she realized that watching it was extraordinarily dull.

The amount of time it took so many people to move so many cables so few feet seemed ridiculously long to her, and finally she dropped out and spent most of her time under a beach umbrella near the water reading.

At night she would have dinner with Cee Cee and the cast and crew from a big Mexican buffet and watch Scott, the young still photographer, flirt with Cee Cee and Cee Cee flirt back. And she suspected that when she was asleep Cee Cee was probably slipping away to be alone with him.

The tropical muggy evenings after dinner were spent in the large bar off the lobby, overlooking the sea, where the grating sound of the blender mixing the margaritas was a counterpoint to the three-piece combo. One night there was a band in the lounge after dinner, and while everyone from the film sat being cooled by the breeze from the sea, Cee Cee went up on the little bandstand and sang, 'Here's That Rainy Day,' and 'My Funny Valentine' and some other really old songs. And afterward while the crew was cheering and stomping for her singing and Scott handed her a bottle of beer, Nina heard her say to him, 'Bet you never even heard of those songs, kid,' and he laughed and put his arm around her waist, and when the band played some other moony love song, he tugged Cee Cee by the arm and pulled her out on the dance floor.

'I think if we dance any closer than this we get thrown in a Mexican prison,' Nina heard Scott say, and Cee Cee laughed.

'Looks like Cee Cee's mushing out,' Nina heard a voice say, and it was Chelsea Bain, whose mom was drinking a margarita at the bar and smoking a cigarette and talking to one of the cameramen. And it was true, Cee Cee was definitely looking with goo-goo eyes at Scott, who Nina had to admit was really cool, but still she felt weird about it. As if she should maybe run over there and stand in front of them so nobody else could see.

'My mom's single too, so I understand,' Chelsea

told her. 'They get horny.' Nina felt her own face and body fill with an uncomfortable heat at that thought. 'Afterward they always hate themselves, but at the moment if you try and warn them, they make you go to your room and play with your Barbies.' Nina knew Cee Cee hadn't had any real boyfriend in a long while, maybe since John Perry left her for the second time. There were dates, guys who came over, took her to a screening at the studio, even some who sent her flowers, but the ones she liked, the men she got all dolled up to be with, talked to in her 'other voice' on the phone, were always the ones who didn't seem to stay around too long, and the ones who were crazy about her, like sweet and wonderful Hal Lieberman, she didn't even consider as boy friends.

'Wanna come over to my room?' Chelsea asked. Nina looked into Chelsea's eyes. There was something she had learned to look for in the eyes of kids who made overtures of friendship to her over the last few years, a subtle, indescribable, too-eager look which meant they had no real interest in *her* but were longing somehow to be connected to Cee Cee. At home in Los Angeles it came in the form of invitations to birthday parties of kids she hardly knew, kids who, probably encouraged by their parents, would invite Nina in the hope that Cee Cee would drive her to the party or pick her up at the party so the parents could meet Cee Cee and tell their friends that they had.

More than once on the playground at school Nina would suddenly spot two or three kids looking her over, saying, 'No she's not. Her last name is Barron, not Bloom. Let's ask her. You ask her. Are you Cee Cee Bloom's daughter?' When her answer was affirmative, sometimes they would just giggle and walk away, sometimes they would ask lots of none-of-their-business questions, and sometimes they would be mean and say things about Cee Cee like, 'I think she's dopey looking.'

In Chelsea Bain's invitation to leave the bar there was none of that stuff going on, so Nina said yes. Leaving unnoticed, they walked silently through the tropical night, up the stone path to the suite Chelsea shared with her mother.

'I'm shooting tomorrow afternoon,' Chelsea said, taking a Coke out of the refrigerator in the bar area and pouring it over a glassful of ice. 'Want some?'

'No thanks.'

'I'm doing my real big scene where I beg my father not to get a divorce. It's the one I did in the test. My acting coach got me ready and we worked real hard on my emotional memory. Know what that means?' Nina didn't. 'It's like, when you're acting a scene, you just work off of things that have happened to you in your own real life that are like the ones you're acting. So I'm gonna just use the way I felt when my real mom and dad split up. Only in real life my dad left my mom for this slut named Karly at his office, and in the movie it's different. You get it? I just say the lines and think about the day my dad left us and I get so sad about that, that I cry and it looks like I'm crying over the characters Cee Cee and Michael Nouri play who are splitting up in the movie.'

Nina thought emotional memory sounded really interesting, and also that she had such a storehouse of emotional memories herself, she could probably be a really good actress too.

'Want to run lines?' Chelsea asked her.

'Huh?'

'You know. Hold book for me. I'll give you the script and you can follow along with the words while I say them and make sure I have 'em right.'

'Okay.' Nina was excited. She was being included. Not just watching the way she did at the taping of Cee Cee's show, but now she had a job, running lines with one of the actresses in the movie. Chelsea handed her a dog-eared script and opened it to a page on which the dialogue and action for the character of Stacy had been highlighted in yellow.

'Ready?' she asked Nina.

'Yes,' Nina said, feeling very important.

'You give me my cues, read the lines before Stacy's, and I'll give you back my lines. Go.'

First came a speech from the character of Mitch, the father. 'I guess you know what's going on, don't you, baby?' Nina read, and when she looked up at Chelsea she could see that the girl was throwing herself into the character, right there in the hotel room dressed in her white OP shorts and a peach La Coste shirt – her little eyes filled with tears and her funny Cee Cee-like face seemed to crumble and she said, 'Yes, Dad, and I want you to love Mommy, and I want you to come home.'

'I do love her, but I can't live with her anymore. There are problems. Insurmountable problems that someday you'll understand . . .'

'Understand. No. I won't ever understand how you can love Linda more than my mom. We were a family, we were like on television, me and you and Mom and Sammy,' Chelsea said, and real tears were coming down her face. By the end of the scene she was sobbing so hard with her head in her hands that Nina set the script on the floor and reached out to comfort her, but before she could touch her, Chelsea's head bobbed up and she was wiping away the tears and laughing. 'So? Are we talkin' Oscar time here, my friend, or what?' she asked. Nina was dazzled, amazed that someone her own age could be so in control that she could pull those tears out when she needed them and then just make them go away.

The knock on the door was Cee Cee coming to find Nina and take her back to their suite. Her hair was messy and her makeup was smeared and she had a glassy look in her eyes that made Nina think she and Scott had probably been 'making out,' or maybe even more. Before the two of them left to go to their suite, Chelsea's mom came in and said, 'Into bed, girl. Big day tomorrow.' Then Cee Cee hugged Chelsea and they talked about how exciting it was that tomorrow was Chelsea's big shooting day, and about how tough it was to shoot scenes out of sequence, since her emotional scene was being shot long before the introductory scenes, and while they talked their actressy talk, Nina felt out of it again.

That night she couldn't get the scene she and Chelsea had read out of her mind, and the way Chelsea had been able just to call those tears up out of nowhere. 'I want you to love Mommy. And I want you to come home.' She fell asleep with the scene replaying itself over and over in her head. It was so early in the morning that it was still dark when she heard the phone ring in Cee Cee's room, but it wasn't just a wake-up call. It was a conversation of which Nina could hear bits and pieces, starting with 'What? Oh no. What do they *think* it is? I thought we warned her about that.'

Nina fell back to sleep, and a few hours later when she woke and dressed and strolled over to the dining room where the film was supposed to be shooting that day, none of the cast and crew were there. 'They're in the lobby,' one of the waiters told her, so she walked downstairs to the lobby where the company was all spread out, their big thick cables, lights, and cameras everywhere as they shot a scene where Cee Cee and the little boy who played the son have a fight while they're checking into the hotel.

'Quiet down, people, we're rolling.'

After the shot Cee Cee noticed Nina sitting just behind the cameras and hurried over with a concerned look on her face. 'Do you feel okay?' she asked Nina.

'Fine,' Nina said.

Cee Cee looked relieved. 'Chelsea was rushed to the hospital early this morning,' Cee Cee told her. 'Montezuma's revenge. Already. And on top of that she was up all night puking her guts out.'

'Thanks for sharing that, Cee,' Nina said, feeling a little queasy herself at the image of poor Chelsea about whose poor health she wouldn't have felt nearly as bad before last night as she did now that the girl had become her friend.

'So we're shooting around her for now,' Cee Cee told her, while her makeup lady powdered her face with a powder brush. 'That's why we're doing these scenes down here so we can put her stuff off for a day or two.'

But a long hot day or two of shooting passed and Chelsea, confined to her hotel room, was still so sick she didn't even want to talk to anyone but Nina who came by and taught her some card games and card tricks, and just to make sure Chelsea would stay fresh for the day when she was well enough to go back to work, they ran lines over and over again. Finally, by the fourth day she said she was feeling better and they were scheduling her first shooting day for Thursday, but that morning when she stood up to walk to the bathroom she collapsed to the floor.

She was so depleted and weak there was no chance

she was going to be able to get on a set within the next few days and play the demanding emotional part. Everyone on the crew was saying that maybe the worse the child looked, the better it was for the story, but nobody believed that, and Martin, the director, spent a lot of time frantically talking on the only telephone the hotel had, which was at a makeshift desk in a little glass cubicle right near the registration desk. Nina pretended to be playing with the big squawking parrot in the cage nearby just to overhear his conversation.

'The child can barely stand up,' she heard him say angrily, as if it was Chelsea's own fault she was sick. 'What about the girl who came in second? The pudgy one who dyed her hair red for the audition? Well, see if we can get her *off* the sitcom. Just for ten days of shooting in a major motion picture. Tell the agent her success will be good for the sitcom. I don't give a shit what you tell him. Just get me somebody fast.'

That night an ambulance came to the hotel to pick up Chelsea and take her to the studio airplane, which was rushing her back to Los Angeles to see a specialist. Everyone from the film crew was there and they all watched as Cee Cee walked over to the stretcher while they carried Chelsea out, and hugged her frail little body, and then hugged her worried-looking mother who followed behind. Nina walked over too and squeezed Chelsea's hand and got a weak smile in return.

It was just as the ambulance pulled out of sight that Cee Cee stood next to Nina and said softly, so no one else in the crowd could hear, and so softly Nina was certain she had to be hearing wrong, 'How would you like to play the part of Stacy?'

'Huh?'

'I mean, I know you don't look like my daughter, but you do look as if you could be Michael Nouri's daughter, and if I coached you I'll bet you could play those scenes. Don't you think? I mean if I hadn't seen you steal the show at the dancing school recital, I wouldn't even mention it, but you did.'.

Play the part of Stacy in a movie, with Cee Cee? For an instant Nina's heart sank with fear, then the idea started to excite her. The idea was so heady it didn't seem possible. Especially because Cee Cee seemed to really want her to do it. Seemed to think she could handle it. 'I mean, what do you think?' Cee Cee asked her, and Nina was embarrassed because she knew her face was flushed with too much need.

'Um . . . I could try,' was all she could say, and Cee Cee slapped her a congratulatory slap on the back and said, 'Good for you, kiddo. I'll tell Martin.'

Late in the day when the sun was starting to set, Cee Cee brought Martin, who smelled of too much cologne, over to the suite where they sat with Nina in the living room going over the part of Stacy scene by scene. Nina felt afraid, but she relaxed a little when she realized how many of the scenes she already knew by heart just from going over them with Chelsea. It felt funny now being the one who was saying the lines while Cee Cee and Martin gave her the cues, encouraging her, praising her, never taking their eyes from her. And all of the line readings were the ones she had heard Chelsea give over and over while Nina was next to her sickbed.

Cee Cee played the scenes with her, treating her the way Nina had always seen her treat the other people she worked with, gently and with a professional respect. And Martin, who had only nodded at Nina perfunctorily at meals and looked at her every time she had been around where they were shooting as if she was a necessary annoyance, was now calling her 'darling' and asking her opinion about whether or not she thought a girl her age would say the words as written in the script, or if there was some other way she wanted to say those words that would feel more comfortable to her.

That night Michael Nouri came over to the suite and he and Nina worked on the big crying scene, the one Chelsea was supposed to shoot the morning she got sick. Martin stayed in the room and worked with them, but Cee Cee said she had some things to do and discreetly slipped out. Nina felt a little afraid, but she remembered Chelsea rehearsing the scene and just copied what she had seen her do, and when she finished she actually had a few tears on her face, and both Martin and Michael Nouri said, 'Nice work.'

'Tomorrow we'll shoot the big scene. After that, it'll be a breeze for you,' Martin told her, and he left. For hours Nina laid on the bed in her room, her head spinning wildly. She knew the truth about all this was that they were desperate. That's why they were giving her the chance to play the part. She had seen them running videos of various kids that casting directors back in Los Angeles had rushed to them, and none of the girls they looked at seemed to interest them. From bits and pieces of things she overheard Martin say to other people, it was clear that Cee Cee had somehow convinced him to take a chance on using Nina in the part. 'Cee Cee says she'll be able to get her through it,' she overheard Martin say to the producer. 'I think her genuine closeness with Cee Cee will play through and work for them both in the mother-daughter stuff.'

Up until the dance recital and all the fuss that went

with it, like the flowers Cee Cee gave her and the raves for her hard work from Miss Olivia and the other parents, Nina had never wanted to be in show business. Thought just the way her mother always did, that it was dumb and brassy and full of showoffs, and the only reason she began taking dancing classes was because it was good for her posture and great exercise. In Sarasota, when she was little, she went to dancing school and the recitals were simply a necessary evil insisted on by the teachers, who wanted to prove to the parents that the money they'd invested in all of those lessons wasn't being wasted, although in most cases it was.

But now Nina was getting the chance that other people only dreamed about and she knew it. 'Are we talkin' Oscar time here, my friend, or what?' she remembered Chelsea saying to her that night. Oscar time. What if *she* was nominated for an Oscar? The Oscars were a subject that could send Cee Cee up a wall. They had snubbed her repeatedly in the early part of her career, and she never failed to look like a wounded puppy anytime anyone talked about them. In fact Nina was sure that the biggest attraction to the part of Jeannie, the wife in this film, was that she was such a sympathetic character, Cee Cee had to get a nomination for playing the part.

But what if she didn't and Nina got one for playing Stacy? Or what if they both did? Didn't that happen one year? Two actresses had to share the Oscar? Cee Cee and Nina would share it. Take turns keeping the statue in their rooms at home. 'I'd like to thank the cast and crew, and most of all Cee Cee, who always believed in me,' she would say. And Cee Cee would say, 'And I'd like to thank Nina.' By the time Cee Cee got back to the room, it was late and Nina was sound asleep on top of the bed with the script lying open on her chest.

In the early morning the wardrobe lady went through Nina's own clothes and picked a few that would be right for her to wear in the film, and Frank the makeup man gently dabbed some makeup base on her face and a lot of powder and then some blusher and used an eyelash curler which he held very close to her eye while she tried not to blink, and then he closed it lightly and asked her, 'Do I have any skin?' and when she told him no he squeezed the eyelash curler hard and curled the lashes of her right eye, then did the same to the lashes of her left. While the hairdresser was brushing her hair, Nina looked in the mirror and saw her very pretty self looking back at her.

Cee Cee flitted in and out of the makeup trailer to see how Nina was, and she seemed much more nervous than Nina had ever seen her when she was going to shoot a scene herself. 'You okay?' she kept asking Nina, but not waiting for the answer. Nina was glad her first scenes weren't with Cee Cee so Cee Cee could watch and tell her how good they were. Just as the hairdresser had the last stray hair sprayed down, Martin's cologne wafted into the trailer followed by Martin, who looked a little shaky when he took Nina's hand.

'How do you feel?' he asked her.

'Great,' she said. 'How do *you* feel?' That made him laugh a funny little laugh and relax a little. People made too much of a big deal about acting. Probably to make themselves think they deserved all the zillions of dollars actors got paid, because this was a snap. All she had to do now was go out there, sit at that table with handsome Michael Nouri, and say the words she knew so well she could say them backwards if she had to, and then the worst part of this would be over. And soon the summer would be over and she could go back to school and wait for the picture to be released. And everyone in her school would come to the premiere and faint at how good she was. In fact, maybe she would get an agent and get jobs in other pictures, or maybe just be in ones that Cee Cee made.

'All right, people, we're going to have a rehearsal,' Martin said, and he sat next to Nina in the seat where Michael Nouri would sit when they started shooting, and he took Nina's hand. The crew was moving around quietly, and Martin spoke softly to her in what was nearly a whisper. 'Nina, I want you to remember all the things we talked about, how deeply this girl is feeling her pain, how enormous a loss it is for her to have her father leave the family.' Then he took a deep breath and moved forward in his chair so he could be closer to her and spoke confidentially, 'Now,' he said, 'you probably remember some of your own losses,' then he paused as if he was summoning the next part of his speech and said, 'Like when your mother died. I know that you were there with her when she did, so you remember what it felt like to suddenly be left alone in the world, to know that you would never see your mother again. To feel her being ripped away from you, don't you?'

The crew was turning the lights on now, trying different ones and moving them around, and overlaid on the already humid morning, it was blasting hot where Nina sat unable to look at Martin's face, so she stared at the gold chain around his suntanned neck and chest, through his open Hawaiian flowered shirt. She knew that he was trying to get her to feel sad so that she would be able to cry. Trying to get her to use an emotional memory, that was what Chelsea had called it, because his words were cutting into her chest and making her feel sick. Up until this minute she had forgotten about emotional memory, and what she had done at all of the rehearsals was just to imitate the way Chelsea looked when she did it. But Martin was telling her now to use her own life.

'Remember the specifics. How she looked lying in that bed on that last day, feelings of fear and rage and need that you had, because that's what Stacy is feeling when she talks to her father and begs him to keep the family together. He's abandoning them just the way you must have felt your mother was abandoning you, and she's longing for a family the way you probably had your whole life.' He was still whispering, and she knew that the usual noisy crew were tiptoeing around at his request so that he could do what he was doing, getting her in the mood, the saddest possible mood so that when he slid out of the seat and Michael Nouri slid into it, she would be hurting and sad.

Martin kept talking to her in his whisper, but she wasn't listening anymore. She was thinking about her mother in that bed in Carmel, how it felt to walk into that room and see her there, the searing pain of her mother's last day on earth when she lay there so gray on the bed, tubes coming from every part of her, not even looking human anymore. And then Martin was no longer next to her, he had slipped away and Michael Nouri was sitting in his place, and Nina's mind was in the sickroom with Bertie, and she sunk low in the chair as there was a bell, a clacker, and from very far away she heard Martin say, 'Action!'

'You know what's going on, don't you, baby?' Michael Nouri said to Nina.

My turn. It's my turn, Nina thought, so hot that she was sure her face was sweating, because her upper lip felt wet. Medicine bottles, hypodermic needles, the intravenous being pumped into her mother.

'Yes, Dad, I know, and I want you to love Mommy.' There. She said it. But Michael Nouri looked different to her now as she looked into his eyes. Worried or something.

'I do love her, but I can't live with her anymore. There are problems. Insurmountable problems that someday you'll understand when you're old enough to have a relationship of your own and when you're an adult and . . .'

Something was wrong. That wasn't the cue she remembered, and her mind was racing trying to figure out why not. Oh, God. She was supposed to have interrupted him after he said 'someday you'll' only she had forgotten, so he went on and now she wasn't sure if she should . . .

'Cut.' Mercifully a fan came on and a few of the lights were turned off and Martin was back at the table now, leaning over the two of them whispering directions Nina could barely hear; she knew her crying line was coming up and then she was going to have to use her emotional memory and she was afraid because remembering the details the way Martin wanted her to didn't work for her the way it worked for Chelsea. These were memories she had spent years trying to shake off. Memories she wished he hadn't made her think about again.

'You're doing fine,' Martin told her. 'We have lots of time, Nina. Don't worry about that. You just concentrate on all the things that are going through your mind and Stacy's mind, and we'll go again.' Then he squeezed her hand and backed away into that other land on the far side of the cameras and again the fan went off and the lights were shining so hot and bright on her they made it impossible to see.

'All right, people, we're rolling.'

'Action.' The way Martin said that word, leaning hard on both syllables, made it almost sound like a sneeze, and for months after this day Nina would hear it over and over in her dreams.

'I guess you know what's going on, don't you, baby?' Michael Nouri said to her again.

'Yes, Dad, and I want you to love Mommy.'

'I do love her, but I can't live with her anymore. There are problems. Insurmountable grown-up problems that someday you'll –'

'Understand?' Nina said, dredging into her mind a picture of Bertie lying on her deathbed, trying to remember those mornings when she would open the door to the room where Bertie lay dying and see Cee Cee fat and pale and drained sitting there holding Bertie's lifeless bony hand, trying to put on a face for Nina's benefit that said, 'It's okay, honey. You can come in,' when she saw Nina at the door. An emotional memory. But it didn't bring tears. It brought a frozen numbness, which was how Nina always reacted to emotion, the way she knew her mother had and her grandmother too, and according to everything she knew about her father, the man had never shed a tear in his life. And there was no way she was going to cry.

Her body felt weak and her mind was a blank, and she had no idea what to do next, so she stood. 'I can't,' she said standing, and it wasn't a line from the script. 'I can't.'

'Cut.' Fans went on, people started moving around.

'I can't do this.'

The hot lights were turned out and Michael Nouri put an arm around Nina, and now she could see beyond the camera where Cee Cee who must have just arrived stood with a look of unmistakable disappointment on her face, hesitant to come forward. But after a moment she did, only Martin was ahead of her, and when he got to Nina he started whispering again, his director's whisper. Telling her that now she was in the exactly right frame of mind. That if she could take the frustration she was feeling about not being able to play the part and bring it to the character, it would take her in exactly the right direction, and as he spoke he tried to gentle her back into the chair, but she wouldn't move.

'Martin,' Nina managed to tell him, 'I really can't do this. I won't do it. We all made a mistake thinking I could and I'm sorry. No, I can't, and I'm sorry.'

Then she walked off the set past him, past Cee Cee, past the handsome crew members, careful not to trip on any of the cables, out of the hotel dining room and back to the suite where she sat in the airconditioned living room on the sofa, hurting so badly she couldn't move.

> I'm gonna make it to heaven
> Light up the sky like a flame
> I'm gonna live forever
> Baby, remember my name.

In a matter of minutes she felt Cee Cee come in and sit on the sofa next to her. 'It's my fault,' Cee Cee said. 'I thought you wanted it, so I pushed it, and I'm sorry. I'm really sorry.'

'You told him about me and my mother and what to use, didn't you?' Nina asked.

Cee Cee felt sick with guilt. 'Yes, and I hate myself for it.'

'It's okay,' Nina said, her face a mask of pain and shame.

'Martin says he's willing to take the whole day just to work with you on this hard scene, because he thinks you have a nice quality and maybe you could –'

'No. I don't know how. And I don't want to. No,' Nina said, never raising her voice.

Cee Cee sat with her for a long time, during which neither of them said anything. The phone rang several times but neither of them moved to answer it. Nina was about to walk into her own room to get away from Cee Cee when Cee Cee said, 'Neen, remember that story I've told you a million times about the day your mother and I met? We were kids in Atlantic City and there was a guy there who –'

'I know,' Nina said, weary of the story she'd heard a million times. 'A guy from Hollywood. And my mother came with you and you auditioned for a part and so did some other girl and the guy picked the other girl to get the part.'

'Exactly. But the reason I'm reminding you about it again is that on that day I thought my life was over. Destroyed. But now *I'm* a big star, and nobody's ever heard of that girl. Even though she beat me for the part. So you get my point?'

'No.'

'The point is that you're like I was then. Thinking it's over, but you're wrong.'

'No, I'm not, Cee Cee,' Nina said looking at her. It was an uncomfortable moment because they both knew Cee Cee was vamping, saying anything she could think of to ease her own guilt and to save Nina's shattered ego.

'I'm not like you in that story, and I'm not like you in real life either. The person I'm like in that story is my mother, who sat backstage and watched you out there, and was happy doing that. You see, you may not believe it, Cee Cee, but some people are actually *happy* doing that.'

For the next few days Nina rarely left the suite. She was too embarrassed to look at anyone from the cast or crew of the film. When she heard from Cee Cee that Chelsea Bain was back, she thought about going over to the set, but she was afraid that if she went over and watched Chelsea doing the scene she had blown, it would make her feel horrible, so she didn't.

That afternoon when she opened the door in answer to a knock, she didn't bother to ask who it was because she was sure it was room service bringing the club sandwich she had ordered earlier, but it was Chelsea, looking fattened up and healthy though the rosy cheeks were due to Frank the makeup man's blusher.

'Hey, girl,' she said. 'I finished working for the day. Want to go body surfing?'

Nina felt as if the sun had just come up, even though she was sure Cee Cee had sent Chelsea over to help lure her out of the hotel room. 'I just ordered lunch,' she said. Now she could see behind Chelsea the room service waiter who was coming up the steps carrying a tray.

'Excuse me,' the waiter passing Chelsea asked Nina, 'do you want this on the table outside on the terrace?'

'She does,' Chelsea said, and she walked ahead of him into the suite and held the door to the terrace for him, then both girls followed him out to the tile patio overlooking the placid aqua sea beyond the pale beige sand beach. After Nina signed the check, the waiter left, and both girls sat, Nina with the large sandwich in front of her.

'C'n I have half?' Chelsea asked her.

'Sure,' Nina said, putting one half of the sandwich and half the potato chips, half the cole slaw, and the entire dill pickle on an empty bread dish and pushing the dish toward Chelsea.

'You can have the whole pickle. I hate pickles.'

'My mom says after this picture we're probably gonna hafta move to L.A.,' Chelsea said, picking up the pickle and biting into it, then wincing a little from the sour taste. 'Only I'm scared, because I don't want to leave my friends and my school.'

'Oh, don't worry,' Nina said, 'you can call me and I'll show you around.' A warm breeze picked up a paper coaster from the tray and blew it to the tile floor. Nina picked it up and put it on the tray and put her water glass on it. 'Oh, and Chels,' she said grinning. 'This time remember not to drink the water.'

Chelsea laughed a blush of a laugh, and the two girls sat back to eat their lunch.

Michael Barron
Barron, Malamud and Stern
1600 Golden Triangle Way
Pittsburgh, Pennsylvania 15213

Michael,

This is letter number I don't know how many, but the time has come for me to cut the crap and get directly to the chase. After your daughter was born I swore to high heaven if you ever tried to see her, I'd personally take her out of the country and go into hiding forever.

As you know, since Bertie's death I have been her guardian and since she has come to live with me I have gotten to know her very well. Now what I feel has changed. I am writing this to tell you that I will do whatever it takes to get you to see her even for a day. Not for me, because as far as I'm concerned my feelings remain the same, but because this girl who is coming into her womanhood needs it. She knows you're out there and I can tell it would help her to see you and to ask you questions and just look at your face and get some idea of where she comes from.

I have heard that you're sometimes in Los Angeles on business, and I am asking if you, on one of those trips, would spend one or two hours with her. It won't hurt you and it could change her life.

Please, Michael, please. Meet her. I swear to God, nobody wants your money, nobody wants to trap you into anything, all we ask, or I should say I ask because I would never tell her I am trying for this, so she won't be disappointed if you should refuse, is for you to give her a few hours of your time. Michael, this is just a personal appeal. Not legal or business or anything like that. If you can only find it in your heart.

Cee Cee

MATTHERS, KENDALL AND SIVITZ

Ms Cecilia Bloom
29 Malibu Colony Road
Malibu, California 90265

Dear Ms Bloom,

I am in receipt of your recent letter to Michael Barron. Please be advised that this office represents all of Mr Barron's legal interests, and that in the future, any questions you have regarding Mr Barron's paternal obligations, i. e., child support, should be addressed to me.

Sincerely,
Ronald J. Sivitz
attorney to Michael Barron

MAUI, HAWAII

1989

A small plane flying very low over the water takes you from the Maui airport to the airport at Hana, and the hotel sends what they call a limousine, which is really a van, to pick you up. Cee Cee was so glad to be out of Los Angeles on a vacation with Nina she didn't care what they sent, or even that two other families were being herded into the van behind them. One of the families consisted of an older couple with a daughter in her thirties who had the same sour expression on her face as her mother. The other family was a tanned, blond, robust preppy-looking couple with three tow-headed children all under the age of ten.

As the van took off through the rich green tropical foliage, Cee Cee watched Nina watching the family with children wistfully. Their togetherness had a brochure dazzle, and an unreality about it that was made even more pronounced by the fact that all five of them were dressed exactly alike in white shorts, yellow-and-navy-striped rugby shirts, and brown Topsiders. Later at the beach they all wore matching red bathing suits and ran out of the surf holding hands with the water splashing symmetrically on either side of them as if the scene of their emerging from the water had been staged for a commercial.

The hotel suite where Cee Cee and Nina were staying was a two-bedroom cottage overlooking the ocean. It was furnished with tan wicker-and-bamboo chairs and couches and headboards, and bright floral-printed fabrics on the pillows, bleached wood floors, white walls, and a ceiling fan that made clanking noises, but neither Cee Cee or Nina could locate the switch to turn it off. Nina searched around in her suitcase, looking for one of her bathing suits, finally pulling one out and putting it on before she unpacked, which was unusually spontaneous for her. When she walked into the living room of the suite and Cee Cee looked at her, she was startled for a minute by her slim perfect legs and long-waisted body with high perfect round breasts poking their nipples forth under the bright blue nylon of the top, and astonished at how adult she looked.

So many times these days she found herself surprised by Nina's growth. A pair of shoes left in the living room couldn't possibly be little Nina's, she would think in amazement. The shoes were bigger than Cee Cee's now. In fact it was probably Nina's hurtling toward womanhood that prompted Cee Cee to call her producer and insist on a few weeks' vacation so she and Nina could take this trip during a school break. The time was moving fast and this person who was a little girl a minute ago was teetering on the edge of an age when her friends' approval meant everything and, if the profusion of recent expressions of mouth turned down and eyes rolled heavenward meant anything, everything Cee Cee had to offer was worthless.

Junior high offspring spend a lot of time in their rooms, usually behind closed doors, wondering why their parents don't understand them. And yet they give us little to go on, few chatty intimate revelations which could make the muddle clearer for everyone. When they do talk, it tends to come in an unexpected rush, a sort of hurrying to get everything said before the next secretive mood descends. And even during these moments, few personal thoughts are revealed.

That was true of Nina most of the time now. But

occasionally if Cee Cee got her alone someplace where it was just the two of them, it was possible to get her to talk. To break through the wall she had always put up, even as a tiny child, and which adolescence had made more impenetrable.

Once over a dinner on trays in Cee Cee's room in the Malibu house, the two of them gabbed while they ate and watched the sunset, and when the room became dark and they were deep in conversation, neither of them moved to turn on a light, as if the cover of the falling night was just what they needed to give them each license to tell the other what she felt. It was after Cee Cee had done some reminiscing about Bertie that Nina told her, 'I'm starting to get to the point where I don't even remember my mother. Sometimes I try but nothing comes. Just a vague picture of a lady with pretty hair who was always hovering over me.'

'Really?' Cee Cee asked, shaking her head in disbelief, as feelings of guilt and inadequacy rose in her chest. She had been sure that her efforts over the years to tell Nina stories about her mother and to have photos of Bert around were enough to keep the memories alive, and if that hadn't worked then she hadn't done her job or kept her promise. 'I can't *believe* you don't remember. It hasn't been that long.'

'Maybe for *you* it seems as if it hasn't. But six years for me is a big part of my life.'

'Do you want to look at some old movies of her? I had all her eight-millimeter movies of the two of you when you were a baby transferred to tape. Of course some of them are nearly impossible to watch because *I* was the one who shot them and believe me –'

'No,' Nina said, and it was unequivocal. 'It doesn't matter.'

'Of course it matters.'

'Why should I set up a situation that makes me feel sad? To look at a picture of someone I'll never be able to see or talk to or be with again?'

'So you can get who she was, and know where you come from.'

Nina shrugged. 'If I wanted to know more about that I would have gone looking for my dad, who's alive. But I don't care. Life goes on. I'm me. Knowing why doesn't change that.'

'You really don't ever want to meet your father?' Cee Cee asked, worried now because she had written many letters to Michael trying to convince him to see Nina, thinking it was big of her to be right out of the King Solomon story, the one who really loves the child is willing to share her and all that kind of bullshit. Michael's response had come from a lawyer telling Cee Cee to fuck off. But somehow Cee Cee still harbored the hope that he would change his mind. Prayed secretly that somewhere along the line he would get a pang of conscience and want to know what his daughter had become.

'No. I really don't care,' Nina said, running her finger around the rim of an empty glass on her tray.

If the father never comes to see the children and they ask you why, I advocate that you tell the truth. If you dream up some cover story for him and the children find out later that you have lied, you will have destroyed your credibility with them.

After Cee Cee had found that advice in one of her books years ago, any time Michael's name came up, she called on the speech she'd practiced in her head about him. *You're a fabulous girl. But your father's screwed up. So badly he can't let himself see you. The poor guy doesn't know what he's missing.* By now she had said those things to Nina many times, and the response was always a kind of absent 'uh-huh,' which made Cee Cee back off, thinking the 'uh-huh' meant the subject was too painful. Now Nina was telling her it was genuine lack of interest. Cee Cee wasn't sure she believed her, but she was surprised at the enormous relief she felt hearing it, because in spite of her efforts to reach out to Michael, the fear that sometimes woke her at four in the morning and other times kept her from falling asleep to begin with was that some day he would show up at her door, push past her, and before she could get to the stairs he'd be on his way out of the house arm in arm with a willing Nina, leaving Cee Cee to that lonely abyss she had called a life before Nina was in it.

'There are a few beaches at this place,' Nina said reading from a pamphlet on the coffee table. 'One of them is a few blocks down, and the closest one, the Red Sand Beach, is just on the other side of that cliff,' she said, pointing out the window.

'Cliff?' Cee Cee said. 'That's a word I usually put in the same column as rope-tow and hang-glider. The heading on the column is "Things to Stay Away From."' Nina, who knew enough about Cee Cee by now to ignore her protests, handed her her tennis shoes, slipped a pair of rubber thongs on her own feet, and they were out the door to the Red Sand Beach. Over the path past a few other bungalows like theirs, to the cliff above the cove.

Nina walked in front down the steep path, reaching back to hold Cee Cee's hand, and Cee Cee, who managed even with her rubber-soled shoes to slip twice, crept along trying to keep her eyes closed so she didn't have to look over the steep drop at the crashing surf on her right, letting Nina's hand guide her until they reached the bottom and stood on the Red Sand Beach.

The sand was a burnt rust color, and after Nina spread her towel out, she sat on it and opened a bottle of Hawaiian Tropic oil, which smelled so powerfully of coconut and pineapple it made Cee Cee's stomach rumble, while she squirted her own white number-fifteen sun protection cream on to her hand and spread it everywhere on herself, then lay back on the big white towel. She loved the sun, even though she'd read all the articles that said it was dangerous and aging, but she didn't care. With a sigh of satisfaction over her wise choice to take a vacation, she stretched out on her back and welcomed the rays of heat, grinning as if the warmth was from the heated body of a lover moving on top of her.

Nina stayed arched up on her elbows watching the waves, then looking at the clusters of people gathered in various spots on the beach. Far off in a cove she could see a tan, lean couple wearing very tiny bathing suits and oiling one another's bodies, and her eyes lingered on them for a long curious time, then moved to the young family from the airport van having a picnic lunch, then to four ladies who had big bellies and varying shades of frizzy hair and who sat on a blanket playing a four-handed game of cards.

'I'm going in the water,' Nina said after a while to Cee Cee's inert body, then stood, brushed some sand from her legs, and ran down to the shore, her long curly hair flying behind her.

Cee Cee dozed and woke every few minutes to look out at the water to be sure she could spot Nina bobbing among the waves. Nina was swimming vigorously with a powerful stroke Cee Cee had seen her use in the pool at home, and confident that all was well, she was about to turn on her stomach again when she caught a glimpse of the family who was now coming down the path to the beach.

What must have stopped her eye was the resemblance the woman had to Bertie, something about her that reminded Cee Cee of her instantly. Not feature for feature, in fact the woman was a blond and Bertie's hair had been a chestnut brown, but she definitely had Bertie's carriage, her style. In the last few years Cee Cee's nearsightedness had worsened decidedly so she could never really trust what she saw from a distance, but this woman really was a Bertie-type, holding on to her little girl's hand in the same no-nonsense grip Cee Cee remembered Bertie using with Nina.

Nina was still stroking away in the water, splashing and jumping up out of the waves every now and then as sleekly as a dolphin. Cee Cee wondered if when Nina saw the woman who looked like Bertie, it would evoke the memories she said she no longer had. Behind the woman trotted a little boy who was whining about something as they passed and behind the boy came a thick-waisted husband who wore mirrored sunglasses and a baseball cap with the letter 'P' on it. The father was reprimanding the boy as they passed, and Cee Cee caught the words '*I* decide what this family is doing and not you, and if you don't get that . . .'

She turned on her stomach now and after a few minutes fell into a sweet warm sleep, which was interrupted by the drops of cold water falling all over her from Nina, who was shaking herself like a dog to dry off, and laughing. 'The waves are awesome,' she said when she sat, the water beading on her oiled body. 'You should go in.' She had brought *A Tale of Two Cities* with her because she was reading it for school. After she dried her hands, she opened the book to the page she had turned down on the flight to Maui from Los Angeles. For a while she read quietly to herself, and when she looked up, something she saw startled her. 'Oh, my God,' she said with such drama in her voice that Cee Cee, who had been trying to drift back to sleep, opened her eyes thinking Nina must have spotted the woman who looked like Bertie.

But that wasn't where she was looking at all. Her eyes were wide at the sight of a long-haired bony-looking woman a few yards away from them who had removed her muumuu and was jaybird naked underneath it, and now was unselfconsciously spreading her blanket on the beach. Next to her, holding a baby, was her muscular, golden-brown husband, who was also stark naked. Cee Cee noticed now that the couple who had been oiling one another down the beach had both removed their suits too. Nina giggled. 'Oh my God,' she said again, with an openmouthed, outraged grin.

'They didn't mention this in the brochure,' Cee Cee said, as the naked man handed the woman the baby, then took off in a run down the beach to the water.

'Or *you* would have been here sooner,' Nina said with the perfect timing of a girl who had spent the last six years of her life listening to jokes being delivered by the best comics in the business. Then she stood. 'Well . . . I'm going up to the room,' she said.

'Is this making you uncomfortable, honey?' Cee Cee asked, looking up at her seriously and shielding her own eyes, which even behind her dark glasses felt scorched by the blazing sun.

'Oh no,' Nina said with a wave of dismissal. 'Does it bother you?'

'I don't even notice it,' Cee Cee said.

Nina slid a T-shirt on over her still-wet suit. 'I'm just running up to get myself a Coke. What can I get you?'

'How 'bout a penis colada?' Cee Cee said, heard herself, and let out a burst of laughter, and Nina looked at her the same way Bertie used to when she said something funny but too outrageous to laugh at, without first giving her a sideways glance of disapproval. Then she broke up, laughing so hard too that she had to sit back down on the towel for a minute to recover, and Cee Cee laughed to see her reaction, and their laughter continued to set one another off until Cee Cee said, 'And hold the colada,' and Nina, still giggling, was off up the hill to the room.

Cee Cee sat up, squeezed the suntan lotion bottle, and felt the hot cream squirt into her hand, then spread another coat of cream all over herself and decided that maybe she should at least dip a toe or two in the water. She was, after all, in Hawaii, and the water wouldn't be like the freeze-your-toes-off water in Malibu. So she stood and moved down toward the shore, passing the naked woman who was now nursing the baby at her breast, and the four fat card-playing women, two of whom reminded her of the De John Sisters, an act she'd worked with in the Catskills. 'Thank God *they're* not naked,' she mused.

In spite of the layers of protective lotion, her face was stinging from the heat, with the cream feeling as if it was bubbling. I should have worn a hat, she thought, as she passed the blanket of the family with the wife who looked like Bertie. What reminded her of the hat was seeing the father remove the baseball hat with the 'P' on it, revealing his partly bald head with gray and brown hair surrounding it like a fuzzy cloud, and this time she heard him say to his son, who was whimpering softly, 'You keep whining, pal, and you'll spend the rest of the day in the room without food.'

God, she hated anyone who could talk to a poor

child that way. With a stony, unsympathetic delivery that was so unfeeling it reminded her of someone in her past for whom she'd felt this same kind of heart-tearing anger, but she couldn't think who. And when she realized, she stopped right there on the sand that was burning her feet, and standing on that fiery-hot beach where there was not even a whisper of a breeze, she was covered with goose bumps because she knew now the 'P' on the cap stood for Pirates. Pittsburgh Pirates, and the balding man whose second wife looked ironically like Bertie was Michael Barron. Nina's father, whom the child had never seen.

It had been years since Cee Cee had seen him, but there was no mistaking him. She turned to face the ocean, trying to collect herself, feeling simultaneously sickened and thrilled. She peeked once back over her shoulder at Michael and his second family, hoping none of them would look up and catch her staring. The baldness that had been promised even by the time Michael was in his early twenties had arrived. In fact, Cee Cee watched him pour some Coppertone into his hand and rub it into his bare scalp. When his little girl picked up his baseball hat and put it on her own head, he grabbed it away and put it back on himself. That's him all right, Cee Cee thought. Still Mister Nice Guy.

When the wife looked right at her, Cee Cee turned quickly and waded into the water, which for the first few minutes felt icy cold on her feet as she walked farther in, trying to decide what to do. Well, how about that? It looked as if Michael was married and had two kids. Jesus. No one ever told her that, or told Nina. I must finally have grown up, Cee Cee thought. Because the old me would have reeled around the minute I realized it was him, run over, grabbed the son-of-a-bitch by the face and shrieked into it, 'How can a man abandon a beautiful child and never have the guts to look her in the face and tell her why?' But now I'm acting like a big girl, weighing my choices. The grown-up Cee Cee Bloom is actually giving it thought. Oh God, stop me from going over and kicking the stinking little slimy bastard right in the balls.

Thank God he didn't recognize me, she thought, but that can't last. Everywhere she went, once people realized she was there they ran up and asked for autographs, surrounded her, spread the word. And this was a small hotel; soon the news would be around that she was there, and the people who were her fans would be looking for her in the lobby, in the gift shop, or out here on the beach. Now the water was up to her knees and she tried to tell herself to be calm. To get clear-headed about what to do. Soon the water was up to her waist and her shoulders were sizzling from the sun reflecting off the water as she watched Michael-that-asshole-Barron sitting in the sand still griping at his poor children, while their mother spread oil on their little bodies.

Cee Cee stood feeling the waves push against her back, watching the members of the Barron family, their oiling tasks complete, lying down across their blanket like a line of gingerbread cookies ready to bake. When they seemed to be at rest, she waded slowly out of the water up onto the beach and then close to their blanket, where she stopped quietly and looked at their closed-eyed faces as they sunbathed.

The wife was sweet-looking and pretty with that same Audrey Hepburn elegance for which Michael clearly had a taste, but at closer range she was not as pretty as Bertie had been. The tiny girl looked alarmingly the way Nina had when she was that age. The boy was on his stomach so Cee Cee couldn't see what he looked like, and Michael, you dirty dog, Cee Cee thought, when she looked down at his wedding band. Filigreed gold, it was the one Bertie had given him. The cheap schmuck.

When she noticed that the little girl's eyes were open and looking at her curiously, Cee Cee turned and walked back to her towel. From a distance she glanced over at them a few times, unsure how she was going to handle their horribly coincidental presence here with Nina, feeling relieved that the girl was taking so long back at the cottage. But when nearly an hour had passed and she wasn't back and the Barron family was hitting a beach ball back and forth, Cee Cee gathered up her towel and Nina's, and the sunscreen and Nina's book, and navigated up the narrow hillside path as though there was no frightening drop-off next to it at all. A mission, she thought as she got to the top, realizing she'd been so afraid of the same walk earlier. That's me. Not much on the everyday stuff, but when there's a mission, I put my boots on and jump into the trenches.

In the cool living room of the cottage Nina was lying on the sofa reading a copy of *Vogue* Cee Cee had bought at the Los Angeles airport. 'Oh, hi,' she said, without looking at Cee Cee. 'I felt nauseated from the sun so I figured I'd stay in here for a while.'

''T'sokay,' Cee Cee said, wondering if she could make up some kind of excuse for them to have to check out of the hotel. She could call Larry Gold and have him call her back when she knew Nina would answer. He could say they had to be back in L.A. in a hurry. Or she could tell Nina the truth. Oh, Nina, there's something I think you should know. The little jerk in the baseball hat is your father. And the 'P' stands for prick. No. She'd say, By a very odd coinci-

242

dence your father happens to be at this hotel. It would give Nina the choice to either watch him from far away or approach him. But how could she do that to Nina? Wasn't it too heavy a responsibility for a child suddenly to come across her father and his new family at a resort and have to figure out how to behave?

'Want lunch?' Cee Cee asked.

'Okay.'

The rich green odor of the tropical growth all around the hotel dining room drifted gently in through the open doors as Cee Cee and Nina followed the muumuu-clad hostess to a table in the front of the room where they could get the best view of the panorama of the lawn and the beach and the sea. Cee Cee wore a big straw hat pulled down over her ears and large sunglasses covering the rest of her face and she was relieved that her disguise, which usually didn't fool anyone, seemed to be working. A quick scan of the restaurant told her the Barron family wasn't around, and she thought with a sad laugh to herself that maybe Michael had punished all of them and banished the entire family to the hotel room without food. The schmuck.

Nina looked over the menu, then out at the view, and Cee Cee saw a calm on her face she had rarely seen there at home. Certainly not recently.

'This place is great,' Nina said. 'So peaceful.'

You should only know, Cee Cee thought, as if Michael Barron hadn't done enough damage to the life of this child, now he was here to ruin her vacation, and Cee Cee couldn't get rid of that clutching feeling in her chest of impending doom. Nina knew what Michael looked like, or at least what he used to look like, from old photographs of his wedding to Bertie, snapshots and films of trips Bertie and Michael had taken together. She hadn't looked at them in years and Michael looked different now, older and chubbier, but there might be a chance she could recognize him. Instinct counted for a lot, and Nina was a sensitive girl.

'I'm going to sign up for a massage later,' Cee Cee said. 'You interested in having one?'

'No way,' Nina answered and Cee Cee realized by the slight blush accompanying the reply that the intimacy and sensuality of a massage was probably too much for a girl her age to handle. She continued nervously to watch the door to the dining room, thinking how ironic it was that she had brought Nina there so that the two of them could have a rest, and now she would spend their vacation feeling panicky and afraid. That was no good, she thought, knowing she would have to do something. Say something.

Nina ordered a hamburger and Cee Cee ordered the grilled mahimahi and passed the time waiting for their lunch to arrive with small talk about the naked people on the beach and the beauty of the hotel. Just as the waitress emerged from the kitchen carrying the tray with their lunch, Cee Cee's heart sank when she spotted the Barrons entering the dining room. Michael was wearing a colorful Hawaiian shirt, and a Panama hat with a black band. The children came next, more quiet and reserved than children should be, and the elegant wife, cool in white Bermuda shorts and a white blouse, was last.

'Booster seats,' Cee Cee overheard Michael's wife say, and her stomach lurched when she saw Nina look over at the four of them being seated. But it was a brief glance with no significance, after which she dug immediately into her lunch, chattering about a bathing suit she'd seen in the hotel shop, and Cee Cee found herself jumping in and yakking inanely about clothes too, hoping to hold Nina's interest so she wouldn't look back at the table where the Barrons were seated.

'No coffee.' Cee Cee waved off the busboy and signed the check immediately. Then instead of exiting the restaurant the way they came in, which would have taken them by Michael's table, Cee Cee steered Nina out onto the front terrace and into the flower-filled hotel grounds for a walk. The early afternoon heat was thick and heavy and Cee Cee wished she had some idea, any idea, about how to handle this. Maybe it would all go away. Maybe Michael and his family would check out after lunch and Nina would never have to know they were there.

Back at the bungalow, Nina sat on the deck outside reading *A Tale of Two Cities*, and eventually she drifted off to sleep. When she had been asleep for a long time, Cee Cee went inside to her room and called Hal in New York.

'Truth is stranger than fiction,' she said after telling him the story.

'Pack up immediately and go to another island,' he said.

'And what do I tell Nina about why we're leaving?'

'Further adventure. I don't know. But you can't confront the guy. He obviously doesn't want them to know about her, and vice versa. This is one of those situations if you saw it in a movie you'd say, "Oh yeah, sure. In the whole world these people end up in the same hotel?" I'd get out of there, Cee. Especially since she's already told you she doesn't want to see him. Pack up and hit the road.'

'You're right. I'll call the Mauna Kea Hotel or the Kahala Hilton. We'll move. I'll tell her we're island-hopping.'

'There you go,' he said. 'And, Cee, don't get too much sun. It's bad for you. Makes you think you're seeing people out of your past.'

'Harold,' she said softly because she thought she might have heard Nina stirring on the lounge outside, 'isn't this too fucking weird? I'm such a nonviolent type. I can't even swat a fly. But I tell you as sure as I'm sitting here in this overpriced room, I could cheerfully put my hands around that weasel's neck and choke.'

'Don't do it. Remember what happened to Claudine Longet?'

'What *did* happen to Claudine Longet?'

'I rest my case. On the other hand, everyone remembers Gandhi. Try being like him.'

'Okay,' Cee Cee said, 'I'll skip dinner.'

When she emerged from her room Nina was still asleep on the deck, so Cee Cee slipped into a muumuu and thongs and wrote her a note on a piece of hotel stationery.

WENT FOR MY MASSAGE
BE BACK SOON.   C.

She listened to the sound of her thongs as they flip-flopped across the gravel path toward the main hotel building, thinking how good it was going to feel to have the strong hands of a masseuse kneading her muscles. Sometimes in the past when the educated fingers of a masseuse pushed on just the right painfully knotted places in her shoulders and back and thighs, the release of tension was so powerful it could make her cry.

It was dark by the time she arrived at the lobby, and on bamboo based tables, fat white candles flickered inside of thick glass hurricane lamps, and people in colorful tropical clothes were meeting to go into the dining room.

A pretty oriental girl in a white coat approached and asked 'Bloom?' when she saw Cee Cee at the front desk, and Cee Cee allowed herself to be led down a long hallway adjacent to the lobby, into a quiet, dimly lit eucalyptus-scented room with only a massage table and a hook on the wall for her clothes. After the masseuse discreetly slipped out of the room to give her the privacy to undress, Cee Cee removed her thongs, her clothes, and her watch, climbed on to the table and put her face into the hole of the face rest and was about to let herself relax when she heard Michael Barron's voice.

He was just outside the door of the room, and Cee Cee sat up alert, listening carefully, hoping to hear him better. He was talking loudly with one of the masseuses, and it sounded from what he was saying that he was just finished having a massage himself, and was signing the tab. Cee Cee grabbed the towel from under her and wrapped it around herself. The timing was perfect. He was alone, and so was she. She could go out there now to talk to him and not worry about his wife's hearing her, or Nina's knowing about it. Tell him she was here with his daughter and see how he handled it. Her heart felt as if someone had reached inside her chest and was squeezing it. This was the fight or flight moment and in an instant she would have to seize it, or let the opportunity of a lifetime pass her by.

Holding her towel together tightly at the top, she kicked the shuttered door open and stood face to face for the first time in many long years with Michael Barron, certain he was going to gasp with surprise when he saw her, but instead he smiled as if he'd been expecting her.

'Hello, Cecilia,' he said. 'I thought that was you on the beach today. And I've got to tell you, I noticed you've put on quite a bit of weight.'

If her rage hadn't made her speechless, just seeing him this close would have. He was such a colossal asshole, he had to open with an insult. Collecting herself as best she could she said, 'Michael, I'm here with –'

But before she could finish the sentence, he put his hand on her arm, the hand wearing Bertie's ring, and she could smell that same disgusting cologne she remembered him wearing. Royal Lyme or something like that, and her worst memory of him rushed into her mind. That night at the Kahala Hilton in 1967 when her husband was sleeping in his own hotel room and Bertie was in the next room sleeping and he'd put the full court press on Cee Cee, trying to get into her pants.

'I've wanted to fuck you since I saw you,' he had said. 'And you've wanted it, too, so what are we waiting for?' The sick slime.

'This was a bad coincidence,' he said to her softly and calmly, as if it was cocktail party chitchat, 'because Helen and the kids don't know a thing. But the good news is that *we've* been here for a week, so we're on our way home in the morning.'

'No, Michael,' Cee Cee said, trying to sound menacing, but having a hard time feeling as if she could intimidate anyone as she stood there wrapped in a towel. 'It was not a bad coincidence, it was a good coincidence because I'm going to tell Nina you're here and let her have the chance to sit down with you in my suite, or in the location of your choice, and take one half hour to see your face.'

'Not a chance,' he said.

'Michael, you're the lowest, sickest, worst piece of garbage in this world,' Cee Cee said, knowing this wasn't the smoothest way to handle the situation and feeling the pressure of tears against her eyes, but willing them to stay in with everything she had. 'Unless you make some kind of peace with this girl.'

'Don't fight me, Cee Cee,' he said in a confidential voice. 'I can have her taken away from you. I can call up shit from your past you can't even remember. You did a lot of drugs in your day, and fucked an awful lot of men. The court would probably want to know about that. Not to mention that "family entertainment" company that puts out your movies. So you just go back to your room and order room service for you and Nina, and just for old times' sake you can put it on my tab. By tomorrow I'll be gone and you can pretend you never saw me. So come on now, do what I say.'

'Don't threaten me,' she said, hearing her voice sound shaky and childlike. 'I'm not afraid of my past. You tell me you'll give this child one half hour. Tell me yes and I'll leave you alone for the rest of all of our lives.'

Michael's jaw was set and he actually seemed to be considering doing what Cee Cee asked, and Cee Cee, who knew this toughness she was putting on was the biggest bluff of her life, held her breath while he did. Please, she thought, make him agree to this and you don't ever have to answer another one of my prayers.

'In the morning,' he said. 'I'll meet her down in the social hall on the far side of the pool. Early, say seven thirty. Tell her I'll meet her there for half an hour. We can talk there and then I'm leaving. If she doesn't want to come, I'll just stay there for fifteen minutes or so and if she doesn't show up, I'll leave.'

Cee Cee felt a rush of triumph, and heroism on top

of it for finally making this evil snake succumb and agree to see his child at long last. It was so heady, for a moment she even felt grateful to the little piece of pond scum.

'Oh, bless you, Michael,' she said. 'Thank you for doing this. You won't regret it. I promise you this girl is so special, and so good, and maybe someday you can find it in your heart to tell your family and get them to know her because she is such a joy.' And while she rambled she already knew this was a mistake, but if it wasn't, and it could create some kind of a positive relationship between Nina and her father, it was worth it. After Michael turned and left, his Royal Lyme still in the air where Cee Cee stood, she moved, exhausted, into the massage room and lay on the table planning what she would say to Nina.

'Nina, the strangest thing has happened. Today when we were on the beach I saw a man who looked very familiar to me and I realized after I looked closely that it was your father.'

'What?'

'He's here. Michael Barron is in this hotel with his family. A wife and two children, and I confronted him. He told me that they don't know about you, and I asked if he would see and talk to you alone, and that I would ask you if under the circumstances you wanted to talk to him.'

'And what did he say?' Nina's eyes were defensive and her posture was stiff as she waited for the answer.

'He said he would. He's checking out tomorrow but told me that he'd meet you down at the rec room near the pool early in the morning. At seven thirty. He said if you weren't there in about fifteen minutes he would leave. That's how he would know that I asked you and you said no.'

'Two kids,' she said with no intonation at all. 'How old are they?'

'Maybe six and four.'

She sighed and looked down, clearly hurting, and instantly Cee Cee was awash with regret. Hal was right, why hadn't she left it alone? Packed Nina up and run away from this place instead of dragging her through the agony of this meeting. What in the hell would she get out of it anyway? Probably she would say no, now. Tell Cee Cee to forget it, sleep late in the morning, and let the son-of-a-bitch go back to Pittsburgh without seeing her. But then there was something in her eyes. A flicker of hope when she said, 'I'll do it,' looking at Cee Cee. 'Did you bring a travel clock? I'll set it for five so I can have some time to work on my hair.'

They played Scrabble and had a room service dinner and though each of them yawned sleepily before they parted to go to her bedroom, Cee Cee didn't sleep at all and she could hear Nina moving around all night too, knowing the girl must simultaneously be looking forward to and dreading the dawn. Finally Cee Cee must have drifted off, because before it was daylight she sensed someone in the room and looked up to see Nina, an apparition at the foot of her bed. She looked as if she had spent the entire night working on her hairstyle. It was waved perfectly and she wore light blusher on her cheeks and a new outfit of silk turquoise shorts and a camp shirt, and she looked as elegant to Cee Cee as if she'd just stepped out of the pages of *Town & Country* magazine.

'I'm going down there,' she said. 'See you when it's over.'

'It's only six forty-five,' Cee Cee said, her voice husky with sleep as she looked at the digital clock on the dresser.

'I know. I want to just sit there for a while and think about things.'

'Okay, honey,' Cee Cee said, and watched her go with her own heart so fearful it pinned her to the bed, where she lay for a long time watching the numbers on the digital clock, watching it minute by minute until it became seven thirty, trying to imagine how the meeting between them was going. What Michael was saying to Nina, and how Nina was feeling, certain that Michael couldn't be anything but smitten with her and her extraordinary beauty. At eight o'clock she got out of bed and took a shower, shampooing her hair with the creamy coconut-smelling shampoo the hotel placed there. And at eight thirty-five, she was glad Nina wasn't back yet, assumed it was a good sign that she wasn't rushing back in tears. Decided that maybe it meant they had really gotten into it, talked about the past, maybe even planned to see one another again.

At eight fifty she slipped into shorts and a T-shirt and some thongs, then put on a big hat and dark glasses and decided to stroll down toward the social hall and tiptoe by to see if she could see any sign of them. A brown-skinned beachboy nodded to her as she passed the pool and made her way across a large grassy area leading to the rec room. Probably Nina and Michael weren't there anymore. Maybe Michael had decided the timing was perfect and took her to the dining room to have breakfast with his family. Right. The rec room was empty, and a hopeful Cee Cee turned and headed back toward the dining room, but before she got to the top of the hill she spotted Nina, sitting tailor-fashion on a chaise longue she had moved away from the pool area, under a tree to face the ocean.

Cee Cee hurried to the spot. 'Neen?' she said as she approached.

'Hello, Cee Cee,' the girl said, looking up at her with vacant eyes. The look from Nina stopped Cee Cee from saying anything back; something had gone wrong. Very wrong. She stood there silently as a morning breeze blew the buttery odor of macadamia nut pancakes from the dining room past her, making her feel suddenly ravenous with hunger. 'He didn't show,' Nina told her, looking back at the ocean.

He didn't show. Cee Cee sat on the grass next to the lounge chair and put her hand on the girl's arm, and they stayed there watching the surf crash on the rocks below, deciding how to spend the second day of their vacation.

HOLLYWOOD REPORTER

CEE CEE BLOOM CALLS IT QUITS

Cee Cee Bloom will not be back as star of her network TV series next season, choosing to exit after seven years of her variety skein. Bloom's decision was announced by her agent, Larry Gold of the William Morris Agency. The network has asked her to reconsider but she has remained firm.

Bloom explained that after the demands of six years and one hundred fifty-six shows, she wanted to be free for a while from the demands of a weekly show.

She is now in discussions with Hemisphere Studios. The final episode of *The Cee Cee Bloom Show* will air May 16.

BLOOM INKS FEATURE FILM PACT

Cee Cee Bloom's 'Bloom Off the Rose' Productions has signed an open-ended development deal with Hemisphere Studios. Bloom will both star in and produce feature film projects developed by her company.

Newport Beach, California

February 1990

Sometimes Cee Cee felt like the guy she used to watch on *The Hollywood Palace* years ago. The one who kept plates twirling in the air on the tops of big long sticks, and whose entire act was based on making sure all the plates were in constant motion at the same time. Under her deal at the studio there were countless projects, each one needing all of her attention to keep it going, and there were days when she felt as if any minute they could all come crashing down on her head.

When it all got to be too much, it helped to glance over at one of the many photographs of Nina she had scattered around her office. So many, in fact, that some of the people who worked for her referred to her office as 'the shrine.' In the middle of a meeting or while she was on the phone, she would look at the pictures and be warmed by them, finding herself almost unable to remember Nina at some of the early stages captured by those shots, many of them taken by Cee Cee with a camera so automatic she called it her P.H.D. camera, for Push Here, Dummy. The array of pictures told stories of the seven years the two of them had survived, and the actual Nina, who was so grown up and beautiful now, was hard to connect to the funny, pouty little girl in the early photos.

There was no doubt she had been, as Bertie promised on her death-bed, good for Cee Cee. An anchor in an insane world, and despite the many errors Cee Cee knew she had made along the way, she could tell the reverse was also true. This was a child whose own mother had said about her when she was only six, 'I feel lucky she's not wearing a tweed suit and carrying a briefcase.' Well, that had to be because Nina had spent her early years being as straitlaced as her stick-up-the-ass father, and more selfconscious about propriety than her lovable but working-too-hard-to-be-gracious mother. Now she laughed with a peal of a giggle so heartfelt it made Cee Cee laugh to hear it, and she talked on the phone too much, and rushed off to the mall after school, and fell asleep over her homework, and pined over certain boys in her class, and went gaga at the sight of certain movie stars, and seemed to have as normal a teenager's life as anybody could.

She had a crowd of friends from school who came exploding into their house, rushing past Cee Cee and up to Nina's room where they slammed the door behind them, then jabbered in shrill rapid-fire voices punctuated by outbursts of laughter with just enough hysteria in them to tell Cee Cee they had to be talking about boys. And eventually when their curfews dictated, they would brush past Cee Cee as they ran the other way, and the house would fall silent. Normal, of course, but Cee Cee hated to admit how left out she felt, knowing those girls had access to a part of Nina that, except for a moment here and there, had slipped away from their relationship completely.

The plop-down-with-snacks-together-on-the-couch-by-the-television days were over. The 'stay and let's talk before lights out' requests, and 'tell me more about my mother' sessions, which always served to make them feel closer to one another, were a part of a little-girl phase that was no more. And saddest of all was the absence of those admiring looks Nina used to give her, the ones with just a bit of awe in them, that had lately been replaced by new expressions, which alternated between impatient tolerance and exasperated disdain.

> Fifteen seeks liberation, yet she still finds many roads
> closed to her because of her age. So she compromises by
> pulling away from her family, manifested in sparse con-
> versation, a locked bedroom door or meals eaten separ-
> ately.

Ain't that the truth, Cee Cee thought, always relieved
to learn from the books she read that others had gone
through this before her.

This morning she looked at the most recent picture
of Nina, which sat on the antique breakfront the studio
had left in Cee Cee's office from the previous tenant, a
director who had moved on to another studio after
three failed films in a row at this one. The photo was
an eight-by-ten taken by one of those photographers
who comes around to the schools, sets up a makeshift
studio where he shoots portraits of each of the students,
then charges the parents some whopping amount of
money to buy them. And Cee Cee, who frequently
referred to herself as 'the queen of overkill,' had naturally ordered the jazziest package the guy was selling,
including a key ring with Nina's picture inside a tiny
frame. Then she sent one of the photos off to Hal, one
to her father and his wife, and even broke down and
sent one to Nina's aunt, Anita-the-jewel-thief-Bennet.

There was something in Nina's eyes in that particular picture that maybe only someone as close to her as
Cee Cee would notice, and the only way to describe it,
the word that floated through Cee Cee's mind every
time she looked at it, was *haunted*. There was an
unmistakable pain Cee Cee sensed there behind the
forced smile she knew the photographer must have
insisted on before he would snap the shutter, and no
matter where she was in the large executive office at
the studio, no matter from what angle or at what

distance, she could feel the pain: when she sat at her desk talking on the phone, wheeling and dealing and arguing with the big bosses about what she thought worked and didn't work for the films her production company was developing; and when she sat tailor-fashion on the sofa instead of stiffly behind the desk, trying to communicate with the screenwriters so they would feel she was working with them and wouldn't be intimidated by all the stardom heaped on her after the success of her last few films.

Lately she would find herself looking long at that one school picture, certain in some mother's inner knowing spot that the hollow-eyed girl looking back was more troubled than she let on. Okay, maybe it wasn't such big intuition on her part. Maybe her worries had more to do with the recent outbursts of anger she'd seen from Nina. The anger toward Cee Cee seemed to come from nowhere and Cee Cee couldn't shrug it off. Instead, Nina's anger could light a fire in Cee Cee's stomach that flared into her chest where she would carry it all day, unable to concentrate completely on anything.

'You look gross in that dress,' Nina would say, and even if Cee Cee had thought when she put the dress on that she looked great in it, she would instantly pull it off and change to another one. 'You're too old for those shorts.' 'Would you go to my school meeting looking like a parent instead of some weirdo?' 'You really bombed on Letterman last night.' 'Why would they want *you* to host *Saturday Night Live*? Are they desperate?'

Any of those comments taken alone was hurtful, but accompanied by Nina's venomous reading, they could make Cee Cee have to sit quietly and remind herself that *she* was the grown-up, the parent, and had to stay in control, and remember how much the kid must be hurting herself to lash out like that. To try to stay composed and not to do what she would if those remarks had come from anyone else, which was to let loose with a big 'Fuuuuck You!!!'

It seemed funny now that in anticipation of Nina's teens, Cee Cee had told herself the legendary mother-and-daughter bloodlettings were reserved for the genetically related. Certain that all the qualities she had detested in Leona were the same ones she saw and hated in herself. Therefore, she concluded, she and Nina would be spared that ritual separation dance. After all, there was precious little if anything of Cee Cee that Nina had taken on. And that was the faulty thinking she had used to lull herself into believing they would beat the odds. But the war between them was escalating, genes or no genes, and Cee Cee was afraid she wouldn't be able to handle much more of it. Last week there had been a big stab in the gut when both of them happened to find themselves in the kitchen foraging for snacks.

'Some girl at school who doesn't know who I am was talking about going to the movies and seeing this really great actress who she wants to be just like?' she said. She was starting to pick up that California speech rhythm, where statements ended as questions, from the kids at school. 'And you're not going to believe who the actress was?'

Cee Cee knew the girl at school was probably talking about her. Her new picture was in wide release and was doing great business.

'Meryl Streep,' she joked.

'No, you!' Nina said, ignoring the joke and devouring her fourth chocolate chip cookie while Cee Cee, who prudently cut an apple in half and then ate only one of the halves, looked on in envy.

'Well, did you thank her?' Cee Cee asked.

'Why would *I* thank her?' Nina asked, a black cloud of anger filling her eyes. 'She wasn't talking about *me*.' And in a huff she wrapped a few more cookies in a paper napkin, shoved them into the pocket of her robe, and left the room.

'Well, didn't you tell her that I'm your . . .' The unfinished sentence hung in the air. I'm your what? Her guardian, Cee Cee would think. It sounds like a matron in a prison. Looking back, she remembered a million reasons she had given herself over the last seven years for not going through with a legal adoption of Nina. Sometimes the reason was her certainty the kid would never go for it, wouldn't want to change her name, and would never really think of Cee Cee as a parent no matter what Cee Cee did, so the idea of going through a ceremony to get a piece of paper saying she was the parent seemed false and unnecessary. After all, she had made a will leaving everything to her father and Nina anyway, so she didn't have to adopt the kid to make her her heir.

And then there had always been Cee Cee's fear that starting adoption proceedings might rock their precarious boat, stir up the ire of that prick Michael Barron, who could rear his ugly head and do God knows what. Or, worse yet, Bertie's Aunt Neetie could come crawling out of the woodwork to use the whole issue as a way to extort money to buy herself some jewelry. Of course, now Cee Cee knew the truth about both of those people after meeting up with them, which was that neither really gave a shit about the kid and would probably agree to let Cee Cee adopt her. But still she didn't call her lawyers and tell them to ready the adoption papers.

Now she decided she wasn't doing anything about it

because they were past it. Nina was a woman, for God's sake, and at this stage going through some legal ceremony to say she was Cee Cee's daughter was completely after the fact. Nina would probably laugh if Cee Cee even brought it up, and think it was dumb. She doesn't want to be related to me anyway, Cee Cee thought. Related to me, hah! She doesn't even want to have a *meal* with me.

That night when Cee Cee walked in the front door carrying a briefcase filled with scripts in one hand and some costume designer's renderings in another, she heard the telephone ringing insistently, so she put everything she was holding down in a heap on the kitchen counter and grabbed the receiver. The call was for Nina. A boy. When boys had first started calling, Cee Cee would run into Nina's room and do a little dance and sing, 'A boy! A boy! Thank heaven it's a boy!' And Nina would laugh. But the adolescent hormones were flying and these days even a smile from Cee Cee when she told her who was waiting on the phone was a reason for a flare-up.

'Neen?' Cee Cee hollered, but there was no answer, and Antonia must have been in the laundry room because the answering machine wasn't on, and the housekeeper usually answered the phone if Nina didn't. 'Neen?' Nothing. 'Hold on,' Cee Cee said into the phone to the boy whose name she didn't ask, not wishing to risk, under the new rules, seeming too nosy, then she pushed the hold button and hurried upstairs. She could hear the shower in Nina's bathroom, which was probably why Nina hadn't heard the phone.

'Neen?' Cee Cee knocked on Nina's bathroom door, but the running water made it impossible for Nina to hear her, so she tried the door. It was unlocked and she pushed it open. Through the glass shower she could see steam rising around the back of Nina's long naked body, and Nina with her head thrown back appearing to love the water as it flowed down her. She was slim and long-waisted, Cee Cee noted with guilt about what she always thought of as her own weight problem. Skinnier than Cee Cee remembered. Of course she hadn't seen her without clothes on in ages. Unlike some of her friends who sometimes wore shorts and halter tops, Nina was modest about her developing body, and most of the time dressed in clothes to conceal it.

Maybe, Cee Cee thought, she should just close the door unnoticed, and go back to the phone and take a message. The boy could call Nina back. But then she reconsidered. Teenaged boys were as weird as teenaged girls. The boy might think it was a rejection if Nina didn't take his call. 'Nina!' This time Nina heard her and she turned, and when she saw Cee Cee standing in the open door of her bathroom, the horrible rage that filled her face was so fierce, for a split second Cee Cee thought it had to be a joke. It was no joke.

'Get out of here. Get the fuck out of here. Can't I have a minute of privacy? What do you *want*?' She was shaking as she opened the shower door and steam poured into the room, and she reached for a giant bath towel, which she threw around her shoulders as if it was a long cape, and now she stood there, wet hair matted against her head, her skinny body trembling, her eyes red with tears.

'Jeez, I'm sorry,' Cee Cee said, feeling stunned and helpless. 'I came to tell you you had a phone call,' and she left the bathroom, walked into her own room, and sat on her bed feeling stunned. Now it was going too far. Now she felt as if Nina really did hate her in that same narrow-eyed and blood-boiling way she remembered hating Leona, and being flesh and blood had nothing to do with it. Maybe every teenager hated every parent in that same way until they separated, until they had their own identity, and then the crisis would pass. That's what it said in all the books.

> Trying to communicate with a teen can be a weary two-step. Forward to closeness, retreat to confrontation. Treat them like a child, they feel patronized; treat them like an adult, they feel anxious. A good way to handle this forward/backward motion is to see it for what it is: part of the long haul to adulthood. Intense though these times are, they will soon pass unless you get all snarled up in them.

For a few minutes after reading the paragraphs of advice in those books, Cee Cee would feel relief. Then her own anger would rise and all reason would spill away, because to be on the receiving end of the kind of wrath Nina had just shown was like getting a kick in the gut, and the pain of rejection it created inside Cee Cee was worse than any desperation she ever felt when a man walked out on her. Certainly far more hurtful than reading some scathing review of her work, because this one hit her so deep inside that, until she started raising a kid, she hadn't even known that place existed. It was hard to believe someone could open you up and twist your vital organs until they ached because you cared about them so much.

She was tired and tense herself, and working too hard, and she always felt apologetic for thinking that thought, because it seemed to be what Hal would call 'a high-class problem,' since it was great to be a successful star after so many years of what a recent *New York Times* article called 'the vicissitudes of La

Bloom's career.' Somehow those studio boys in suits expected her to move from picture to picture without a pause in between, convincing her that this time if she built up 'a body of work' she would 'never slide back' again. Slide back. That meant doing television, or worse yet Vegas or Atlantic City.

And even though she realized what they were telling her was just a way to scare her into doing what they wanted her to do, knew that they were manipulating her by using the terror most performers have of waking up one day and finding themselves out in the cold, still she bought into it. Because it had been so hard-won, because she never quite believed it was really happening for her. And because as much as she hated even to say the words to herself, as hard as she tried to keep it from showing, the truth was she was starting to feel it was harder to keep running on the kind of energy she once had, because she was getting older. Aging. Shit.

In her own bathroom she pulled her sweater over her head, then slid her jeans down to the floor, unhooked her bra, which had left the mark of the too-tight elastic around her, and, dressed only in her black lace panties, looked at herself in the full-length mirror on the door. After just seeing Nina's body, every lump and bump on her own looked even worse than she remembered. Her middle was a little too round, but the legs were still great for her age. And the tits, well the size was perfect, but gravity was definitely having its way with them.

She laughed to herself, remembering Marlon Brando's line in *The Last Tango in Paris*, where he told the young girl that someday she'd be playing soccer with her own tits. Now she cupped a hand around each of hers, lifted them a little higher to where they used to be, and for a fleeting instant entertained the thought of calling a plastic surgeon and getting a tit job. A bra tuck they called it, pull them up a little just like this. 'Get serious, Bloom,' she said, as the thought passed. Why would anyone in her right mind let someone touch her with a knife unless it was to remove something that might kill her? Then she moved her hands to the sides of her breasts, squeezed them together so the nipples pointed straight at the mirror, and said, 'Reach for the sky,' to her reflection. The tits were still okay.

'Besides, there ain't nobody beating my door down to look at them anyway,' she said, shrugging, and ran the water into the bathtub where she sat for an hour replaying that moment of Nina's rage, wondering how and when and if they would ever get back to laughing together, reading together, gabbing away like buddies. Missing her as much as if she'd gone far away, because the Nina she knew had done just that.

The next morning Nina made herself a fast breakfast and her eyes avoided Cee Cee's as she moved to the front door with relief when she heard the honking car horn of one of her friends who had come to take her to school. Today was Valentine's Day, Cee Cee noticed by the date in the newspaper, which she lingered over, reading everything she might ordinarily skip like 'Dear Abby' and 'Peanuts' while she sipped some lukewarm coffee. Then she read the 'Astrological Forecast,' feeling foolish every morning when she checked the View section of the *L.A. Times* for it, hating the fact that even though she really believed it was bullshit, she was irresistibly attracted to it.

'*Refuse to be intimidated by family member's anger.*' Hah! Everybody who read this asshole thing must have a teenager at home. The rest of the message said, '*Phone call brings long-awaited gratification.*' 'Sure,

sure,' she said, not letting herself think about what that could possibly mean, as she poured more hot coffee and headed upstairs, carrying the cup with her. Maybe she would stop and shop for some Valentine goodies on her way in to the office this morning, and later she could leave them on Nina's bed. Then at least for a minute or two while Nina's eyes lit up at the sight of yet another stuffed animal to add to the huge collection she already had, there would be a truce, and maybe the two of them would share even a brief moment of warmth. A moment Cee Cee craved so powerfully she didn't even care if it took bribery to get it.

She pulled some fresh towels out of the linen closet, and just as she passed through her bedroom the phone rang and she picked it up.

'H'lo.'

'Hey there! Cee Cee Bloom.' It was Larry Gold. There was an excited edge in his voice, which always meant he had some good news. 'Hold on to your hat, lady.' Cee Cee's insides were shaking because she knew what it was he could be about to tell her. Something she had tried hard not to hope for, to think about, or to need, superstitious that the hope would make it go away. 'Best actress nomination for the Oscar! How about that for the kid from the Bronx, ladies and gentlemen? Is that a good way to start your day?'

Cee Cee sat on the bed so suddenly that the hot coffee from the newly filled cup she was holding splashed on her robe, but she didn't care. 'It sure is, Larry. It sure as hell is.'

'The official letter will be coming in a day or two with the date of the ceremony, I think it's the twenty-sixth of March, and all the info will be in that. Mean-time, congratulations, kiddo. We made it.'

When she put the phone down she lay back among the pillows on her unmade bed, enjoying the quiet feeling of elation combined with disbelief. Feeling what it meant finally to be where she had been heading every day of her life. Well, *almost* there. To *really* be there would be to stand on that stage hanging on to that gorgeous gold statue, looking out at America and spouting one of the many speeches she'd rehearsed every night of her life since she could remember. *I'd like to thank my director* . . .

With a sensation of lightness she hadn't felt in years, maybe since John Perry proposed to her when she was nineteen, she showered, dressed, and gathered up the papers she needed to take into her office for her ten o'clock meeting. When she got into the car and reached her foot out toward the gas pedal, she realized the front seat had been pushed back, as if someone taller had driven it. But nobody else ever drove her car. Antonia had her own little Plymouth Fury and Nina was too young to drive. She pulled the lever under the seat and moved the seat closer to the dashboard, turned the key in the ignition and the radio came blasting on, but not to her station, 105.1 KKGO. This was some jarring heavy metal station. So she pushed the button until she found KKGO and pulled out of the driveway to go to the studio.

When Nina called her at the office from the Santa Monica Mall to ask if she could buy herself a new pair of stretch Levi's, it was as if nothing bad had happened between them at all. Hormones, Cee Cee thought, knowing that her own could sometimes make her feel as if she needed an exorcist. Fair was fair and Nina was entitled to her bad times too. 'Yes, you can buy the Levi's,' Cee Cee told her. 'Oh, and Neen . . . I got the nomination.'

'Cee Cee!' Nina squealed. 'That is so cool. That is awesome.' It was genuine excitement. And when she added, 'You deserve it,' she sounded just like Bertie used to, and Cee Cee felt a pang of nostalgia. Then Nina rattled on about how she hoped Tom Cruise, her new favorite heartthrob, was nominated so they could sit near him at the ceremony, and while they talked Cee Cee looked over at the shelf across from her desk at the huge white stuffed rabbit she had just bought Nina for Valentine's Day. The rabbit held a red heart which read SOME BUNNY THINKS YOU'RE GREAT. There were other little goodies for her: a heart-shaped bud vase and some heartshaped soap, and a charm bracelet with tiny heart charms dangling from it, and she'd even found some of those old-fashioned heartshaped candies that had YOU'RE CUTE and BE MINE printed on them.

All the way home from work that night she thought about the best way for them to celebrate the nomination. Maybe the excitement would carry them along and after Nina opened all of the Valentine's Day gifts they would go to a movie in Westwood or order dinner in from the Chinese restaurant or pack a picnic and take it out on the sand and watch the sunset.

When she walked in the door of the Malibu house, which usually had a slight mildew scent, this time she was engulfed by the sweet thick smell of flowers, and she was astonished by the number of baskets and vases that filled the living room. Roses in bright yellows and deep reds, rich purple irises, and pink peonies with open lettucey faces by the dozen everywhere. One by one she collected and read each card, one from her business manager, Wayne, one from Larry Gold and another from the entire William Morris office, a massive basket from Hal, another from the studio executives, another from the producer of the film. And every card held some variation of the message that an Oscar nomination for Cee Cee had been a long time in coming. High with joy, she picked up one of the baskets and carried it upstairs to her bedroom, where she put it on her dresser, then took all of the goodies she had bought for Nina and went into Nina's room to leave them for her.

The room was neat. Cee Cee had to give the girl that. Nina was like Bertie in that way. Not a slob like Cee Cee, who always had everything so out of place she never knew where to find it. Sometimes she could waste an hour trying to find some sweater she wanted to wear and thought she'd mislaid, then remember she'd sent it to the cleaners. But not Nina; even when there was no cleaning lady around, her room was perfect. And despite her protests of womanhood, the room looked very much like the room of a little girl, with stuffed animals all over the bed and on every shelf.

Stuffed dogs and lions and elephants on the bookshelves, the windowsills, the desk, and the bed. Winnie-the-Pooh and Tigger and Eeyore, and a giant Minnie Mouse in the corner. Some of the animals Cee Cee could remember buying for her, but most of them had been gifts from or traded for with her friends. Alone in the girl's silent room, Cee Cee put the new Valentine's Day bunny in the middle of the bed, placed the other gifts on the night table, reached across the bed and stroked a furry white toy cat gently, then picked up the mama kangaroo, sat on the bed, and held it on her lap.

Nina, she thought, we will get through this. As soon as I finish the next picture we'll go away somewhere and have time to talk. Guiltily she remembered how she'd said that before, planned other trips with Nina that had fallen through. Since that painful trip to Hawaii, quite a few of their vacation plans had gone awry. The first because of an urgent business problem, and a few months ago because Nina had come down with a violent stomach flu, and by the time she was well enough to reschedule, Cee Cee was too caught up in some project she couldn't interrupt. Well, this time they would do it. Of course it would have to be after the Oscars because between now and then she had to concentrate on getting into shape, work out with her trainer every day for hours, and decide what dress she was wearing to the ceremony and get fitted for it.

The mama kangaroo had big eyes and a funny round nose, and Cee Cee could see that the baby stuffed kangaroo, which should have been sitting in the mama's pouch, was sitting on Nina's dresser instead. As she stood to leave the room, she picked up the baby and was going to slide it into the mama's pouch, but it wouldn't fit, couldn't slide in. As she tried to force it, it felt as if something was at the bottom of the pouch taking up the space. Absently she slid two fingers into the soft belly of the kangaroo to feel what it was, and when she pulled her fingers out, between them was a small plastic Ziploc bag filled with an unmistakable powdery white substance Cee Cee recognized immediately as cocaine. Dear God, no. With a snap in her chest everything fell into place. The moods, the skinniness, the seat in the car being pushed so far back. Probably even the mysterious stomach troubles a few months ago. No, please don't let this be happening. Not to this kid who's had so much to fight through already. Nausea overwhelmed her and she sat back down on the pristine bed to pull herself together and decide what to do.

★

There was a certain detached expression Bertie used to get on her face when she couldn't or didn't want to handle something. Cee Cee still remembered very clearly how that expression became more and more closed in direct proportion to how emotional the situation was. Like the time Cee Cee screamed bloody murder at her in the lobby of that hotel in Miami Beach, and Bertie just stood there, not even blinking. And then there was that year in Malibu right after Bertie found out Michael Barron was on a business trip in Los Angeles at the same time she and Nina were visiting Cee Cee in Malibu, and Bertie rushed out the door to find him and beg him to see his daughter. Naturally the lowlife cocksucker had refused, and Cee Cee would never forget the way Bertie had come back to the house wearing that stoic nothing-can-get-me expression, which was how Cee Cee knew the minute she saw her what Michael's answer had been.

Now Nina had that expression on *her* face, while she looked at Cee Cee who was waving the Ziploc bag of drugs in the air, and Cee Cee knew as she heard herself say every out-of-control word that came into her head that she was doing every wrong thing imaginable in this situation, if in fact there was a situation, which she prayed that there wasn't. Even as she shrieked in anger, she held on to the hope there would be a reason, an excuse, an explanation for drugs being in the room of this child.

'Who the fuck do you think you're talking to?' she railed at Nina. 'I know what this is and I want to know why you have it and where you got it, and I want to know right now, goddammit, or you're never walking out that door again, except to go to school. Do you hear me? And don't give me any bullshit either because

I've been around the block more times than the ice cream man and I'm not some naïve housewife you can con.'

'Cee Cee,' Nina said, without a trace of emotion, 'I already told you, I don't have any idea where that came from. I don't even know if the kangaroo used to belong to Jody or Lindsay or Beth or Allison. It's been sitting in my room for at least a year. Why are you doing this?'

Please, Cee Cee thought, please let that be true, and that I'm getting crazy for no reason at all here. 'Nina, tell me you don't do drugs and that you never have.'

'I don't do drugs and I never have,' she said without a flicker of any emotion on her face.

'You swear?'

'I swear.'

'I don't believe you.'

Nina shrugged, but it wasn't a hostile shrug, it was an indifferent one.

'If I walked into your room with a knife and cut open every stuffed animal, would I find more dope?'

'Not that I know of,' Nina said. Her coolness was remarkable. Even if she wasn't guilty, it would be impossible for a kid to be so undaunted by the red-faced out-of-control carrying-on Cee Cee was doing, about which she was beginning to feel really foolish. Dumb. A kid this cool had to be innocent, didn't she?

They were standing in the kitchen, and Cee Cee walked to the sink and, without taking her eyes from Nina's, emptied the bag of white powder into the garbage disposal, ran the water, and then ran the disposal for a long noisy time. Nina watched, with the same stoic expression she'd had on her face since the confrontation began when she walked in. Outside a car horn honked.

'Who's out there?' Cee Cee asked.

'Melissa.'

'What does she want?'

'We're going over to Allison's. May I go now?'

'We're not finished here.'

'Okay, then she'll wait.'

'Nina, where did the drugs come from?'

'I don't know.'

The car horn honked again.

Maybe she didn't know. Maybe she was telling the absolute truth. And if she wasn't, she was the one who ought to be nominated for a frigging Oscar for this performance here, because there wasn't a blush, an extra blink, even a trace of defiance in her expression that would give her away. Cocaine. Imfuckingpossible. But which one of those other girls would have had it?

'May I please go?' Nina asked, again without impatience.

'Yeah,' Cee Cee said, 'sure, go on.'

When she got to the door Nina turned back again.

'Thanks for the Valentine's Day presents,' she said, and Cee Cee watched her leave. The house was quiet, but in her head she could still hear the echoes of her own hysterical accusations as she walked back upstairs, picturing what the whole scene would have looked like to an outsider. Nina was taller than she was, and there Cee Cee had stood, looking up at her, screaming like some irrational idiot. Like Mammy Yokum wagging her bossy little finger at Li'l Abner. For a while she sat on her bed leafing through copies of *Rolling Stone* and *Ms*, but she couldn't shake the way she felt, when she'd looked at that little bag of cocaine.

It had to be a mistake. Maybe she should call each of those girls and confront them, or better still call their parents and try to get an answer out of them.

Obviously the drugs had been left in the kangaroo pouch by someone else. Had to be. There was no way Nina could afford to buy drugs. Her allowance was so limited and so carefully doled out to her, it would take her forever to be able to afford even what was in that one little bag. In spite of the fact that Cee Cee bought her nice clothes and they lived in a big fancy house, the girl's personal cash situation was practically nil. Anytime she wanted to buy something, she had to call Cee Cee and get her permission. Okay, so maybe Cee Cee gave the permission a little too often, but there was never any cash involved. There wasn't a way in the world she could have paid for drugs like that.

'Nina, Cee Cee brought you here because she's afraid you might be using drugs and that maybe we could talk about it.'

'Well, there's nothing to talk about, because I'm not,' Nina said in a small voice. 'So there's no more to say.' The girl was neatly dressed as always and the light makeup she wore was carefully and tastefully applied. She looked more like a photograph in a teen magazine than someone who had been coerced into the room by an adult suspecting her of drug use.

'If I were you I wouldn't want to talk either. Cee Cee drops you here into the office of some adult you don't even know and expects you to trust me. Why should you? You don't even know me, but maybe you could tell me why Cee Cee was so panicked on the phone.'

'I don't know.'

'Is she always that way?'

Nina didn't react.

'What's it like for you when she gets that way?'

Nina looked over at the door to the waiting room.

'She can't hear us out there, these walls are sound-proof, and I told her she could come in to our private session only when you felt comfortable about it. So even though she's waiting out there, we don't have to let her in at all if we need the time for ourselves.'

Nina shrugged. 'It doesn't matter to me.' Again there was silence.

'When Cee Cee acts that way at home, how do you deal with it?'

'I don't.'

'Do you hide?'

'Well, I wouldn't call it hiding, but I try to stay away from her.'

'And what do you do the other times? The times when you can't stay away?'

'The other times . . . I guess I tell her what I know she wants to hear.'

'Good heavens!' Florrie Kagan, the family therapist Cee Cee had tracked down after frantic phone calls all over town, sat back in her chair, and Nina saw a pleased-with-herself expression on the woman's face that meant she thought she'd found an inroad. 'You must have to play a role all the time. What role do you play with her?'

Nina took a long look at her. The woman was about Cee Cee's age, but much prettier with pouffy blond hair and giant piercing blue eyes. She wore a sweater that came down past her narrow hips over a long skirt and boots. 'Is it the role of the people-pleaser, or the role of the good daughter? Tell me who you play.' Nina wasn't sure where this was going or even what she was going to answer, until she heard it come out of herself as she said it.

'I play my mother.'

'What does that mean?'

'It means I guess I act like I'm her friend who thinks she's great. Her loyal, perfect friend.'

'And that's who you think your mother was to Cee Cee?'

'I *know* that's who she was.'

'What happened to your mother?'

Nina looked down at her lap.

'You know what, Nina? I just saw a wall come down. This must be so hard for you. How did your mom die?'

Nina didn't look up.

'Nina. I know this must be tough. Can you tell me what happened to your mom?'

'She died of cancer.'

'How old were you?'

'Eight.'

'How long was the process of dying?'

'She was sick off and on for two years.'

'Did you realize what was happening?'

Nina spoke but didn't look up. 'At the end . . . she had this plan? To go off to Carmel? So I wouldn't have to see her the way she was when she was real bad at the end. But Cee Cee went to Carmel to be with her and Cee Cee told her she had to send for me. So she did and I got to be with her for the last few months.'

'And how was that for you?'

'Well, you can trust me, it wasn't the prom,' she said, and as her answer rang through the office she thought how much she sounded like Cee Cee.

'Did you have a chance to say goodbye?'

'At the time I didn't even know what that meant. I guess I always thought she was going to come back.'

'And now?'

Nina's eyes looked up, but far away and not at the doctor. 'Now I know she's not.'

'Nina, these are tough times for kids your age in terms of the availability of drugs and the peer pressure to use. Cee Cee called me because she found cocaine in your room, which you said you didn't know was there. Do you know of any of your friends who are using?'

'No.'

'Do you know any kids at your school who are?'

'I'm sure it's around,' she said, 'but ...' She shrugged as an end to the sentence.

'You and Cee Cee have been through quite a few painful experiences together. Your mother's death, your father's abandonment, Cee Cee's personal problems and career problems. All very heavy for a girl your age. Can you talk about any of that?'

'No.'

Cee Cee sat in the waiting room staring at the same page in *Better Homes and Gardens* she'd been staring at for the last fifteen minutes, her insides throbbing with fear, knowing this could be a turning point from which she and Nina might never come back. A break between them that could never be repaired. She remembered the way it happened with Leona. How one day in 1956 or '57 she had looked at her mother and said to herself, I'll tolerate my life with her until I can get the fuck out, but that's it. I'll never tell her one more thing about me. Never let myself care about her, never. Never confide in her or let her know who I am. And now she had the agonizing certainty that Nina was not only having those feelings about her, but was taking drugs to dull the pain.

When after nearly an hour had passed and the door from the inner office opened, Cee Cee jumped to her feet, and after Florrie gestured gently for her to come in, she walked slowly toward the inner office wondering what had transpired while she'd been sitting out there imagining the worst.

'Cee Cee, Nina says she thinks you're overreacting. She says she doesn't use drugs and has even agreed to be tested to prove it. What do you think of that?'

I think she's lying through her perfectly straight teeth, Cee Cee thought, then thought, Thank you, God, then wasn't sure what she thought. 'What do *you* think of that?' she asked the lady shrink.

'Well, I suggested that even though there may not be drugs involved, the two of you might want to continue to come in here together a few times just to work on your relationship, and she agreed to that.'

'She did?' Cee Cee's heart jumped with hope. Nina's face was expressionless.

'How about if we set a time in a week or so for the two of you to come back?' Florrie asked.

Nina nodded. Florrie opened a calendar book and mentioned some possible appointment times. None of them were good for Cee Cee, who was scheduled up to her ears at work, but she didn't say that. 'Whichever one is good for Nina is good for me.' Nina picked a Friday appointment in a week at three thirty.

That week was crazy busy for Cee Cee. The Oscar nomination had created a flurry of events in her career, offers to field, magazine layouts to do, phone calls from Barbara Walters wanting her to tape a show in a few days which would run on Oscar night. Thankfully, and unusually, everything at home was so calm and almost back to pleasant, she didn't even mention the idea of drug testing for fear of stirring up an argument.

In fact, she was starting to feel as if maybe the whole drug thing had been her paranoia, another example of her going too far, and that finding the drugs one of those bratty little girls had hidden in Nina's room had been God's way of getting the two of them to counseling so their mother-daughter problems could get fixed. On the morning of the appointment with Doctor Kagan, the shrink, Cee Cee told Nina she would pick her up at school at three o'clock.

She was early so she was able to get a parking spot right in front of the school where she sat for a while thinking about what the two of them might say to one another in today's session, feeling hopeful that things between them were on the mend. It was hot in the car, so after a while she got out and leaned against the door and watched the kids pouring out of the building. For a long time her eyes followed one particular group of girls who were a little older than Nina, walking along laughing and talking, and she was impressed with how womanly and sophisticated they seemed. More sophisticated than she had ever been at that age. At *any* age, she thought to herself, and wondered how those girls got along with *their* parents. In another passing group she noticed a tall straight-haired blond girl dressed in a plaid skirt and green sweater who was clearly the focal point of her friends. The girl was talking away and gesturing, and as she did, Cee Cee noticed that on the third finger of her right hand was Bertie's emerald ring.

The answer, the cash. That's how she got it. Goddammit. Goddamn her. I won't fucking have it. A crashing rush of adrenaline flooded through her. Stop it, she told herself. You're imagining things. The girl had walked by pretty fast, so she could be mistaken. There were a lot of emerald rings in the world. In fact the emerald was the birthstone for the month of May, so maybe the girl's birthday was in May and it was her own ring, which just happened to resemble Bertie's from a distance. But instead of staying by her parked car where she had promised Nina she'd meet her, Cee

Cee moved quickly after the girl and her friends who were now about a half a block away. You're crazy, she told herself, you're going to make an asshole of yourself and of Nina because you're a certifiable lock-up case.

'Hi, Nance,' she heard a boy's voice yell from across the street, and Cee Cee saw the girl who was wearing the ring raise a hand high to wave at the boy. The wave gave Cee Cee another look at the ring, and this time, even from the distance, she was sure it was Bertie's ring. Nina's ring. Now she moved faster, and when she was a few feet behind the girls who had now turned the corner she shouted, 'Nancy!' The girl turned around to look at her and so did her three friends. Cee Cee noticed the friends exchange looks when they saw who had stopped them. When they realized it was Cee Cee Bloom, not just anybody's mother but a movie star, they looked nervous. That gave Cee Cee enough of a feeling of power to move closer to the girl with the ring, who, she could now see, looked as guilty as sin.

'I need to talk to you,' Cee Cee said.

'Okay,' the girl replied and gave one of those nods to the others that a gangleader in a bad crime movie gives to the gang to tell them 'It's okay to leave, but don't go too far away, just in case.'

Cee Cee braced herself as the girl walked farther down the block next to her, with a brash confident walk that only a girl who looks that good can, and the minute the other girls were out of earshot she said, 'She told me it belonged to her, not you. That she needed the money. She said that her real mother left it to her when she died so she could do whatever she wanted with it.'

'She told you the truth,' Cee Cee said, looking down at the girl's perfect hand holding on to a history book, and there was the ring, looking just the way it had once looked on Bertie. Cee Cee flashed on that time in Miami when she'd spotted the ring on Neetie's hand and had gone bananas over it, and how that night when they had arrived at home in Malibu and Nina put the ring back into her musical pink ballerina jewelry box that plunked out 'Love Makes the World Go 'Round' she had thanked Cee Cee gratefully for retrieving it.

For so many years Nina's hand had been too small to wear the beautiful piece of jewelry on her ring finger, even with ring guards, but last year she tried it on and came running in to Cee Cee's room to show her that it fit her on the same finger where Bertie had always worn it, and it was like a rite of passage. Coincidentally, two days later she got her first menstrual period. Since then she'd worn the ring for special occasions, always when she did stopping frequently to look down at her hand to admire it.

'It did belong to her. But her mother was my best friend, and it belonged to her grandmother first, and it would mean a lot if you would sell it back to me.'

The girl sighed a sigh which said, I don't want to do what you're asking, but you're an adult and if I don't you'll probably start a big stink about it.

'How much did you pay for it?' Cee Cee pressed.

'Seven hundred dollars.' The goddamned ring was worth a hell of a lot more than that.

'I'll give you nine hundred.' The girl was pouting and looked as if she was thinking about giving Cee Cee a hard time. 'I don't have that much cash on me,' Cee Cee apologized, knowing the girl might just get up and storm away if she didn't handle her properly. 'But if you give me the ring now, I'll have my secretary meet you here tomorrow at this time on this spot with the money.'

As if she was ending an engagement, the girl reluctantly slid the ring from her finger and handed it over to Cee Cee. 'Tomorrow at this time on this spot,' she said looking into Cee Cee's eyes.

'You got it,' Cee Cee said, and turned to go when the girl's voice stopped her.

'She threw this into the deal too.'

Cee Cee turned back. In the girl's hand was a compact. It had fake rhinestones on the lid, and had been a gift from someone at the studio to Cee Cee for Christmas. Kept in her room, in her own jewelry box. The kind of glitzy item teenagers liked, and Nina had taken it to sweeten the deal when she sold the ring. Stole it from Cee Cee and sold it. It was hard for Cee Cee to think those words. When she got back to her car, stinging with the ugly truth, Nina was sitting in the passenger seat, waiting for her.

'Where'd you go?' Nina asked.

'Down the street,' Cee Cee answered and got into the car.

In Doctor Kagan's waiting room, Cee Cee, too numb to even think about what she was going to say when they got inside the office with the cool I've-seen-it-all lady doctor, watched through a veil of fear as Nina paged through some schoolbook, a legitimate way to avoid conversation with Cee Cee. She was wearing a nearly angelic look on her face, and looking at her sitting there, Cee Cee remembered when she was a kid and Leona took her to see Patty McCormack in *The Bad Seed* on Broadway. When the mother in the play realized her child was a murderer passing herself off as an innocent, the look Nancy Kelly who played the part wore on her face had to be the same one Cee Cee wore now. Stiff, pained, shocked, hurt.

'Well, now,' Florrie said, leading them into her

office, and Cee Cee felt a terror of what would happen next, because she knew she was about to break open the blister of lies that would have to release the poison into their lives. Had to tell Nina now that she knew her secret. And after she did there was no outcome she could imagine that wouldn't be painful. Every ending for the scene she had played in her mind as she drove blindly to Brentwood and parked and rode up in the elevator to this office was horrible.

'Well, how have you two been doing this week?' the doctor asked.

Nina shrugged and made a noise which sounded like 'N'kay,' and Cee Cee said nothing. She thought seriously about grabbing Nina by the neck and shaking her hard enough to scare the shit out of her, and to maybe scare out a confession, too, knowing that the shrink would pull her off before she really hurt her.

'Did you have a drug test, Nina?' Florrie asked matter-of-factly.

'No,' Nina said. 'Why *would* I?' As though a drug test had never been discussed in this office.

Florrie looked at Cee Cee as if to ask her why anybody who had been as crazily convinced one week ago that her kid was taking drugs wouldn't have pushed her to take the promised test, but Cee Cee looked away from her at Nina.

'Nina,' Cee Cee said, pausing before she asked the next, wishing she didn't have to. 'Where's the emerald ring?'

'What?'

'Your mother's emerald ring. The one Neetie tried to take from you. Remember how excited we were when it finally fit your finger? And you wore it a few times to parties. Where is it?' There was a long pause, during which the silence drummed away in Cee Cee's ears.

'I lost it.'

'When?'

'A while ago.'

'Why didn't you tell me? You knew it was insured. In fact that was why we decided it was okay for you to wear it every now and then. I could have reported it and you could have had the money to replace it. Do you remember where you lost it?'

'If I remembered where I lost it, I could go there and get it and it wouldn't be lost, would it?' The bitchiness in her voice helped Cee Cee to proceed, and ask a question to which sadly she knew the answer.

'Are you lying?'

'I forgot about the insurance,' Nina said, looking hurt and slumping into the chair, 'and I know how emotional you get and I thought you'd go crazy. Besides, it was *my* ring. My mother left it to *me*. So why should I have to answer to you? I lost it.'

'Well, I found it,' Cee Cee said and pulled the ring from her pocket, where she had been holding it tightly in her fist all the way to the doctor's office from the school, and which she now held up as the three of them looked at its deep green glow catching the overhead light. 'I stopped Nancy at school today and bought it back for you. And my compact too.'

'Oh, shit!' Nina cried with an embarrassed agonized howl. 'I hate you so much,' and she covered her face with her hands.

'So you've been conning us, Nina. Conning Cee Cee for a long time. Covering your tracks very well. That must have been a hard job,' Florrie said quietly.

'Did you take my car out at night?' Cee Cee asked.

From behind her hands, Nina nodded a slight nod. 'When you were sleeping. A lot of times.'

Cee Cee felt cold all over. 'Nina, what did I do?

285

Where did I screw it all up? Why didn't you tell me what I was doing wrong?'

Nina took her hands away from her face now and got to her feet. All her coolness was gone and her face was splotchy with anger and her hair askew. 'Guess what?' she said, glaring into Cee Cee's face. 'This time it isn't about you, Cee Cee. For once in our lives, something isn't about you, it's about me! Me! I am sick of you trying to make everything in the world about you.' And she rushed to the door and with a grunt pulled the inner door toward her, then forced herself against the outer door, ran through the waiting room, and with a slam of that door was gone.

When she wasn't home by ten that night, Cee Cee sat with the high school roster and called the home of every girl she ever remembered being in her home. Some were asleep and their sympathetic-voiced parents said they had no idea where Nina was. Some phones didn't answer. Soon in her anguish Cee Cee wasn't sure which ones she had called and which ones she hadn't. She thought about calling Kevin Myers, but over the past year, probably because hanging around with him hadn't been considered cool, Nina had pretty much phased him out of her life.

At two in the morning she still sat with her hand on the phone, trembling with exhaustion, not sure if she should call the police or drive the streets and look for Nina herself. *Runaways*. She had skipped over that chapter in the book about parents and teenagers, not even imagining it would ever be necessary to read it. Now she read it.

Running is almost always a cry for help, and you must face these needs and learn to deal with them. Over a million teenagers choose this solution every year and the average runner is a fifteen-year-old girl. Usually within a few days your child will be back at home.

Please God. As the sun came up, Cee Cee walked upstairs with a blinding headache and a heart that felt ripped in half and called Doctor Kagan. When she got the answering service, she begged them to let her hold on while they tracked her down.

'Cee Cee, what news?' the doctor said within minutes.

'What should I do?' she asked. 'Tell me what to do. Should I drive all over town looking in alleys? Should I hire a detective? Should I call the hospitals and the morgue? Please tell me what I'm supposed to do, because I can't stand not knowing where she is. What if she needs food? What if she thinks I won't *take* her back? I have to tell her that I'm going to help her through this.'

'Cee Cee, what I'm going to tell you will be the hardest thing for you, but I think you need to wait, to give it another day or two, let her play this out, because I believe she wants to come home and that you'll hear from her very soon.'

Barbara Walters and her crew would be arriving in a few hours to tape an interview with her, and Cee Cee knew she looked as horrible as she felt. So what if I look like shit, she thought. Dear God, bring me my kid back safe and I'll turn in all the fame, all the nominations, and every fucking ticket anybody ever bought to come and see me anywhere. But the phone didn't ring with any word of Nina, and after a blazing hot shower, which Cee Cee took with the shower door open and the phone pulled across the bathroom so she could hear it in case it rang while she was in there, and three cups of coffee she brewed so strong they could wake the dead, she answered the door to her makeup lady by saying, 'I think you've got your work cut out for you today, girl.'

She could hear Barbara Walters's crew arriving as the base coat and concealer and blusher were being applied, and while her face was being powdered in place, and her hair was teased, combed, and sprayed into obedience, she tried desperately from some reserve tank of wherewithal to dredge up some enthusiasm for the interview she had made a commitment to give. Finally with a face painted on that magically brightened her own pale-with-fatigue one, she dressed in a soft pink jersey shirt and pants and went into her living room, which was now filled with cameras and technicians and lights, to chat with Barbara Walters. And as she passed the assistant producer, she thought she heard the young woman doing a last-minute check on details before they started to shoot.

'Telephone bells turned off?' Cee Cee heard her ask.

'No!' Cee Cee whirled around and shouted. 'You can't shut the phones off, I'm expecting an urgent call!'

'But we –'

'No! You can't shut the phones off and that's final!'

The young woman looked over Cee Cee's head at the producer, who gave an everybody-has-their-own-craziness nod back to say it was okay to leave the phone bells alone, and Cee Cee went in to meet Barbara Walters. But the phone didn't ring at all.

'You're a busy lady. A movie star, a producer, a single mother. Tell me about your daughter.'

The lights were hot and Cee Cee held tightly to the arm of the sofa. She was trembling and weak and so sick inside she was sure it had to show, but she fixed her face into the Cee Cee Bloom position and answered. 'She's sensational,' she said. 'A joy and a gem and the light of my life.'

The interview seemed to take all day. Questions about her past, her marriage, her television show, her films, her future plans, but later when the lights were turned off and Barbara Walters left after thanking her for a great interview and the crew had cleared out, she sat by the telephone again, and all she could remember about the interview was what she had said about Nina.

There was no word that night either, and the next morning, after about an hour's sleep, she went to have her dress for the Oscars fitted at Bob Mackie's studio. The dress was long and slinky and covered with bugle beads, and when it was finished it would fit her like a glove. Cee Cee stood still as Bob Mackie circled her, congratulating her for the nomination with his sweet boyish smile, amazed at how thin she was these days. And that was when she realized she hadn't eaten anything in nearly two days.

When the fitting was over, she went into the three-way-mirrored dressing room to slip the dress off carefully to avoid the pins, but before she did, she leaned against the center mirror and watched as an infinite number of Cee Cees in all directions covered their faces and wept.

Three days had passed. It was a Monday afternoon and Cee Cee was in her office, in a meeting for her next film. The director, the writer, the two producers, and all of the development people, Cee Cee's and the studio's, sat spread around the room, on chairs, on the sofas, and on the floor, talking about the script and some of the last-minute changes, when the door opened.

'Cee Cee,' her secretary said, 'it's Nina.' Her face

looked alarmed. Cee Cee left the meeting, walked to her secretary's desk in the outer office, and took the phone.

'Hello?'

The voice on the other end of the line was Nina's but in a panic that made it sound shrill and eerie. 'Cee Cee, you have to help me. I can't breathe and my face is swollen and I . . . I'm sorry, but I snorted something at Lisa's and I . . .'

'Where's Lisa's house?' Cee Cee asked her.

'On Tigers Trail. Six four one.'

'Hang on, I'm coming,' Cee Cee said and hung up.

She drove like a maniac over the canyon, running stop signs and red lights, and when she reached Lisa's house she double-parked and ran up the steps, tried the door, and barged into the house. There were dozens of crumpled tissues all over the floor and the chairs, and Lisa sat crying on the sofa, holding bunched-up tissues to her face.

'I'm okay,' she said, 'but she's really bad.'

Cee Cee heard a loud moan, which she recognized as Nina's, and followed the sound to a little chintz and ruffled powder room where Nina crouched over the toilet retching and vomiting. Cee Cee put an arm around her, brushed her hair from her face, and held her head.

'Sorry, Cee, I'm sorry,' Nina said.

Cee Cee wet a washcloth with cold water to wash Nina's face, which, now that the girl turned to her, she could see was swollen and distorted. And when Nina looked up and caught sight of herself in the mirror, she wailed, 'Oh God,' and Cee Cee could hear by the gurgled sound of the wail that her throat was closing.

The doctor in the emergency room told Cee Cee they

had to intubate Nina because her vocal chords were swollen and her airway was in jeopardy of obstructing, which could have killed her if they'd been a few minutes later. The swollen face was an angioneurotic edema, caused by the drug. It was crank, a mixture of speed and God knows what else that had been used to cut it. Lisa had been put into a separate hospital room from Nina with only a dripping nose, and by the time her parents, a curly haired conservative-looking man in a gray suit, and a pretty blond mother, arrived at the hospital, Cee Cee was standing beaten and drained in the waiting room, placing her fourth phone call to Florrie, but still getting only the answering service. The parents didn't see her as they passed, but Cee Cee, who recognized them from school meetings, heard the father say to the mother, 'I told you Nina probably got drugs from that piece of garbage Cee Cee Bloom and then gave them to Lisa. But you'd never listen, would you?'

'Shut up, Frank,' she heard the woman answer.

Cee Cee's first impulse was to run after the guy, grab him by the throat, and scream obscenities into his face. To tell him it was *his* kid who got the dope, not her kid, and she started out the door to go after him, but stopped when she saw Florrie walking briskly down the corridor toward her.

'I got your message and came immediately. Is she all right?'

'The doctor said she will be,' Cee Cee said.

'Can I see her?'

'I'll take you in.'

Nina had a tube in her nose that was draining and a tube coming out of her mouth, and though Cee Cee had already seen her, each time she looked at her this way she had to hold on to the footboard of the bed to keep her knees from buckling under her. Nina narrowed her eyes when she looked at Florrie and realized who it was, and she wouldn't even look at Cee Cee.

'Nina,' Florrie said, 'it must feel pretty horrible being in that bed with all of those tubes in you, knowing that you came very close to dying. And I think it's significant that you called Cee Cee to come and save you instead of calling an ambulance yourself. Does that just mean you were afraid the police would find out about the drugs? Or does it mean that you're finally ready to accept Cee Cee's help with your drug problem?'

Nina stared at the ceiling. Cee Cee's face and body hurt with anxiety and pain, looking at this baby, this young child, so disfigured and destroyed by the abuse she'd brought on herself in this horrible way. God give me strength, she used to hear her own mother utter every day of her life. And now it was what she found herself asking, God give me the strength to get through this one. *Leona*, she thought, *I'm using your prayer because I finally get it, I finally understand you, and I'm sorry for every time I ever made you worry about me. For every time I shrieked at you, hated you, wanted to hurt you and didn't know why. Because now, at last, I understand how you felt. How a mother feels. And I wish you were around to say you told me so.*

'Dear girl,' Florrie said to Nina, 'perhaps now we can begin our treatment, because I'm sure that after this you'll be willing to make a commitment to stop using drugs. Won't you?'

Nina's response to Florrie's question was to turn her face back to the ceiling with an expression that, despite the helpless state and her supine position, still managed to look defiant. Florrie took Cee Cee by the elbow and moved her out of the room into the hospital corridor.

'What do I do?' Cee Cee asked.

'You put her into detox and then a rehab program. I know an excellent one in Newport Beach. You take her there, you leave her there, you do whatever you can to find out why she uses and try to change that, which can be a long and painful process. But Cee Cee, mostly . . .' Florrie put her hand on Cee Cee's arm. 'Mostly you pray.'

The sky was a muddy brown as Cee Cee drove south on the San Diego Freeway. Nina was asleep in the passenger seat; her face, though still puffy around the eyelids, was almost back to its normal size. That morning at St. John's Hospital she had stared out the window, sullen and pouting while Cee Cee packed the few toiletries she had used in the last few days and was allowed to take with her to the rehabilitation clinic. Her clothes were packed and waiting in the car per Florrie's instructions that Cee Cee take her directly to the drug clinic, because a stop at home could be disruptive to the process.

'Many times parents have said, "We're just stopping off to pick up some clothes," and when they got home, they were manipulated into changing their minds.'

For a few minutes before they checked out, Florrie sat with the two of them in the cold, metallic, stripped-bare hospital room. A nurse came by pushing a wheelchair as standard hospital procedure to take Nina down to the car, but Cee Cee waved her off.

'Nina,' Florrie said very softly, 'can you connect with the specific pain you're feeling when you use?'

Nina didn't answer.

'What does being high give you that you can't get on your own?' It looked as if Nina wasn't going to answer, because she continued to stare out the window at the hospital wing opposite, but then she said, 'Because my outsides don't match my insides. Outside I'm the nice quiet, okay-looking girl, but inside I want to be something else.'

'What kind of something else?'

Again she thought for a while, then said, 'I want to be able to be funny and tell jokes and have people like me because I have guts, and wear something with rhinestones in it . . . and unless I'm high I'm too scared.'

Cee Cee couldn't believe what she was hearing. The kid was gorgeous; so many times she had looked at her in awe of her burgeoning beauty, thinking that she looked like all the beautiful girls Cee Cee had envied all her life. And with a brain and a sense of humor to match that beauty. How could she not know that about herself? 'So I get high to go to school, because otherwise I'm nobody, and if I have to be nobody, I'd rather be dead.'

'Nina, when you're high, who's your behavior model?' Florrie asked her.

The answer was so obvious Cee Cee wanted to blurt it out and would have if Florrie hadn't raised a hand to stop her. When Nina replied, there was amazement in her voice, because she spoke the answer just as she realized what the answer was.

'When I'm high, I act like Cee Cee does all the time. Gutsy, saying anything I feel like and cracking people up.'

Dear God, Cee Cee thought, why would anyone want to act like that? I do it because it's all I know how to do.

'Has it been hard over the last seven years to keep up with whatever it means to belong to Cee Cee Bloom?'

There was a silence, then Nina smiled, a smile that looked eerie on her bright red face, and said in a voice that sounded odd coming from her, 'You bet your ass,' and all three of them laughed a laugh of recognition.

Now as Cee Cee pulled up to the admitting entrance of the hospital in Newport Beach, what at another time might have brought rage simply caused a blanket of weariness to fall over her, because standing in wait, festooned with their cameras, was an army of fan-magazine photographers. Somehow the sons-of-bitches knew everything, maybe from someone who worked at the other hospital, maybe from someone on Cee Cee's own staff who was selling the information about her troubles. And there they stood, waiting to take shots of Nina's entry into the hospital so that they could sell the pictures to the tabloids.

Instead of pulling into the portico where they stood, Cee Cee stopped and with a screech of tires backed up and found herself waking Nina and walking her into the hospital through an obscure entrance she found, just behind the linen service man who was making a delivery.

A nurse frisked her. Cee Cee stood and watched a big black nurse, wearing a plastic pin that said that her name was Marvel, actually frisking Nina for drugs, while Cee Cee stood there feeling as guilty as if she had been caught red-handed killing the very person she cared about the most.

While the nurse patted Nina down Cee Cee noticed Nina hung her head in a way that looked so tough, she must have seen it in some old 'women in prison' movie on television. It was almost as if she was relishing the role of the beaten-down bad kid because it was so unlike the perfect girl she'd been, or pretended to be, up until so recently. Cee Cee's stomach was cramped and twisted, and she could feel every touch of the nurse's hands on Nina as if she was living through the humiliation herself. Marvel handed Nina a plastic specimen cup and was ushering her toward a door marked RESTROOM.

'You can leave any time now, honey,' Marvel said to Cee Cee, with more than a little hint of I'm-running-the-show-here. 'She's starting detox right after her shower, and after that you're not allowed to even talk to her for about three weeks.'

Cee Cee made a noise in her throat to indicate that what the woman had just told her was absurd. 'You mean I can't *see* her. But it's okay to call her on the phone. Right?'

'You can call *me*,' the nurse said. 'I'll be glad to let you know how she's doing,' and she gave Cee Cee a little wave of dismissal. 'But, no you can't call her, and she can't call you. Not till the doctor says so.' When Cee Cee looked as if she was about to give her an argument, Marvel looked at her closely and said, 'Why don't you stop by Doctor Pappas's office and get the packet we give out to the parents. The rules are all in there real clear.'

Nina was in the bathroom now and Marvel was using her own foot, wearing white Nike tennis shoes, as a doorstop to hold the door partially open, until Cee Cee saw Nina's hand pass the urine specimen out to her. Marvel looked down just long enough to mark BARRON with a grease pencil on the side of the plastic cup and then looked back at Cee Cee. 'You go on now,' she said. Nina emerged from the bathroom, and Cee Cee walked closer to her, hoping to give her a parting hug, but before she could, Nina shook her off. 'I'm leaving,' Cee Cee said.

'Bye,' Nina said, and walked with Marvel down the hospital hall.

'You've got to be joking about the three weeks,' she said to the doctor. 'I'm not gonna make it through that. Anyway, why keep *me* out? I'm not going to bring her any drugs.' Doctor Pappas was in his late fifties, handsome in an Anthony Quinn sort of way, olive skinned with white hair and a slight Greek accent.

'No, but you might perhaps be a reminder to her of why she's been using them.'

'I don't get it. You mean *I'm* the reason? Hey, I know I'm a pain in the ass, but Doctor Kagan sent you her records. Her mother died a grisly death when she was eight years old, and her father is the worst prick that ever lived. You *know* what her life has been like. And what about peer pressure? That's what pushes kids to use, isn't it?'

'Ms Bloom, it would be too easy to blame any and all of those things. The reasons for adolescent addiction are mixed and complicated. The sad fact is that today thirty percent of the addicted population are adolescents. They're a perfect target for the drug sellers, as is anyone who is fearful, feeling rebellious, anxious to be attractive to the opposite sex. And it's also classic for the child of an overbearing and famous parent to seek independence from that parent, and solace in substance abuse from the sad fact that he or she will never be equal to that parent. Maybe since you caught Nina so early in life, by working together we can find out what her particular reasons are and infuse her with enough confidence in herself to make her want to get and remain sober.'

'What can I do? Tell me and I'll do it.'

'After she's been detoxed, I want to put her in a private rehab program not far from here which I facilitate. You can go home, and come to a family meeting there when I think she's ready to have you. At least three weeks. In the meantime,' he said, handing her half a dozen small paper booklets, 'it would be good if you would attend some of these.'

Cee Cee looked down at what he had given her. Brochures from Alanon, Naranon, AA, Cocaine Anonymous, CODA, Adult Children of Alcoholics. 'Those are lists of meetings of Twelve Step programs of various types. Programs that will help you to understand what we do here better than my explaining it to you. Go to them, find one or find several where you're comfortable, and go every day, at least once. We like to say ninety meetings in ninety days, but going to more than that won't hurt you. Because if you sit there long enough, eventually the commonality of the situations hits home and you learn through the pain of others how to overcome your own.'

'I don't have . . .' She started to say she didn't have time to go to a bunch of meetings. To explain she had work to do, the Oscars to prepare for, but she stopped herself. 'Look, it's not my pain that worries me. I'm okay. It's the kid's pain we're talking about here. This is a kid who could have O.D.'d on crank. Who told me she had to toot up just to make it through a schoolday. And I don't remember the last time I saw her arms. She could be mainlining for all I know.'

'You seem to have the lingo down already,' the doctor said, looking long at her, and she felt herself flush.

'I'm in show business,' she said.

'I'm very aware of that fact,' Pappas said, 'but I'm in the reality business. So now we're going to deal in

Nina's reality. As unpleasant as that may turn out to be.'

'I'll go to meetings,' Cee Cee said, 'and I'll see you' – she looked at Pappas for an answer but he had none for her – '. . . when I see you,' she said, and she left his office and walked through the quiet corridors of the hospital, feeling cold and tired and not sure what day or time it was. When she got to the delivery entrance where her car was parked, she noticed for the first time that it was dark, and she got into the car and drove into the night alone. Somewhere along the free-way her stomach growled. She was hungry, so she pulled off at the next exit and into the drive-through entrance of a McDonald's.

'Next, please,' said a disembodied voice.

'Big Mac, side of fries, and a Coke.'

After she picked up her food, she pulled the car into a parking space in the brightly lit parking lot, looking through the windows at the families inside McDonald's enjoying their dinners, and she envied them.

'God grant me the serenity to accept the things I cannot change, the courage to change the things I can, and the wisdom to know the difference.'

The next morning she stood on the beach in Santa Monica before sunrise, holding the hands of two people she'd never seen before in her life. In fact, she was part of a large circle made up of dozens of people she'd never seen before. She was wearing her disguise, the hat and the sunglasses, and it seemed to be working. So far not one person there had asked if she was Cee Cee Bloom. The Serenity Prayer, she thought. That ought to be called the mother's prayer.

As the meeting began she sat on the blanket she'd brought, holding a Styrofoam cup of hot coffee and four cookies, which she ate in rapid succession, not caring if they were going to make her look fat in her Oscar dress, and she watched carefully and listened to the welcomes and to someone reading the Twelve Steps, and then she realized they were going around the group and everyone was saying his or her name. Just the first name, after which everybody said 'Hi' to them by name, but Cee Cee was such a funny name that if she said it and they took a good look at her, everyone would know who she was.

'I'm Pat,' she said when it was her turn.

'Hi, Pat,' everyone said, and she felt relieved when they went on to the next person and nobody seemed the wiser that she wasn't Pat, but she hated herself for lying at the same time. Mostly what happened at these meetings, she was figuring out now, was that people got up and told their stories. One young girl in her twenties said that her husband was so physically abusive she had to move out on him, because it was one thing for him to hit her before, but now she was pregnant, and she thanked all of them for being there for her because, she said, 'Without you people I would have nobody.'

Then a very straight-looking, handsome, gray-haired man said that last week was his birthday, and he was trying to figure out why that depressed him, and then he remembered that when he was a kid he always hated his birthdays because he had to have his birthday dinner at a restaurant that had a bar in it, so his father could leave the rest of the family and sit at the bar and drink, and how his father still ran his life, and he wanted to stop wishing his father would die already.

One girl said she spent the money her parents sent her to buy books and clothes at college on drugs, so she had to go to the college bookstore and steal the books, and then to the clothing stores and steal clothes. And now that she was sober and working her program, she was up to Step Nine, which said, 'We will try to make direct amends to people we have harmed, where amends are possible to make,' so she had gone back to those stores she had stolen from years before and offered to pay them back for the merchandise.

An older woman said she used the twelve noon, twelve midnight plan. 'I never ask myself how I'm gonna get through the day. When I wake up I tell myself I'll just try to get to twelve noon, and at twelve noon I say, I'll just try to make it to twelve midnight. It's how I survive my husband's drinking.' Cee Cee reached into her purse and took out a pen, and the only paper she could find was an old envelope, so on the back of it she wrote herself a note that said, TWELVE NOON. TWELVE MIDNIGHT. She would try that.

Maybe these meetings worked, or maybe they were just a bunch of slogans and coffee. But she needed something, anything, so she sat tailor-seat on her blanket on the sand listening to it all, taking it in, hearing the way other people lived with their problems. These little bits of people's lives are better, sadder, more human, and much more moving than any of the stories the writers who come in to meet with me at the studio ever bring, she thought. These people are spilling their real beans all over the place, and feeling better for it, and even getting applause after they do. She could never do that in front of strangers. When a character she played was in pain, that was okay. She could cry and scream and writhe and suffer publicly as someone else, but not as Cee Cee Bloom, who thankfully no one at this meeting seemed to realize she was.

When the meeting on the beach was over, she helped

some of the others pick up coffee stirrers and half-empty Styrofoam cups, and put them in a trash can, then walked to where she'd parked the BMW in the lot, slid in, and picked the pile of lists of meetings up from the passenger seat. At nine o'clock she was at a rolls-and-coffee breakfast meeting in the basement of a church in Woodland Hills.

> Our Father
> Who art in Heaven,
> Hallowed be thy name.
> Thy kingdom come
> Thy will be done . . .

'Well, don't *you* look familiar,' she heard a woman's voice say very loud at the break, and she cringed, wondering what she was going to say to some fan, how she was going to explain why she was here, but then realized the person who had said that wasn't talking to her, but to another woman, and the two women hugged and went off to find two seats together so they could chat until the break was over. Cee Cee sat in the back, close to the exit door so when it got boring she could leave early. But she was never bored and she never left early. Not from that meeting or from the candlelight meeting in Hollywood she attended that night, or the meeting that was conducted while the group took a walk on the Venice bike path. Or even at the meeting of gay men and transvestites she went to by mistake, where a short bald man came over and said to her, 'Jim Dale does a great Cee Cee Bloom, but you know what? I think yours is better.'

She went to a Cocaine Anonymous meeting in the north valley and a guy wearing a pin that said THERE IS NO PROBLEM WHICH CAN'T BE SOLVED BY THE

DIRECT APPLICATION OF EXPLOSIVES asked if she would give him her phone number. She declined politely, hoping he wouldn't apply the explosives to her face. In that meeting she looked around and decided she was probably the only person in the room who didn't have a tattoo. In fact, when she first walked in and saw the people who were showing up, she was so unnerved by how tough they all looked it made her want to leave, but as they stood one by one to tell their stories, they looked different to her.

A recovering drug dealer-user who had his first honest job, working for a cold storage company, told everyone how the minute there was some quiet time at work, he sat in his seat high atop the hydraulic lift, read his Twelve Step study book, and meditated. Then there was a recovering heroin addict whose wife had committed suicide three months and one day earlier, who received a ninety-day chip at the meeting as his reward for being sober for three months. He had started on his road to sobriety the day after her death. They were all filled with gratitude for the safety of 'these rooms' as they called the places they came to meet with one another, and support one another, and get each other through the difficulty of becoming and staying sober.

At a meeting in Brentwood, Cee Cee stopped on her way in the door because inside she saw a few people she knew. One of them was a woman studio executive, very high up in the Hollywood hierarchy, and when the woman saw Cee Cee she came right over to her. 'If there's anything I can do' was all she said, and she squeezed Cee Cee's hand warmly. Cee Cee decided not to go back to that meeting, or to any other one where there was a chance they would go around the room and give their names. In those, she always allowed herself to lie and say she was someone else. Until she understood by the end of day ten, by which point she had been to more than thirty meetings, the queen of overkill, that nearly everyone had known all along she was Cee Cee Bloom and that it didn't matter.

One by one she had canceled the fitness-training sessions she had booked after she'd heard about the Oscar nomination, canceled her firming facials and a photo session with *People* magazine because she wanted to spend the time at meetings. She postponed two of her new projects and didn't go in to the office, just went to these meetings, day after day, night after night, trying to get it. And she had some private sessions with Florrie too.

'Why the compulsion to work so much, so hard, so constantly?'

'I don't know. Because it feels good, and makes me feel powerful, important. Sometimes I think I need it to feel alive.'

'What happens when you stop?'

'Well . . . I'm okay for a little while and then . . .'

'And then?'

'If I stop . . .' She paused and then laughed an embarrassed laugh and admitted, 'I guess it's my drug of choice.'

Florrie nodded as the two women's eyes met.

'When she gets out of rehab she's going to need you. I think you should take a long look at your future schedule and make it one that gives you a lot of time for her, even if that means cutting back on your own productivity. Will you do that?'

'I want to be able to do it.'

'But will you do it?'

'I can probably do that.'

'Cee Cee, will you do it?'

Cee Cee didn't speak.

'Answer the question for yourself, not for me,' the doctor said.

On day twelve, at her thirty-sixth Twelve Step meeting, she felt herself standing and wanted to sit down, but was called on by the leader before she could change her mind, and with the rapidly beating heart of a first-time performer with stage fright said, 'Hi, I'm Cee Cee.' Then wondered what in the hell she was going to say.

'Hi, Cee Cee,' everyone said back to her. Then she waited a beat to listen for snickers or for people saying 'Don't we know it,' but nobody did, and she went on. 'I'm raising a teenager, thought I was doing pretty good at it, but recently I found out she's into drugs. So I've been trying to learn about my part in that by coming to these meetings. About the times I've given her things instead of giving her me, and the times I've looked the other way when she walked out of the house with friends I wasn't sure about. And the times I said to myself I have no right to control her, because I'm not her real mother, and even if I was, I hated my mother for controling me and I don't want my kid to hate me that way so I'll back off.

'And if kids learn by example, my own life hasn't exactly been a shining one. I'm disorganized and sloppy, I'm moody and unpredictable. I used to do drugs myself, a lot, and though I stopped, I have an addiction of my own. You see, the reason I was able to stop using drugs was because they were hurting my performing, which means the drugs were getting in the way of my bigger addiction, because I have one and it took me all this time to realize what it is.

'I'm hooked on the high I get from performing and

stardom, and some version of success I made up when I was a little kid and never bothered to change. But even though that's not what I think success is about anymore, I don't think, I mean, I'm not so sure I can kick the habit of scoring that high again and again, because it was how I turned on for so long. And because of that, I've pushed aside my personal life over and over again to get the phony synthetic kind of love that comes from an audience, instead of taking in the real blast that comes from being loved by the people I love.

'I don't mean to knock my career. It's wonderful that I'm good at what I do and that people like it, and that when they see me up there in the movies they laugh and cry with me, but over the last seven years, *that* was never what really did it for me ... gave me unending joy, filled me up. That was done by my little girl. Being with her was what made me glad to be alive. When that little face told me she thought I was funny or brave or important ... that was when I got the real goods.

'And the horrible thing is, you never figure when you watch that little pink person come into the world, so cute and scrawny and helpless, that one day she'll be taking your car while you're asleep and going out to score drugs with money that she got by selling her belongings and yours too, and you tell yourself, even when you look right into the jewelry box and things are gone, that you probably left them somewhere or maybe the plumber took them on his way past the closet to fix the bathroom faucets. But now I know that I just kept denying and denying, and thinking when I looked at her that she couldn't need anything more grown-up than her teddy bears.

'And because I took her innocence and her goodness

and her love for granted, and didn't pay close enough attention, she started using drugs. The kid had to get high just to go to school, to be with friends, to feel okay about herself. And now I'm afraid that I let the most valuable person in my life slide away, and that I'll never be able to ... I have to make this right. Have to get her to know she's more important to me than ... oh my God, oh my God.'

The man next to her, who was big and beefy looking, wearing a baseball cap with a short ponytail sticking out of the adjustable part in the back, stood and held her in his arms, and she stayed there for a while with her face against his shirt that smelled of starch and sweat. Then, finally when she was able to, she said, 'Thank you for letting me share,' and everyone applauded for her, as she sat down wondering what she had accomplished, but some of it was starting to sink in, as she sat with the Twelve Step literature, the Alanon day-by-day messages, and the Blue Book, and read and thought and wrote and took stock of the past seven years.

It was a Sunday afternoon when she got the word from the doctor telling her that next week Nina would be ready to have her come to a family meeting with the other boys and girls in rehab and the members of their families, and she was jubilant. She was in her room when the phone rang, so she scribbled the date and the time and the directions down on the pad next to her bed, and as she did she thought excitedly about what she would say, and how good it was going to be to see Nina's face, ready to have her there. Maybe Nina would rush to her and hug her, maybe ... As she looked at what her hand had written on the page, she realized that the family group in Newport Beach at the rehab center was being held on Monday night, March

26, at eight o'clock, which would be halfway through the Oscar ceremony.

'Thank you for calling,' she said into the phone. 'I'll be there.'

The small row of dormitory houses belonging to Seaside Sobriety where Nina had now lived for nearly three weeks sat on a narrow street across from a wide expanse of a beautiful off-white sandy beach, in what was in other parts of the neighborhood a pricey vacation home community in Newport Beach. The neighborhood reminded Cee Cee of the way it had looked in Beach Haven, New Jersey, when she was in summer stock. In fact, the accommodations reminded her of the place where the cast had lived, but it was clear by looking at the faces of the young people who filed into the living room where tonight's meeting was being held that they weren't here to be in a musical play.

When Cee Cee saw Nina walk in among a group of girls, she felt afraid that the girl would be embarrassed by her and wish she wasn't there. Maybe she would do her usual and say the wrong thing in front of the other kids, who, she could see by the laughing and the elbowing and wisecracking among them, had become Nina's new group of friends. Nina waved a little wave to her, but stayed with the friends, none of whom moved to speak to any of their parents, who were forming a group right near where Cee Cee stood. It wasn't until the door to the living room was pushed open with a flourish, and handsome Doctor Pappas moved through the parent group and pulled a big frayed armchair for himself to one end of the room, that the others began pulling chairs into a circle.

Now Cee Cee noticed how each of the kids carried a pillow. As she moved into the group, she saw the other family members sit on their chairs in an outside circle, and the kids put their pillows on the floor in the center of the circle, then sit on them. A few of the kids positioned themselves directly in front of their mothers. Cee Cee saw Nina notice that and then plop her own pillow in front of Cee Cee and sit facing into the circle. According to the rules, the only treat parents could bring their kids was sugarless gum. Cee Cee saw one of the mothers offer some to her own daughter, so she offered some to Nina, who shook her head to decline.

'Okay,' Pappas said, 'let's have a feelings round. Say who you are and how you're feeling. Bobby, why don't you begin?'

'Hi, I'm Bobby, I'm an alcoholic, addict.'

'Hi, Bobby.'

'I'm feeling scared because my dad's here for the first time.'

'I'm Gary. Addict.'

'Hi, Gary.'

'I'm feeling glad because next week's my graduation from this place and I get to go home, which is cool since I haven't seen my dog in three months.'

Everyone laughed, especially Gary's mother whom he resembled, who said, 'Thanks, pal.'

'I'm Jenna, I'm an alcoholic.' This girl looked as if she was nine years old. Tiny and dark skinned, with giant brown eyes.

'Hi, Jenna.'

'I'm three weeks sober, and I'm feeling bummed out because neither one of my parents is here tonight, and last week they hardly came to any meetings either, and I hate their fucking guts.'

'Hi, I'm Nina. I'm an addict.' Cee Cee hoped no one noticed how she flinched when she heard those words.

'Hi, Nina.'

And all the way around the circle. Addicts, alcoholics, many of the kids said they were both, and not one of them was over the age of seventeen. Cee Cee had to stop herself from shaking her head in disbelief at the straightforward way these kids spoke in front of their parents with no holds barred. Now the focus moved to the outside of the circle, to the parents. Cee Cee had been looking them all over carefully. One of the mothers sat behind her daughter and tenderly brushed the girl's hair. A father massaged his son's shoulders. One couple sat far away from their son and clutched each other's hands so tightly that their knuckles were white.

'I'm Harv, Bobby's dad. I'm an adult child of an alcoholic, an alcoholic, a co-dependent, and a sick son-of-a-bitch for not coming to any of these meetings before tonight. I'm feeling glad I'm here.'

'Hi, Harv.'

'I'm Edith, Gary's mother.'

'Hi, Edith.'

'I'm feeling glad Gary's coming home soon, too, because I'm sick of taking care of the goddamned dog.'

'I'm Cee Cee. I'm with Nina, and I'm feeling fine,' she said.

A chorus of kids' voices rang out, and because they were trying to top one another in volume it was hard to make out exactly what they were saying at first, but they repeated it at her a few times. 'Fucked up, insecure, neurotic emotion.'

'What?' Cee Cee asked, looking around nervously.

Doctor Pappas was smiling. 'The group has an aversion to the word *fine*,' he explained. 'They think it's a catchall, a cover-up for real feelings. They say it's an acronym for fucked-up, insecure, neurotic emotion. A way to conceal how you really feel.'

Cee Cee had to laugh a little laugh. After all the meetings she'd attended, she should have known these kids would have an instant bullshit detector. 'They're right,' she said. 'I feel real scared.'

'I'm Joanne, I'm Danny's mother.'

'Hi, Joanne.'

'And I've got to say what I'm feeling, which I'll bet is what a lot of people here would like to say, which is that I'm feeling uncomfortable because Cee Cee Bloom is here, and knowing she was coming tonight had everyone around here gossiping for the last few days, and I don't know if I can be myself with some movie star in our group. I don't feel like she's one of us.'

Cee Cee's heart sank, and all eyes went to Doctor Pappas. 'Joanne, when Cee Cee is in this group, she is a mother just like you, except for the fact that she has . . .'

'Several million dollars in the bank,' someone quipped, and a few people laughed, but Cee Cee felt tense now because she saw by Nina's back that her body was tensing up.

'. . . a higher profile,' Pappas went on. 'She hurts over her family's problems just like you do. She cries when her child is suffering just like you do. So let's go on.'

The next parent and the next and the next said their names, but Cee Cee didn't hear them. She watched Nina's body language as the girl pulled her knees to her chest and put her head forward so her chin rested in the space between them, trying to make herself small enough to be unnoticeable.

'Nina, you look particularly unhappy,' Pappas said. 'Can you say why?' Cee Cee would have bet that Nina, in a group this size, would never talk about what was going on with her, but the weeks in this place must have had their effect because she spoke right up.

'Because here I am trying to get over the worst thing in my life, and just like always it gets to be about Cee Cee Bloom, and I'm sick of that. All I ever wanted even with my real mother was to be in a regular family, ordinary, you know? Where the mother cleans the oven, and the father comes home and says, "What's for dinner?" And instead I went from a bad situation as the daughter of a single mother to living with Cee Cee and being the . . .' And then she said a few words that were unintelligible, after which she stopped short and everyone was uncomfortably quiet until Pappas asked:

'The what, Nina?'

Nina shook her head no. She was refusing to finish the sentence.

'Come on, Nina,' one of the kids said, 'you told all of *us*.'

'Living with Cee Cee and being . . .' Pappas said, leading her.

'The nobody to a star.'

'Why a nobody?' Pappas asked quietly, and no one moved while they waited for her answer.

By the time Nina spoke, it was in a tortured voice that would have been painful to hear no matter what it said, but the words delivered the killing blow. 'Because I'm not her daughter. Sometimes I lie and tell people I am, but that's what it is. A lie. I'm nobody's daughter, not my mother's, my father's, or Cee Cee's. She never cared enough to make me her daughter or she would have adopted me when my mother died. And I've thought about that every day of my life for the last eight years. Sometimes Cee Cee would come home and say, "I have a surprise for you," and I would always think, "This is it. Today's the day she's going to say she'll adopt me, and that will be the surprise."

But it never was. It was always a stuffed animal or a sweater or tickets to a play, and I was always afraid to say, "Don't you get it, *that's* not what I want. I want *you*. To belong to *you*, to belong *with* you. Because I'm a person who doesn't belong to anyone." But I never said that because I was afraid she'd say no.'

Pappas gave Nina what looked to Cee Cee like a conspiratorial congratulations for being able to say what she had in front of Cee Cee. Obviously it was information she had shared with Pappas, with the whole group of kids before this. Then the doctor looked at Cee Cee as if to ask her if she wanted to respond. *How can I do it?* she thought. *How will I ever be able to tell her what I should have told her every day for the last eight years?* Then she cleared her throat, which had become clogged with nervousness, and spoke.

'For a big part of my life I thought the same thing about myself that Joanne over there said about me. That I was different than other people. But over the last eight years of living with Nina, and now after coming to these meeting rooms for even this little while, what I know for absolute certain is that what Doctor Pappas said was true. I'm the same as everybody else. In spades. I'm raising a child and I want the best life has to offer for her just like all of you want for your kids. I work hard at what I do and I want it to go well, just like all of you feel about your work. I want to be loved and respected the same as everyone in this room does. And just like every parent here, because it's all trial and error, I raised my kid making a lot of mistakes. Like being in her face too much when she doesn't want me around, and being out to lunch too often when she does want me to be around, and I wish I could turn back the clock to that first day and do everything right but I can't so . . .'

'Cee Cee,' Doctor Pappas interrupted, 'may I suggest that you talk directly to Nina.' Then he made a little gesture to Nina to move inside the circle so she could turn around and look at Cee Cee, and she did. Her pretty but pale face turned up at her, her eyes blinking fast in a way Cee Cee knew she always used to hold in her tears.

'Nina,' Cee Cee said, 'it took your mother's death to make me think I grew up, because taking care of her when she was dying was the only unselfish thing I've ever done in my life. By the end, I guess she knew it, so that even though it was pretty obvious I was the candidate least likely to succeed at the job, she must have figured, from the way I finally set everything aside but her, that I had the potential to be a caring person and it would be okay for her to appoint me as your guardian.

'At the time it made me happy, but I didn't even have a clue that first day you and I were together what it was gonna mean. In my wildest dreams I didn't imagine that the job description of motherhood was that one day you start feeling so close to another person that when she hurts even the least little bit, it kills you, and that without even thinking about it, you get so attached to that person and need her love so much, that even if she looks at you crooked, you want to cry. And maybe I never told you up till now, but what being with you taught me that I never knew was that it was possible to love another person more than I love myself. I know I don't always show it, doing dumb things, making wrong choices, but believe me, it's true.'

She paused for a moment, and when she did Dr Pappas spoke. 'But after saying all that you still haven't said the words.'

'Huh?' Cee Cee asked looking at him.

'You still haven't simply stated what it is I believe you want to tell Nina.'

'You mean . . .?'

Pappas nodded and Cee Cee looked into Nina's pathetically ringed and bloodshot eyes and said, 'Neen, I love you. I love you as if I was the one who gave birth to you in that delivery room myself, instead of the one who fainted. I couldn't love you any more if you were born from my body. But I have to admit there hasn't been one day that we've been together when I didn't fear I wasn't good enough, smart enough, understanding enough, loving enough to live up to being as good as your real mother would have been for you. And that was the biggest reason I was afraid to adopt you. Because of what *I'm* not.'

Nina looked down into her lap now with what seemed to Cee Cee to be a look of relief.

'And believe me when I tell you, your mother wasn't perfect. Sometimes she could be a cold, judgmental pain in the kiester. Holding feelings inside, being too rigid about how things were supposed to be. But she had other stuff about her that I loved, and her best quality, at least for my money, and the thing that I know made her a great mother, was the way she'd stand up with an opinion about things I did that she didn't like, even if the risk was rejection or me mouthing off at her, which I did a lot. And on the other side of that coin, she was just as unafraid to say, "Goddammit, you did something great and I'm proud of you," and never thought that saying that meant she was putting herself in second position by getting out of the way and making me feel appreciated.'

Now there was a little smile on Nina's face as if she was remembering those aspects of Bertie too.

'I hope it's not too late for me to say I want to try harder to be that way for you. Not scared to point out what I think is wrong for fear you'll hate me if I do, and thoughtful enough to pat you on the back as often as I can. I have lots of fears that have plagued me and run me for too long, and one of those is what's kept me from admitting to you what I'm about to tell you now, which is not what I planned to say here tonight, but I have to.

'For a big part of my life I was a user too. A heavy user. It was one of the reasons your mother was planning at first to give you to your Aunt Neetie instead of to me. I smoked grass and sometimes hash to go to sleep and for the longest time I tooted up to go to work, and then used some more to get me through the work day . . . and to get me through the fact that I felt fat, or unattractive, or different than everybody else. Your mother once screamed her head off at me, trying to get me to stop. And the reason I never told you or anybody that about me is because I was afraid if it came out, it would somehow be what separated us, that you would think I was garbage for having that in my past. It's also part of the reason I never tried to adopt you, though I've thought about it every day for the last eight years too, and wanted to but was always afraid if I started the process and social workers came and checked on me, they would find out I once did drugs and say what I feared. That I didn't deserve to be your mother.

'Having you in my life has made me a human being, given me a reason to wake up on mornings when I was too depressed to move. I couldn't believe it when you said that you did drugs so you could be like me. Because I've spent a lifetime wishing *I* could be like *you*. Beautiful and dignified, smart and classy. Knowing just how to behave, and being in enough control to pull it off. I admire you so much, and if I never told you I loved you all these years, I realize now that the reason was probably that I was afraid to, since I've lost everyone I've ever loved.'

Nina nodded knowingly, then spoke softly. 'Me too.'

'And you know what else?' Cee Cee said. 'Not that this makes it okay, but you've never said you love me either.'

Again there was silence, interrupted only by the cracking of one of the kids' chewing gum and what sounded to Cee Cee like a floor polisher somewhere off in the distance in the hospital corridor.

'Nina,' Doctor Pappas asked, '*do* you love Cee Cee?'

Nina didn't answer, and the silence was killing to Cee Cee, who figured it could go either way now and the kid could say no, and that would be the worst thing she could ever hear, but then Nina's lower lip trembled and her face collapsed, and she cried, that kind of cry where no sound comes out and the crier seems to be inhaling all of the tears and can't say a word. Then she nodded, a very slow nod, and took in a huge breath, and Doctor Pappas asked softly, 'Well, why don't you tell her?'

Nina took a few breaths and tried to gain control, as Cee Cee sat forward in her chair expectantly. 'I love you, Cee Cee,' Nina said, punctuated by intakes of breath. 'I really do love you a lot.'

Thank you, God, oh thank you for that, thank you, Cee Cee thought.

'I love the way you always stick up for yourself and for me. And I think it's so cool the way you try to be so nice to your fans even when they bug you, and the way you try to act real tough but inside you're really full of mush.' That caused a light giggle to ripple through the group, and brought a smile that started inside Cee Cee's chest and moved to her face, and her smile seemed to buoy Nina to continue.

'You're what some of the kids in this group call "truly awesome." But, see, one of the things I've been finding out about me is that I can't always handle awesome too well? Because what I really need is real? And I don't know if you and I will ever get there. To being real. Because you're still always going to be you, Cee Cee Bloom, and I'm still going to be me, wishing for a real life with real parents. And that's the kind of stuff that all the meetings and groups in the world can't change.'

Doctor Pappas handed Nina a wad of Kleenex, and she wiped her eyes and blew her nose and went on. 'What I'm saying is, I think I'm scared that talking about not using won't make me not want to get out of here and use again. But yes . . . I love you, and I've been superafraid to tell you that before tonight. Before I knew that you love me . . . and that I wasn't someone you got stuck with because your friend died.' She bit her lip and looked straight and hard at Cee Cee, waiting to see what would happen next, and Cee Cee moved to the middle of the circle, took Nina's hands, lifted her to her feet, and pulled her into her arms where they wept, and Doctor Pappas passed a box of Kleenex around to many of the other people in the group who needed it too.

The moon lit the narrow beach street as Cee Cee and Nina walked toward Cee Cee's car, arms around one another's waists. Some of the tiny, funky, one-story houses they passed had wind chimes, which hung quietly in the still night. A few of the houses just beyond the row of Seaside Sobriety houses were lit only by the flickering lights of televisions.

'Doctor Pappas said he thinks you'll be able to come home in a few weeks,' Cee Cee said as they reached the car, which was parked just opposite the open sliding glass door of a house inside of which Cee Cee spotted an older couple, watching the Academy Awards.

'I'll come back on Wednesday for the next family meeting,' she said, taking Nina's hand, 'and for every meeting after that. I promise. I'm going to do everything I can to get us through this.' Nina squeezed her hand gratefully, then looked past her at the television in the little house, and when Cee Cee followed her gaze back to the small set she saw Billy Crystal introducing Gregory Peck, who strode handsome and elegant up to the podium, and when the applause ended he said something about five gifted women. And then he named them, and as he did a piece of each of their films rolled by. Isabelle Adjani, *Camille Claudel*. Jessica Lange, *Music Box*. Cee Cee Bloom, *Lives of Sophie West*. Cee Cee, who never liked the way she looked on film, was relieved that the clips were so short.

When Gregory Peck had announced all the nominations, he opened the envelope and announced, 'And the Oscar goes to Jessica Tandy for *Driving Miss Daisy*.' In an instant the audience rose to their feet and Cee Cee took a long deep breath as Nina put a supporting arm around her shoulder and held on tight, and they both watched as Jessica Tandy took the stage. The old couple in the house were applauding along with the television audience.

'I never expected in a million years that I'd be in this position, and I thank my lucky stars ...' Jessica Tandy said, 'and Richard and Lily Zanuck, and that forgotten man Bruce Beresford. I'm on cloud nine.'

Cee Cee turned away from the television and looked at Nina. She could hear the old woman in the house they were standing next to saying, 'Well, it's about time she won one of those things.'

'Do you feel awful that you're not the winner?' Nina asked her.

'Oh, kiddo,' Cee Cee said. 'That's where you're wrong. I have you. And that makes me the biggest and luckiest winner I know.'

They hugged again, and Cee Cee got into the car and Nina waved goodbye as the car pulled away, and then she walked slowly back to the small house where some of the group were waiting for her.

LOS ANGELES, CALIFORNIA

August 1990

It was seven years exactly from the day of Bertie's death, one of those eerie coincidences Cee Cee remembered thinking when she entered today's event into her appointment calendar. Now it crossed her mind again while she sat in the back of the limousine, which snaked with funereal slowness through the relentless freeway traffic. Her father, Harriet, and Hal sat with her, staring out of the darkened windows, lost in their respective thoughts, and as the oddly mixed architecture of the downtown skyline came into view signaling their imminent arrival, Hal reached over and took Cee Cee's hand.

'How're you holding up, old girl?'

She answered with a fervent squeeze of his hand.

Within minutes the limo slowed and Cee Cee leaned forward to look out the window in amazement at the size of the group waiting for them at the curb. So many of Nina's friends were there, all of them wearing what were for them somber clothes, and every one of them was serious-faced. Particularly Kevin, who stood in the front of the group and nodded a nod of encouragement to Cee Cee as she opened the door for herself and emerged from the car.

And then Jake, looking very official today in a uniform, including the rarely worn chauffeur's cap, opened his own door and walked around to the front door on the passenger side, opened that one with a flourish, and out stepped Nina. A cheer rose from the group, as all of the friends ran to greet her, to encircle her, hugging and congratulating her noisily, and finally they nearly lifted her off her feet to usher her along the sidewalk and up the steps to the courthouse.

Cee Cee took a deep breath and stopped at the bottom of the steps just to watch, filled with a grateful, joyous ache at seeing Nina getting the demonstration of love she needed so much now. Then, needing some support herself, she put an arm around her father and one around Hal, and with Harriet hanging onto Nathan's arm, the four of them bounced excitedly up the steps like the quartet from *The Wizard of Oz*.

Jim Andrews, Cee Cee's bespectacled, handsome, tweedy-looking lawyer, who was waiting in the marble hallway, smiled when he saw the size of the group. 'I don't know if the judge's chambers are big enough to seat this many people,' he said.

'So we'll stand,' Nathan Bloom told him.

The last months had been a grueling series of painful sessions for Nina and Cee Cee. Sometimes Cee Cee would have stomachaches before going to a group meeting or an hour of therapy with Nina in anticipation of what she would hear next. Once, sitting on the far end of Doctor Pappas's sofa, as far as she could get from Cee Cee who sat on the other end, Nina confessed, 'For a long time I blamed you for killing my mother. I thought if you had taken better care of her, if you hadn't sent away the nurse, she would have lived. So I hated you.' Then she turned and put her face against the back of the sofa and cried silently. There was no way Cee Cee could respond to that. Another time, in a rage, Nina cried out, 'It's not fair that someone as wonderful as my mother died and someone as horrible as you is still alive.'

Then, immediately regretting it, she stood and went to Cee Cee and held her, saying, 'I'm sorry. I'm so sorry.'

And there were lighter times.

'Cee Cee, how did you learn to parent?' Doctor Pappas asked.

'Are you kidding? From my lunatic mother. I vowed I was never gonna be like that. She was loud and crass and when she showed up at school to take me to an audition I used to die of embarrassment. Everywhere I went, before I got into the room there was Leona, talking too much and talking too loud and saying all the wrong things. It made me nuts so I . . .' She stopped because the doctor and Nina were both grinning at her. 'Oh yeah,' she said. 'I guess that's where I learned.'

They celebrated on the day Cee Cee filed for adoption, and on the day when the phone call came from the lawyer telling them Michael Barron had signed the release of abandonment, so the only possible impediment to setting the court date would be an investigation by a social worker.

'Both Doctor Pappas and Doctor Kagan say that despite all that's happened, you've worked hard to be a good mother to Nina,' the social worker said. 'Do you think that's right?' He was a young man of about thirty dressed in a suit and tie, unawed by Cee Cee's stardom, and that was the last question he asked her during a long and exhaustive interview.

'I can only tell you I've had moments I could kick myself for, but I've also had some moments I think I've been more mother than Harriet Nelson and Donna Reed rolled into one. Of course, the bottom line about being somebody's parent is what you learn. And for me, raising another human being has been the most important, most creative, most humbling experience I've ever had, and that's why it would mean so much

323

to me and to Nina if we could . . .' That was when she had lost it for a second, but she stopped until she was able to talk again and said, 'If we could, if I could . . . make it legal.'

Now Hal and Nathan sat on a marble bench talking about the stock market, and Richie Charles entered, greeted by a very surprised squeal and a hug from Nina, and Florrie Kagan bustled in at the last second moving quietly to Cee Cee to give her a warm and approving embrace just as the door from the courtroom opened and a guard in a khaki uniform poked his head out and gestured to Jim Andrews, who said, 'Okay, people, here we go.' Then the guard opened the door to the tiny courtroom wider and ushered them through, walking single file to a large dark wood door at the back, upon which he knocked, and after a moment he gestured for all of them to follow him into the judge's chambers.

The judge was a pretty, page-boyed woman in her fifties, and she smiled a big smile and stood as she watched the gang of people troop in and find places to sit, or stand, to watch what was going to happen next.

'Looks to me like a party,' she said.

'That's what it is,' Harriet said.

The emotion in the room was palpable, the joy and the hope and the wonder, and the relief brought a giddiness to each person there, as Cee Cee's lawyer spoke. 'Good morning, Your Honor, James R. Andrews appearing on behalf of petitioner Cee Cee Bloom and the extended family.'

A court reporter took everything down as the judge said, 'This is the matter of Cee Cee Bloom. The petitioner is present as well as the minor and their attorney, Mr Andrews. The report from the County Bureau of Adoptions is admitted into evidence by reference. Please raise your right hand.'

Cee Cee did. 'Do you solemnly swear before this court that the information you have given is the truth, the whole truth, and nothing but the truth, so help you God?'

'I do,' Cee Cee said.

'I assume you are here because you want to go ahead with the adoption?'

'That's right,' Cee Cee said, and, continuing to look at the judge, she reached out her hand in Nina's direction and felt Nina take it.

The judge looked at Nina now and spoke gently. 'Nina, when a child your age is being adopted, it is required of the state to ask that child if she can whole-heartedly say she consents to the adoption of her own free will. Do you want Cee Cee Bloom to adopt you, to be your legal parent forever?'

All eyes were on Nina now. She knew it, and she was flushed and bright-eyed. 'Yes I do,' she said, and it was forthcoming and clear.

'And, Cee Cee? Do you promise you will treat her in all respects as your lawful child? To make the child your own, to care for her and treat her as your rightful heir forever?'

'I sure do,' Cee Cee said emphatically.

'I have a consent form I would like you to read, and if you approve, sign it.'

Cee Cee bent over and shuffled around in her purse to find a pair of reading glasses. 'This is what happens when you have an older mother, dear,' she joked to Nina, and everyone laughed as she put the glasses on to read the form the judge had given her. When she'd read it, she nodded to Jim Andrews, who said, 'Let the record reflect that the petitioner has read the consent in the open court.'

'Since you have read it, if you approve, please sign

your full name in black ink. According to the court the report is approved and filed.' There was a lot of stamping of papers, and Cee Cee relaxed against the back of her chair for the first time.

The judge now looked at Cee Cee and Nina standing together, and smiled a very warm unjudgelike smile. 'The court finds that it's in the best interest of the minor that the petition be granted. The petition is therefore granted, and hereafter you have the relationship of mother and daughter. All the responsibilities of that relationship and the duties thereof. I'm signing the decree.' And she did. 'Congratulations,' she said.

Cee Cee would always remember that nobody moved for what seemed like a long time, then Nina came to her and looked at her and put her arms around her neck, and Nathan said, 'Somebody take a picture,' and a few flashbulbs went off. 'Take one with the judge,' somebody else said, and Cee Cee and Nina stood with the judge, and more flashbulbs went off. One of the kids had a camera, and Hal pulled one out of his pocket too. Everyone was carrying on and laughing now, and Nathan called out, 'I want another picture. Let's have another picture,' and Nina called out, 'Come on, Hal, give your camera to someone else to take a picture of us. I want you to be in the picture with me and my mother.'

Cee Cee beamed when she heard those words, and as Hal handed the lawyer his camera to take their picture, he put a loving arm around both Cee Cee and Nina.

'Smile, ladies,' Nathan said, and each of them was glad to oblige.

After they moved out of the courtroom and back into the corridor, it seemed as if nobody from their group wanted to leave. The kids' voices and laughter echoed down the high-ceilinged hall, and the high spirits of the morning made everyone feel friendly and talkative. Richie and Hal were reliving old times, and Florrie was getting to know Nathan and his wife. Cee Cee looked over at Nina, who was at the edge of the group talking animatedly with Kevin, and watched as she touched his arm, said, 'Excuse me,' and slipped away from the group down the corridor toward the ladies room.

'Remember that time we worked that club in Pittsburgh?' Richie asked Cee Cee, and he launched into some story about a guy who owned a club they'd all worked in years ago, as Hal laughed along remembering the character Richie was describing. But Cee Cee wasn't listening. Her eyes were glued to the ladies room door, and after what seemed like an eternity she started away from the circle of people nervously, and made her way down the hall with what she hoped looked like a casual gait. Something was wrong. She heard her heels tap-tapping against the marble floor, or maybe it was the sound of her heart pounding as she pushed the door to the ladies room open hard, and when she didn't see anyone she shouted.

'Nina!'

The silence was long, and then there was a flush, after which the door to one of the stalls opened and Nina emerged.

'Are you okay?' Cee Cee asked, walking to her and looking up into the girl's eyes. Thank God. They looked normal.

Nina held her gaze knowingly. 'I am okay,' she said. 'For now. But I had to get away from everybody for a minute because my stomach felt funny. I think it was just butterflies from all the excitement.' Then she went to the sink and washed her hands, pulled a paper towel from the holder and dried them. She was wearing the emerald ring. She was a beautiful young woman, even prettier than Bertie had been, but it was clear by the way she glanced at herself in the mirror that, for her, the beauty still hadn't begun to reflect.

'I guess I'll always worry when I see you slip away. Even if it's just to go to the ladies room,' Cee Cee said now, looking at their two faces together in the mirror over the sinks, thinking how changed they both were since this same day in 1983.

Nina turned away from the mirror now, looked at Cee Cee, then lovingly took her arm. 'I guess you will,' she said, and the two of them turned, their arms linked just the way they used to be long ago when they walked on the beach in Carmel, and together they walked across the wide hall of the courthouse to join the others.

Published or forthcoming

HAVING IT ALL

Maeve Haran

Having it All. Power. Money. Success. *And* a happy family. Liz really believed she could have it all. So when she's offered one of the most important jobs in television, she jumps at it.

But Liz discovers that there's a price to be paid for her success and that the whole glittering image is just an illusion. And one day she's faced with the choice she thought she'd never have to make.

Liz decides she *will* have it all – but on her own terms.

'Will touch cords, tug heartstrings. Every woman's been here' – Penny Vincenzi, author of *Old Sins*

'Realistic, compassionate, but still as pacey as they come' – *Cosmopolitan*

SIGNET

Published or forthcoming

The Stars Burn On

Denise Robertson

On New Year's Day 1980, Jenny and seven friends watch the dawn from a northern hill. On the brink of adulthood, confident of their futures, they vow to meet there again at the end of the decade. Just two weeks later, one of the group is dead. The others, irrevocably affected, go on to pursue careers in the law or media, and make new lives for themselves as husbands, wives and parents. Jenny, who establishes herself as a successful journalist in London, remains their lynchpin – and only Jenny knows that the secret that binds them is a lie.

'A saga that'll keep you turning the pages ... told with perception and humour' – *Prima*

'Her prose has a fine flow, her knowledge of the region is deep and instinctive. Above all, her compassion and great understanding of life show in all she writes' – *Evening Chronicle, Newcastle on Tyne*

SIGNET

Published or forthcoming

Lilies of the Field
Maureen O'Donoghue

Invited back to Trewythian, her long-lost island home, Sally leaves the sophisticated charm of London for the golden memories of her childhood.

As she is drawn into the warm embrace of the villagers, and intoxicated by a new romance, Sally's homecoming promises to be a joyous occasion. But the idyll turns sour when she stumbles upon a shocking secret from her family's past − a secret shared by a murderous assailant who stalks the island determined that she will never leave Trewythian again.

Unfolding against the sweeping moors and boundless skies of a gaunt and beautiful island, *Lilies of the Field* is a stirring, sensual tale of romance and adventure.

S SIGNET

Published or forthcoming

THE GLITTERING STRAND

Judith Lennox

The Levant trade of the 1590's offers wealth and danger in equal measure. And, always, dreams ...

A dream for Serafina Guardi, captured by corsairs and sold into slavery *en route* to her profitable betrothal, struggling with the intrigues of the Italian cloth trade to reclaim her heritage – and revenge herself. And for Thomas Marlowe, the English pilot wrecked on the Barbary Coast, dreams of a ship such as the Mediterranean has never seen and wider seas to sail her in.

Chance and treachery conspire against their hopes while irretrievably entangling their fates. There will be long, hard years before either Serafina or Thomas comes near to their dream – only to find the dream is no longer the same...

SIGNET

Published or forthcoming

Liscombe Hall

Anne Griffiths

When an illicit liaison with Lord Liscombe ends in heartbreak, Kate Tranter sets out in search of a new life. Driven to protect a secret borne of passion, she rises beyond her humble beginnings to become a wealthy restaurateur; indomitable, proud, admired – and haunted by the searing memory of a love that could never be.

Set amidst the rolling hills of the Dorset countryside, from the turn of the century to the post-war era, *Liscombe Hall* follows the tangled destinies of two families and the powerful passions that bind them.

SIGNET

Published or forthcoming

SLIVER

Ira Levin
author of *Rosemary's Baby*

Thirteen hundred Madison Avenue, an elegant 'sliver' building, soars high and narrow over Manhattan's smart Upper East Side. Kay Norris, a successful single woman, moves on to the twentieth floor of the building, high on hopes of a fresh start and the glorious Indian summer outside. But she doesn't know that someone is listening to her. Someone is *watching* her.

'Levin really knows how to touch the nerve ends' – *Evening Standard*

'*Sliver* is the ultimate *fin de siècle* horror novel, a fiendish goodbye-wave to trendy urban living ... Ira Levin has created the apartment dweller's worst nightmare' – Stephen King

SIGNET

Published or forthcoming

THE RATING GAME

Dave Cash

Behind the glass-fronted walls of CRFM's 24-hours-a-day nerve centre in the heart of London, three people fight for control of their lives as the tycoon powerbrokers of international finance move in for the kill...

Monica Hammond, the radio station's beautiful and ruthless Managing Director – nothing was allowed to stand in her way ... until one man discovered her fatal weakness.

Nigel Beresford-Clarke – CRFM's greatest asset – hopelessly betrayed by his love for a schoolgirl...

And **Maggie Lomax**, uncompromising and tough as nails – then her outspoken broadcasts pushed the wrong people too far ...

They're ready to play ... *The Rating Game*

Published or forthcoming

TRIAL

Clifford Irving

They called it suppression of evidence and disbarred him from the 299th District Court for two long years.

Criminal Defence lawyer Warren Blackburn came back from the wilderness to pick up the crumbs – and found two cases just like the one that brought him down.

But this time he was ready to back his judgement and fight. Fight for justice and a fair trial against a legal system that would do anything as long as it got a deal...

'Riveting legal edge-of-the seater ... Has Texas and American Justice systems by the tail' – *Daily Telegraph*

ON FOOT THROUGH
CLYDESDALE

BY

IAIN C. LEES

ILLUSTRATED BY JOHN WHITE

BIRLINN

To

the Memory

of

my Mother

This edition published in 2015 by
Birlinn Ltd
West Newington House
10 Newington Road
Edinburgh
EH9 1QS

www.birlinn.co.uk

ISBN: 978 1 78027 330 3

First published in 1932 by Blackie & Son Ltd, Glasgow

British Library Cataloguing-in-Publication Data
A catalogue record for this book is available
on request from the British Library

Facsimile origination by Brinnoven. Livingston
Printed and bound by Bell & Bain Ltd, Glasgow

FOREWORD

Many members of the Carvel family have a copy of *On Foot through Clydesdale* gracing our bookshelves. Some of us return to its charm and elegant prose time and again, gaining inspiration, rather like repeated viewings of a fine painting and enjoying a fresh aspect each time.

We believe the original 193-page hardback volume, published by Blackie & Son in 1932, was such a masterpiece. We also believe our great-uncle and grandfather, Iain C. Lees (pseudonym for John Lees Carvel, 1895–1959), was an artist of high calibre. Perhaps I (DC) am biased. Several years ago, I chose to live and work in arguably the finest village in Clydesdale, and I see the beauty around me, and his words, written more than eighty years ago, come alive each day. In the whole of Lanarkshire, with the demise of coal mining and the expansion of towns, Clydesdale has changed the least in these intervening years.

John was a journalist by trade who was perhaps best known for his work as political correspondent of the *London Evening Star*. Before heading south of the border in 1934, he was sub-editor of the *Scottish Daily Express*. He delighted in capturing the spirit of his native country, speaking to locals along the way. After *On Foot through Clydesdale* came *The Campsies and the Land of Lennox* (1933), and after the move south he returned to write *Byways from Tyne to Tay* (1936). These later books included photographic plates rather than the charming illustrations of his friend and walking companion, John White.

On Foot through Clydesdale was originally dedicated 'To the Memory of my Mother' (Jeanie Lees). And here is the clue to the pseudonym. In those days, editors did not approve of their journalists writing books. Serialising them in one's own newspaper was unimaginable. (Consider how things have changed!) So, John took his mother's maiden name as his *nom de plume*. 'John' changed easily into its Scottish form, 'Iain', and Carvel hid itself as the middle initial, 'C'. This would hardly have fooled Alan Turing and other cryptologists at Bletchley Park, but it was enough to keep John's editor happy.

In later years these sensitivities must have eased because John wrote several books and manuscripts under his own name, which mainly catalogue and describe the history of light and heavy industry in Scotland. These include *The Coltness Iron Company*, *The Alloa Glass Works* and *Linthouse Shipbuilding*.

John's father, James, was quarry master at Auchenheath Quarry, Blackwood, but John showed no desire himself to enter industry, and his only sibling, my (DC) grandfather, William Carvel, was a market gardener in the Clyde Valley. John had one son, Robert, a political journalist and commentator, and he in turn had one son, also John (JC), who became social affairs editor of the *Guardian* newspaper.

When Birlinn offered to republish this book after so many years, the family was delighted. We hope that whether you live in, or hail from, this often overlooked part of Scotland, or have yet to visit, you might walk with us, and in John Carvel's literary footsteps, once more through Clydesdale.

David Carvel
Biggar
Clydesdale

John Carvel
Buckhorn Weston
Dorset

May 2015

CONTENTS

MAPS on Pages 38 and 39.

PREFACE

Most people think of Lanarkshire as a world of collieries, steelworks, and factories, yet all the coal-pits, iron foundries, and other works do not cover more than one-tenth of the county. There are, in fact, districts which are unsurpassed for picturesque beauty, the glory of their orchards and waterfall scenery, where every square inch is rich in romance.

Kings, princes, nobles, warriors, and churchmen, all pass along the screen of the story of Clydesdale, which sometimes fought for its king, but was as often opposed to him. Its people were ever fighters for liberty and stout opponents of oppression.

The Romans made Clydesdale their centre, and Wallace made it his home. Kings held their councils within its bounds, and Covenanters made it their hiding-place. Princes made it their hunting-ground, and industrialists extracted their wealth from its mineral resources.

Clydesdale is, indeed, a place of great traditions, honourable dealings, and stirring romance.

That romance gripped me as a boy when I roamed the moors and hills about my home, spending many happy hours listening to the stories of the farmers and villagers, and learning some delightful folk-lore. Its spell increased with the passing of years, and after I had left the district for the busy haunts of men I stole back as often as I could, renewing old associations and making new friendships. I told others of the happy days I had spent in the county. They wanted to share my joy and desired a guide to find it. That is the reason for this book.

I walked the county from Glasgow to its southern boundary, and found walking a spirited game that is far more entertaining than flying through dust-clouds in a motor-car, an everlasting source of delight, of fascination, of joy, fair day or foul. It made me eat like Gargantua, and sleep like a night watchman.

Good company enhances the delight of a walk as it does the delight of a meal. I pay tribute to the companionship I enjoyed on these outings. My friend was an artist, and while he sketched I was free to talk with the inhabitants, peep into little-known corners, sit by the roadside and study plant life, or lean over the parapet of a bridge and watch the weeds and fishes. I thank him for his companionship and for the sketches which are used to illustrate this book.

A small part of the contents of this volume has already appeared in substance in the *Daily Express*, and I desire to express my gratitude to the Editor for his ready permission to make further use of the material. The greater portion, however, is now published for the first time.

My acknowledgments are also due to the staffs of the Mitchell Library and Baillie's Institution, especially to Mr. Robert Bain and Mr. John Dunlop of the former and to Mr. James R. Anderson of the latter, for the facilities afforded for research.

GLASGOW, *March*, 1932.

CRAIGNETHAN CASTLE

ON FOOT THROUGH CLYDESDALE

CHAPTER I

Scotland's Oldest Royal Burgh

Ru'glen's wee roun' red lums were reekin' briskly as I crossed the Clyde, and left the noise and bustle of Glasgow behind. Once Rutherglen was the chief port on the Clyde, but it has long since been eclipsed by its young neighbour a little lower down the river. Still, it is a thriving and busy town. Its streets are full of life, and you are never far away from the touch of engineering on which its prosperity rests.

Rutherglen has many claims to renown. It is the oldest royal burgh in Scotland; at least, none can produce evidence of greater antiquity. Wallace made peace with the English in its old church, and in the same building Sir John Menteith agreed to hand over the patriot to his enemies. Bruce and his brother drove the English from its castle, which at a later date was demolished by Regent Moray. Armed Covenanters burned the Acts against conventicles at its Cross.

1

The parish church stands in the heart of the town, and the tower of the ancient Norman church is in the churchyard nearby. Like " Alloway's auld haunted kirk ", it seems to have been the scene of strange on-goings at times. At least one of its ministers had an experience similar to Tam o' Shanter's. He was riding home after dark, and as he passed the church he believed he heard strange sounds coming from it. He dismounted, and made his way among the tombstones as best he could. The church was lighted, and, looking through the windows, he saw members of his flock dancing with the Devil and his minions. Devils or no, he would put an end to this convention of the damned.

" In the name of God, begone!" he cried. " Ye'll no' deny this the morn, ye limmers." Then, turning on his heel, he crossed the graveyard, remounted his horse, and resumed his journey.

He had been seen, and was followed. The witches and warlocks overtook him, and began to dance round him. They would not allow him to go until he had promised not to divulge the names of those whom he had seen in the church. The promise was kept.

There would be only one explanation of a story of that kind nowadays. Ministers had greater licence then.

The burgesses of Rutherglen were a gay lot. They were the champion Sabbath-breakers and the heart-break of the presbyteries. They danced to pipes in the streets, produced plays, fished for salmon in the Clyde, and paid accounts on Sundays instead of going to church! They were reprimanded by kirk sessions and presbyteries, but that only made them worse. One of their number drove four ministers from the town; another said he would kill two before he was satisfied. And so they made merry!

Politics to them was also a great sport, the choice of a member of Parliament often being accompanied by hilarious proceedings without parallel in the history of the country. In pre-Reform days the town shared a member with Glasgow, Renfrew, and Dumbarton. The electors were the town councillors, who chose a commissioner to go to the presiding burgh and record his council's vote for the candidate they had decided to support. Each burgh, in turn, was the returning burgh, whose commissioner had a casting vote in the event of a tie.

Three candidates took the field in the election of 1831. They were Joseph Dixon, the son of the Provost of Dumbarton, Kirkman Finlay, a Glasgow merchant, and Archibald Campbell of Blythswood, the retiring member. Glasgow pledged itself to support Kirkman Finlay, while Renfrew declared for Archibald Campbell, who, however, withdrew from the contest in favour of Glasgow's nominee. Dumbarton was the returning burgh. Rutherglen was thus the deciding factor. If Finlay received its vote he would be elected, and if it were given to Dixon, Dumbarton's casting vote would secure his return. Consequently, both candidates devoted a great deal of attention to Rutherglen.

Rutherglen councillors were delighted to have for their candidate a robust champion of reform like Joseph Dixon, but his opponent was not easily turned aside. He persisted in his canvass, and sought to win the support of the councillors through the distribution of handsome gifts to their wives. By this means he did all he could to drive

Tower of Norman Church, Rutherglen

young Dixon out of the burgh where Dixon had received pledges from fourteen of the eighteen councillors.

These fourteen men were so sorely tormented by Finlay and his friends that at last they asked Dixon to deliver them from temptation. They were taken to Dumbarton, where they could remain in safety until the day of battle approached.

Provost Dixon entertained them lavishly. They were taken up Loch Lomond to Rowardennan, whence they climbed Ben Lomond. Frequent halts were made on the mountain-side to quench their thirst. The summit was reached after great difficulty and many halts for stimulants. A council meeting was then held. A council meeting on Ben Lomond! An incident without parallel! The Rutherglen men renewed their vows of fidelity to Joseph Dixon in flowing bowls of the best champagne.

At last the day for electing a commissioner dawned. The fourteen were still absent. The day wore on, and none appeared. At six o'clock the reformers in the burgh began to despair of their return in time for the council meeting. As the minutes passed, Finlay and his friends began to think there had been a miscarriage in the arrangements, and that they would have it all their own way. The town bell had actually begun to ring its summons to the meeting before the " lost men " appeared. They took their places in the council chamber, and elected the provost as their commissioner to attend at Dumbarton and vote for Joseph Dixon.

Kirkman Finlay was a bad loser. He lodged a petition alleging bribery and corruption. A Parliamentary Committee was appointed to try its merits. The petition was dismissed. The entertainment had been provided by the

Provost of Dumbarton, and the son could not be held responsible for the actions of his father!

From Rutherglen to Cathkin you must climb through Burnside, and as you rise you have time to think of Scotland's saddest woman. Here, legend tells us, Queen Mary, in her flight after her last gamble at Langside, was intercepted by two rustics who threatened to end her misery with their reaping-hooks. Another legend says she spent the night before the battle at Castlemilk, which nestles among the trees at the foot of Cathkin Braes.

Glasgow has something to be proud of in her parks, but Cathkin Braes Park is in a class by itself. It has retained its natural ruggedness. I have brought many people here. They have confessed that it was their first visit. Yet in this park, belonging to the citizens of Glasgow, is a lovely open space with a fine panoramic view of Clydesdale from Tinto to Dumbuck and the surrounding country. From Queen Mary's Seat, the highest point of the park, the eye takes in its sweep the peaks of central Scotland from the Pentlands to Ben Lomond, the Cobbler, and Goat Fell.

There is certainly no other city in Britain which has on its fringes a point that can show scenes of such majesty and grace.

An old road runs over the hill from Cathkin Braes to East Kilbride, past the old Peel of Mains—just the kind of road wayfarers like. No motor-car can follow.

The Comyns lived hereabouts at one time. The last of the race to own Mains was the Red Comyn whom Bruce slew at the high altar in the church in Dumfries.

" I doubt," stammered Bruce, as he hurried from the church, " I ha'e slain the Red Comyn."

"Doubt!" said Roger Kirkpatrick, "I'll mak' siccar."
He ran to the altar, and thrust his dagger into Comyn's
body. Others, including James Lindsay of Dunrod,
followed his example.

The Comyn lands were forfeited, and John Lindsay of
Dunrod, a son of Bruce's companion, received the castle
and lands of Mains for his father's part in the struggle
for national independence.

The Lindsays were a proud and turbulent race. The
last to own Mains exceeded all his ancestors in pride and
extravagance. He never left his home without twelve
attendants on white horses. Feuds with his neighbours
reduced him to poverty. He sold part of his property to
provide the sinews of war, and the rest was taken from
him to recompense those whom he assailed. In his later
years he was a vagabond, taking shelter where he could
find it, and dying at last in the barn of one of his former
tenants.

Tradition associates him with the witches and warlocks
who held high carnival in Inverkip Glen.

> Auld Dunrod was a goustie [1] carle,
>   As ever ye micht see;
> And gin he was na a warlock wicht,[2]
>   There was nane in the hail countrie.

> Auld Dunrod stack in a pin,
>   (A bourtrie [3] pin) in the wa',
> And when he wanted his neighbour's milk,
>   He just gied the pin a thraw.[4]

---

[1] Ghostly.   [2] If he was not a potent wizard.   [3] Elder tree pin.
[4] Gave the pin a twist.

He milkit the laird o' Kellie's kye,
  And a' the kye in Dunoon;
And Auld Dunrod gat far mair milk
  Than wad mak' a gabbart soum.[1]

The cheese he made were numerous,
  And wonerous to descry;
For they kyth't as gin they had been grule [2]
  Or peats set up to dry.

He was also associated with those who raised stormy weather on the Firth of Clyde in order to hinder the fishing or damage the boats of those whom he did not like. The credulous seafaring folk paid him blackmail to refrain from injuring them and to prevent others from doing so. Yet, notwithstanding his reputed powers he died of starvation.

The tall square tower of Mains Castle remains on a knoll which runs out as a spur from a low hill to the north. No trace remains of the arched gateway and drawbridge, but the tower has been carefully preserved—a memorial of the distant past and stirring events.

East Kilbride is beyond the top of the hill on which Mains Castle stands. I like this old village whose streets run in all directions. I like particularly its old houses, and above all I like the gargoyles which peer down from the eaves. These are, indeed, monuments of a leisurely age, when village craftsmen knew nothing of time clauses, and thought no building complete without decorations.

Masons hereabouts were proud of their work. The builder of the parish church made sure that his name would not

---

[1] Float a flat river boat.   [2] Appeared like moss dried in the sun.

be forgotten. It is carved in a tablet above the main door for all to see.

Beside the church, whose fine tower dominates the village, is an old hostelry with a " loupin'-on stane " in front. No one could resist the appeal of this relic of the days when men rode to kirk and market. Food and re-freshment are as necessary as ever they were. They can be enjoyed where the romance of those stirring times lingers, undisturbed by the march of progress.

Loupin'-on Stane, East Kilbride

CHAPTER II

By Calder Braes to Bothwell Banks

It is really surprising what yarns you meet in country districts—tales of ghosts, secret chambers, subterranean passages, and hidden treasure. East Kilbride has its mystery woman. Her ghost does not walk, but the villagers talk in whispers of her doings, as if they were afraid that she might appear and challenge their veracity.

She is Jenny Cameron. Her home was about a mile away from the village—at Mount Cameron.

Jenny Cameron was the mystery woman of the " Forty-Five ". The pamphlets of that time are full of her. Some say she was the cast-off mistress of Prince Charles, others that she was a quiet Highland widow who took no interest in Jacobite intrigue. The villagers are emphatic in their assertion that she roused the men of her house after the Prince arrived, and led them herself in the rising. She went with them, they say, to Derby, and, after the return of the Highland army, was captured at Falkirk, and imprisoned in Edinburgh Castle. They are proud to think that this brave woman came to spend the last years of her life in their parish.

There seem to have been at least three different women of the name, all of whom, it has been alleged, were associated with the Prince. On the other hand, Jacobite writers claim that Jenny Cameron was the invention of their enemies. Wherever the truth lies, it cannot be denied that a Jenny Cameron died at Mount Cameron, and was buried in one of her own fields. No monument marks her resting-place.

Women seem to have made all the running in East Kilbride. Local legend associates Kate Dalrymple, the heroine of William Watt's comic song, with the village. The wee thatched cottage, in which, it is said, she lived, has disappeared, but women repeat the song, and youths whistle the air. Kate will live for ever.

Joanna Baillie, the poetess and dramatist, also lived hereabouts. She came to Long Calderwood after the death of her father, who had been Professor of Divinity in Glasgow University. Her mother was a Hunter of Long Calderwood, a sister of the famous William and John Hunter, the one a scientist and the other a surgeon, whose names are perpetuated in the Hunterian Museum in Glasgow University.

It is easy to understand how difficult it would be for a youth to settle down to study in this lovely countryside. John Hunter preferred the outdoor life to his studies, and was given up as hopeless by his tutors. He grew into his teens with only a smattering of English and without thinking of a profession. His father died when he was only ten, and no provision was made for maintaining him in idleness. There seemed nothing for him but a business which would occupy his hands rather than his head. He was apprenticed to a cabinetmaker, and learned to make chairs and tables. This might have been his life's work but for the failure of his employer, when John had to look in another direction for employment.

His elder brother, William, who was a doctor in London, had already begun to distinguish himself as a lecturer in anatomy. News of his success awakened ambition in the younger man, who offered his services as an assistant in the dissecting room. The army was the alternative. The offer was accepted, and the manual dexterity acquired as an apprentice cabinetmaker helped him to success with the scalpel. He passed the tests set by his brother, and so rapid was his progress that in little more than a year he was giving demonstrations to a class of his own. In a few years he was at the head of his profession, and did more for surgery than any other investigator who had gone before.

The land in this region was held for five centuries by the Maxwells. Their home was Calderwood Castle, on the Rotten Calder less than a mile from the home of the Hunters.

The Maxwells and their neighbours were never long at peace. It did not take much to start a feud. Men would batter each other for a day over a silly remark about the sweetness of a woman's smile.

They were saved from extinction on one occasion by a minister. Dr. Baillie, the father of the poetess, had a dream that something terrible was about to befall this house. His wife tried to calm his fears, but he could not rest until he had warned them of impending disaster. He took his horse from the stable at midnight, and rode across to the castle. He explained, after anxiously inquiring about the safety of every member of the family, the reason for his visit at that hour.

" I am not superstitious," he said, " but it is strongly impressed on my mind that the family are to be wiped out, and I have come to warn you."

He then asked Sir William Maxwell to go with him over the castle, as he wanted to see the east wall. He was certain the castle was going to fall into the river below. There was a large rent in the wall when they arrived in that quarter. The members of the household who had gone to bed were roused, and the family records, which were kept in the tower, were removed.

Nobody slept that night. At half-past nine next morning the whole of the east side of the castle went over with a tremendous crash.

The castle was rebuilt. The Maxwells, however, no longer occupy it, but their coat-of-arms and motto, " I am ready; Think on ", remain above the main doorway.

The Calder leaps over the rocks far below the castle. Its banks are covered with trees of many kinds and numerous hues. On the rocks above are traces of Craigneath Castle, and down their face is the mausoleum of the early Maxwells.

Crossbasket, once a seat of the Lindsays, is a mile lower down the valley, and behind it, in the distance, is Dechmont Hill, where early man had his settlement and lit his Beltane fires.

The roofless keep of Gilbertfield stands in an open plain at the base of Dechmont Hill. It was built for a Hamilton, and for long was the home of a family of Cunninghams, one of whom was the mother of Tobias

Smollett. Its fame, however, rests on the fact that it was the residence of William Hamilton, who inspired the muse of Allan Ramsay and kindled the patriotism of Robert Burns.

Scotland, no doubt, would have forgotten Hamilton but for Burns's acknowledgment of his debt to him. Hamilton published a modernized edition of Blind Harry's *Wallace* in 1722. It was of this book that Burns wrote: " The story of Wallace poured a tide of Scottish prejudice

Gilbertfield

into my veins which will boil along till the floodgates of life shut in eternal rest."

It was also Hamilton's poem, " The Last Dying Words of Bonnie Heck ", which fired Ramsay with the ambition to sing.

Glasgow and its smoke, which can be seen from Dechmont, are forgotten when the wayfarer begins the walk to Bothwell Banks. A road on the left, beyond the bridge which carries the Hamilton road across the Calder, leads to the Clyde. A path through a strip of wood beyond the railway gives access to the site of Blantyre Priory.

Little remains of the priory, which was founded by King Alexander II. It stands on a promontory over-hanging the steep bank of the Clyde and directly opposite Bothwell Castle. All traces of the chapel have vanished, but the gables and other fragments of the prior's house have withstood the ravages of Time. There is nothing forlorn and desolate, however, about the place, although so little remains of the building, and although the floor is covered with a carpet of grass. Instead of thinking of it as a ruin, the emblem of man's ambitions, hopes, and labours falling into decay, it would seem that Nature had arranged her rockwork in approved architectural designs, and had decorated it with plants of her own choosing. Birds sweep through the sanctuary where monks once gathered and prayed. Flowering plants have found a foothold in the broken stonework.

There is a vault from which you can look down to the river bed far below. It frames a charming scene. Trees rise to great heights on either bank, and round the bend is a fertile stretch of land where fruit has been grown since the monks laid out the orchards. The old castle opposite is the grandest ruin of its kind in Scotland.

Bothwell Castle has played a great part in the history of Scotland. It knew the ebb and flow of the tide of invasion, the sharp turns of the fortune of war. King Edward I seized it from Sir Andrew Moray, the first Scots noble to enrol under Wallace's banner, and the last to leave him when his struggle ended. Bruce bestowed it on his brother-in-law, and Edward III recaptured it. Its owner wrested it from the invaders, and, believing that it had been of greater use to the enemies of his country than it had ever been to its rightful owners, destroyed it. A Douglas rebuilt it, making it stronger and bigger than ever. It changed hands a number of times after his day, but eventually reverted to his descendants.

Archibald the Grim, a natural son of the Black Douglas who died fighting the Moors in Spain, and who threw the casket containing the heart of Bruce into the charge before him, was the first of his house to live in Bothwell Castle. He was well named " The Grim ". He defied his king, and murdered his enemies. He tortured his slaves, and built churches to relieve his conscience.

Not only did he buy slaves to do his work, but he tried to buy a husband for his daughter. He secured the husband, a prince of the royal house, but it is doubtful if he ever paid the price. This unusual bargain was made at Bothwell. The uncle of the young Duke of Rothesay, the heir to the throne, proposed a marriage between the duke and the daughter of the noble who should offer the highest bid. Douglas made an offer, but another offered more—the Earl of March. Douglas, however, was not a man to suffer eclipse. It was nothing to him that the offer of his rival had been accepted. The Duke of Rothesay would be his son-in-law or remain a bachelor for life.

The duke was a willing accomplice to thwart the purpose of his wicked uncle, and defeat the Earl of March in his plan to increase the dignity of his house. March raged and stormed when he heard of the Douglas alliance with the prince, and sought to enlist the nobles in his cause. While he fulminated, and prepared for war against his rival, the duke came secretly to Bothwell and married Elizabeth Douglas.

CHAPTER III

Two Davids who became Goliaths

David Dale was a herd boy. He was happy with his sheep on the Ayrshire hills until he saw a vision. Then, like the prophets of old, he answered the call to higher service. He was to lead his countrymen to the greatest heights of industrial success. The road was not an easy one. He worked long hours for a pittance at a loom in Paisley, Hamilton, and Cambuslang — but he became a master of his craft. Then followed a period during which he tramped the country as a packman, distributing flax to cottagers, and collecting the yarn they made from it. His commercial success was founded on blistered feet, for in a short time he was recognized in the west of Scotland as the keenest buyer and salesman on the road. His integrity became proverbial.

A momentous decision was made in 1763. He opened a linen warehouse in the High Street of Glasgow. Twenty years later he became the father of the cotton industry in Scotland.

Richard Arkwright, a Lancashire barber, placed in Dale's hands a machine with which Dale outstripped all his competitors. It was the spinning-frame. His competitors were sceptical, but Dale, ever shrewd and far-seeing, appreciated the possibilities of the invention. He established a mill at New Lanark in 1785, and another soon after at Blantyre.

Dale and James Monteith, a Glasgow weaver and linen merchant, were the creators of modern Blantyre. Little remains of their early mill, but the houses which clustered round it are a mile up the Clyde from the ruined Priory of Blantyre.

Dale's successor as industrial leader in the west of Scotland was another Monteith—Henry Monteith, the friend and partner of Macintosh and Tennant, and all of them pioneers of bleaching and dyeing.

There was no eight-hour day, and there was no Children's Charter in those days. Work began at six in the morning, and continued for twelve hours. The tasks, too, were of such a nature that a child, with its nimble fingers, soon became proficient.

One boy, who, like the founder of the factory, began work in the mill when he was ten, saw a vision. It was not one that led his feet to the bottom of the industrial ladder, but one that kindled in his bosom the desire for knowledge so that he might become the instrument for breaking the shackles of slavery in the darkest corners of the world. That boy was David Livingstone, who dealt the slave trade in Africa its death-blow. He was the greatest missionary-explorer who ever left this country. He conceived, developed, and carried out to success a noble and many-sided purpose, with an unflinching and self-sacrificing energy and courage which have placed him among the great and strong who, unaided, materially influenced human progress.

The house in which he was born, and the picturesque

Shuttle-row adjoining, have become a place of pilgrimage. They are Scotland's memorial to her distinguished son.

A suspension bridge links Blantyre and Bothwell. The road rises from the riverside by a wall that skirts the policies of Bothwell Castle. Bothwell is a lovely village

Livingstone's Birthplace, Blantyre

with a lang pedigree. Modern mansions have, however, taken the place of the early houses which sprang up round the old Church of St. Bride.

An interesting church it is, too. It shows growth, alteration, and restoration. The oldest part was built by Archibald the Grim. A new church was added to it early last century, and the whole renovated and restored at the end of last century. A large pointed window with the Moray and Douglas arms on the mould, a stained-glass window depicting the Nativity, and monuments to the Douglases and the Hamiltons are the principal features of this old building. The roof, too, shows the skill of the old craftsmen.

Epitaphs always interest me. I found some unusual types here. One is a long catalogue of the virtues of a parish minister, a sister's eulogy. But a different estimate of the man is found in these lines recorded elsewhere by a brother minister:

> There lies interred beneath this sod,
> That sycophantish man of God,
> Who taught an easy way to Heaven,
> Which to the rich was always given.
> If he get in he'll look and stare,
> To find some out that he put there.

Rhymsters seem to have been numerous in this parish. Their aid has been invoked by bereaved families in all stations. The quaintest of all inscriptions is over the grave of a blacksmith:

> My sledge and hammer lies declined,
> My bellow's pipe have lost its wind,
> My forge's extinct, my fire's decayed,
> And in the dust my vice is laid.
> My coals is spent, my iron is gone,
> My nails are drove, my work is done.

Hour-glasses, skulls, and cross-bones are numerous, while on one stone is hewn the head of a dog with a shuttle in its mouth—a reminder of the time when Bothwell was a weaving hamlet. The story behind this emblem is one of a dog's sagacity. Its owner was a weaver, and the dog used to run between his workshop and his home with the pirns which were filled by the family while their father tended his loom.

The outstanding monument in the churchyard is the one placed near the entrance to commemorate Joanna Baillie's association with the parish—she was born in the manse when her father was the minister of Bothwell.

There are many unrecognized and long-since forgotten battlefields in Scotland, but there is one near Bothwell which Scots will never forget. The battle of Bothwell Brig marked the opening of one of the darkest chapters in the history of the country, when " murder stalked redshod in every valley and by every farmstead in the west and south of Scotland ". The monument at the bridge commemorates the stand of an army of untrained rustics for Kirk and Covenant.

There was great excitement round Bothwell the day before the battle. The Covenanters lay on the opposite bank of the Clyde. The Duke of Monmouth had just arrived with reinforcements to avenge the defeat of Claverhouse at Drumclog three weeks before. There were brave men among the Covenanters—men like Robert Hamilton, their leader, and Hackston of Rathillet. But the rank and file could not forget their differences on the Indulgence, and when they should have been preparing for battle they were engaging in theological discussions.

The battle began early on a Sunday morning in June, 1679. The bridge was the key to the situation. Hackston, with two hundred men, held it until ammunition gave out. Then he had to abandon the gatehouse which stood on the middle of the bridge. A victory for Monmouth, after the fall of the bridge, was a matter of minutes. The defeat of the Covenanters became a rout and then a disaster. Many were killed in the indiscriminate butchery which followed.

The bridge which spans the Clyde at Bothwell is the same one that Hackston defended. Three of the original arches remain, but the rest of it has been so altered that the wayfarer finds it hard to think that the fight for spiritual freedom took place round it.

The town of Hamilton, which is little more than a mile away, once demanded a fee from everybody who entered by the bridge. A battalion of toll-keepers would be necessary now to cope with the traffic which comes this way! Hamilton is the Charing Cross of Scotland. It has been an important town since the fifteenth century.

Cromwell sent a force here to bring the Covenanters to his terms, and Claverhouse was a frequent visitor when he was rounding up those men whose only offence was their stand for freedom of worship. An odd memorial of that time is to be found in the churchyard adjoining the parish church in the heart of the town. The monument, which consists of the rudely carved heads of four martyrs, bears the following inscription:

> Stay, passenger, take notice what thou reads,
> At Edinburgh lie our bodies, here are our heads,
> Our right hands stood at Lanark; those we want
> Because with them we sware the Covenant.

The four men were captured at Rullion Green, and executed for their part in the Pentland Rising.

Hamilton is a smart town, and has its best expression in Cadzow Street. Its inhabitants have resolved to keep pace with architectural advances. The fresh additions to the town's buildings are shedding their influence not only in directly improving the town, but in stimulating other owners of old property to improve their buildings also.

The town's greatest glory and chief attraction of an earlier day—the palatial home of Scotland's premier dukes—has gone, but the dome-roofed mausoleum, built by the tenth Duke of Hamilton a century ago, stands alone in the centre of the park which surrounded the palace. It was built to hold the bodies of this noble race, its designer thought, for all time; the ashes of its tenants were removed to the public cemetery in 1923. It cost £130,000 to build; the town bought it for a trifle.

What a story its tenants could have told. It contained the ashes of the duke who was defeated by Cromwell at Preston, and who was beheaded for his loyalty to the Stewarts; the body of another wounded at Worcester in 1654, of another who fell in a duel in London, of another who married one of the beautiful Gunning sisters, and of Alexander, who built the mausoleum to be a fitting tomb for his own coffin, formerly the sarcophagus of an Egyptian princess, for which he paid £10,000.

The story of the Hamiltons is the history of Scotland. Kings made them ambassadors, and the people their champions. One of the greatest of his family was Sir James Hamilton of Finnart, the designer of royal palaces and the confidant of his king. His character, however, was stained by numerous acts of cruelty and oppression. He took a prominent part in the persecutions of the early Reformers, and no hand was more deeply stained than his with the blood of his kinsman, Patrick Hamilton, the first Protestant martyr, who suffered in 1528. Ultimately he fell into disgrace, was accused of embezzling the royal funds and also of treason, and was beheaded in 1540. Had he occupied the position of his feeble father and still feebler brother, he would have been the supreme ruler of Scotland during the troubled minorities of James V and his ill-starred daughter, Mary.

His brother, the second Earl of Arran, was " everything by turns and nothing long ", and by his combined feebleness and fickleness brought great misery on his family and his country. He was an adherent of Queen Mary at one time, at another her most bitter enemy. He was a Reformer when he was courting Queen Elizabeth. He took the other side after she refused to have anything to do with him, and when he tried to woo his own queen. When she, too, declined his suit, his family carried her off by force. He died an imbecile.

Successive heads of the Hamilton family were notorious for their weak and facile character. Sir Walter Scott, who thoroughly understood and appreciated the family character, makes John Gudyill, the butler of Tillietudlem, say of the first duke, who was illegally put to death by the English Parliamentarians, " that he lost his heart before he lost his head ", and that his brother and successor was " but wersh parritch neither gude to fry, boil, nor sup cauld ".

The marriages of the Hamiltons always created a stir. No duchess ever had a more rousing homecoming than Elizabeth Gunning, who became Duchess of Hamilton in 1752. She was the younger of the two famous beauties who, coming from the wilds of Connaught, threw Dublin into a state of high excitement in the winter of 1745. They won the homage of every man, from the Lord-

Lieutenant to the meanest jarvey. They were the daughters of a poor Irish landlord, whose main occupation was keeping the bailiff from his door, but through their mother they had Plantagenet blood in their veins.

Dublin, however, was not considered a good enough market for them. Mrs. Gunning brought them to London, hoping to make suitable matches for her offspring. No man beneath a duke or an earl would ever marry them, she declared. All London raved about the newcomers. They were toasted at Court and at coffee-stalls. Curious multitudes followed them whenever they walked abroad. All the gallants were at their feet, and the young sisters had refused a number of coronets before they had been many weeks in town. Never before had such beauty been known.

Each counted her wooers by the score, and in the end each capitulated to a favourite suitor. Maria married the Earl of Coventry, and Elizabeth accepted the young Duke of Hamilton, who fell in love with her at a masquerade. One evening, when he called to see her, he determined to marry her without further delay. He sent for a parson, who, however, refused to perform the ceremony without a licence or a ring. The duke swore he would send for the archbishop. At last they were married with a ring of a bed-curtain at half an hour after midnight in Mayfair Chapel.

The journey from London to Hamilton after the honeymoon was one long triumphal procession. They drove through long avenues of cheering people in every town they had to pass. Men and women fought for a glimpse of the famous beauty who had made so romantic a match. Some of them ran for miles behind their coach.

Elizabeth's married life was not happy. The duke was

young, but worn-out with the excesses of a misspent youth. His duchess longed to leave her Scottish palace and its solitude, and return to the scene of her early conquests. The duke died in 1758, and she was free to go back to the gay circle she had left behind.

The duchess did not wear the widow's weeds long. In little more than a year, after she had rejected the suit of a number of nobles, she married Colonel John Campbell, who later became the Duke of Argyll. He was able to boast: "My dear, your 'poor soldier' has been able to make you a 'double duchess'."

The early home of the House of Hamilton was Cadzow Castle, about two miles from the town. It was at one time a royal residence. It is a place to be visited, for its situation is unrivalled.

> Cadzow's towers, in ruins laid,
> And vaults, by ivy mantled o'er,
> Thrill to the music of the shade,
> Or echo Evan's hoarser roar.

Its ruinous state is due to the fact that Parliament, after the battle of Langside, in which the Hamiltons had thrown all their weight in the scale for Queen Mary, greatly feared the existence in Clydesdale of an irritation and a set-back to the convalescent country—a rough spot tending to re-open the sore. So soldiers were sent, and it seems to-day that their orders were executed with unnecessary thoroughness. The ruin stands on a high bank of the River Avon, and is a pathetic reminder of the glory it might still have boasted.

The steep slopes of the Avon are covered with massive trees, but these are young compared with the veterans of

Cadzow Forest near at hand. The gnarled branches and hollow trunks of this remnant of the great Caledonian Forest, which once stretched from the Clyde to the Cheviots, bear silent witness of days that stand dim and vague on the horizon of history.

I have seen nine people stand inside the biggest of these oaks, under whose branches graze white cattle, the survivors of the cattle which roamed the Caledonian Forest. They are pure white, except for black ears, muzzles, and hoofs. A sort of despotic monarchy is the form of government among these cattle. The herd has its king, and his accession to the throne is almost invariably accompanied by bloodshed. The duels which have been fought over the kingship of the Cadzow herd have often been fierce and deadly. They graze peacefully in the great park, through which visitors are allowed to walk. The cattle may be wild. Their wildness, however, takes the form of timidity unless something has happened to disturb the domestic peace of the herd. Still, it is unwise to take any liberties with them. A notice reminds you that " the cattle are dangerous ". Follow the advice of a man who has worked among them for a long time: " Admire them with one eye, and keep the other on the nearest gate."

CHAPTER IV

The Capital of the Iron Kingdom

A traveller from the south approaching Motherwell once said to a train attendant as he looked towards a great smudge of smoke in the distance, " What's that?"

" That, sir," said the attendant, " is Motherwell. It is smoky, but that's what makes the money."

Motherwell is the Capital of the Iron Kingdom. The steel throne of His Industrial Highness is here. He leads his people with a cloud by day and a pillar of fire by night, the one the smoke from the blast-furnaces, and the other the flames that darkness shows up.

Motherwell was a small town of 700 inhabitants in 1841; to-day the combined burghs of Motherwell and Wishaw have a population of one hundred times that number. Steelopolis is the product of the nineteenth century.

The full beauty of the town is not revealed until the shadows of night fall, and it is seen at its best from the high ground a few miles up the river. Go, when Motherwell is busy, as I have gone, to that high ground, and you will think the sky has been inverted, and the landscape sprinkled with stars. They twinkle precisely as they do in the heavens, and they are tinged with colours. The "Milky Way" runs right down the Clyde, planets glow here and there, and occasionally through the gleam of the evening haze there is the suggestion of the moon. At other times the lights shimmer off like the tails of comets. These are the reflections of enormous furnaces, fires casting their gleam upon the sky. But watch!

Here is a volcano on the edge of this Clydesdale town. The flames burst out, and those who realize that it is simply a blast - furnace casting off iron - ore impurities know that from time to time the lava, in the shape of slag, is being poured off. Then another volcano, and another, and another breaks forth. Those near at hand hear the roar of charging machinery. It all means that Motherwell's industries never rest. Day and night they go on with thunder, and fire, and smoke.

It was after the middle of last century before the manufacture of iron and steel was begun on a lasting basis in the town. The venture of the pioneers has brought wealth and prosperity to Clydesdale. The names of the Colvilles, the Findlays, the Bairds, and others are recalled at once with this marvellous industrial development. The great foundries and mills they began are their best memorial.

Motherwell's success is, however, responsible for its difficulties. It is practically a one-industry town. It is prosperous when times are good, and extremely hard hit when dull times come. But the meaning of the steel trade to the town is of deeper significance. The condition of the steel trade has come to be a barometer of commercial progress for the whole country. When prosperity rules it means that Motherwell is probably more prosperous than any other place in the country.

It was not until I went through one of these steelworks that I realized what they mean, and that it began to dawn on me that right here in the heart of Clydesdale the forces are put into play that have developed our railways, reconstructed our great cities by transforming their buildings, made it possible for Britain to become Mistress of the Seas by building her navy and her mercantile fleet, and that into this industry there enter the highest skill of the chemist, the immeasurable courage of the manufacturer, as well as the brawn of physically the most highly developed Scots working men.

When Motherwell is busy scores of great sheds and mammoth furnaces are in use. A network of railway tracks fills every one of them. A roar like the sound of a bombardment smites the ears. The crashing of man-made thunder is in the air. Enormous ladles convey sixty tons of molten steel with the greatest ease, and almost human tools toss heavy ingots as easily as a child throws a ball.

A furnace is the most spectacular manufacturing thing in the world. A blast of compressed air is discharged into it after it has been filled with the molten steel, and a great flame leaps out at the top, throwing out sparks that make fireworks of fascinating shapes. At first the flame is a deep yellow colour. It becomes gradually lighter in shade, and then the fireworks cease. The skilled worker looks at the molten mass, wearing blue spectacles to protect his eyes. He knows exactly when to stop the blast, when the metal is pure enough to cast into ingots.

It is a common saying that iron and steel have made Motherwell. It is true enough, but it may be said also that the rich coal deposits in the neighbourhood have made the iron and steel. No one will dispute that.

This district has a strong Covenanting tradition. One

of the first to denounce Charles II for his oppression of the Scots was Hugh McKail, the chaplain and tutor to the family of Sir James Steuart of Coltness. McKail was a youth of twenty-two when he went to Edinburgh to preach from his uncle's pulpit. That day he referred to the miserable state of the country, when there was an Ahab on the throne, a Haman in the State, and a Judas in the Church.

A reference of that kind was more than the King, the Earl of Lauderdale, or Archbishop Sharp could stand. They resolved to punish the youth, but he had escaped to Holland before they could lay hands on him. He returned four years later, and took part in the Pentland Rising of 1666. He was subsequently captured, tortured with the boot, and executed.

McKail was only twenty-six when he mounted the scaffold. His last words left a deep impression on the crowd round it. They were:

" Farewell father and mother, friends and relatives—farewell the world and all its delights—farewell sun, moon, and stars—welcome God and Father—welcome sweet Jesus Christ, the Mediator of the New Covenant—welcome blessed Spirit of Grace and God of all consolations—welcome glory—welcome eternal life—welcome death!"

The Hamiltons of Belhaven were not behind the Steuarts in their allegiance to the Covenant. The first Lord Belhaven fought with King Charles against the English Parliament. He led a force across the Border. When they reached Berwick they halted. Belhaven asked why they did not enter the town. He was told they were considering whether the Governor of the town should be consulted before they entered.

" Ride through!" exclaimed the Scots leader, and the order was obeyed. Those words are now the family motto of his descendants.

Lord Belhaven was a keen gardener. The Barncluith terraces at Hamilton were designed by him.

He was careful of the bawbees, and his skill as a horticulturist helped him to evade the heavy fine imposed by Cromwell. To avoid this imposition he decided to disappear for a time. He thought it would be easier to hide in England than in Scotland, and left with a servant for the south. He dismissed the attendant when he reached the Solway, giving him a letter to take home to Lady Belhaven. The servant, on his return, reported that his master was lost when crossing the Solway sands.

Lord Belhaven did not perish in the sands. He found his way to London, and thence to Richmond, where he was given a job as gardener in Richmond Park. His skill was soon recognized, and he was sent to Holland to buy bulbs and plants. He became the messenger between the exiled Charles II and the Royalists at home. At the Restoration he resigned his post as gardener, and returned to his flowers at Hamilton.

The second Lord Belhaven was the husband of a granddaughter of the first holder of the title. He was the most distinguished of all who held the honour. His lot was cast in the troublous " Killing Time ". He had been Lord Belhaven only two years when the oath known as the " Test " was framed to crush the spirit and extinguish the cause of the Covenanters. He was imprisoned in Edinburgh Castle for a speech he made against this measure.

He contributed not a little in settling the crown on William and Mary, and commanded a troop of horse at

Killiecrankie, where he displayed as much courage in the field as he had shown wisdom in the Senate.

The memory of this able and disinterested patriot has, however, been preserved by his famous philippic against the union with England—without doubt the most eloquent speech ever delivered in the Scottish Parliament — in which he held up that measure to public reprobation as the total surrender of national independence, as dangerous to the national Church, as degrading to the nobility and the army, and as ruinous to every section of the people. His appeal to the Estates to lay aside their dissensions and to unite in saving the honour and independence of the country produced an extraordinary effect on the public mind, and could scarcely have been heard without emotion even by the hardest crusted politicians of the day. This speech is the only specimen of Scottish parliamentary oratory which has found its way into English collections of rhetorical masterpieces.

" Where are the Douglases, the Grahams, the Campbells, our peers and chieftains, who vindicated by their swords from the usurpation of the Edwards, the independence of their country, which their sons are about to forfeit by a single vote?" he asked.

" I see the English constitution remaining firm; the same trading companies, laws, and judicatures; whilst ours are either subjected to new regulations, or are annihilated for ever. And for what?—that we may be admitted to the honour of paying their old arrears, and presenting a few witnesses to attest the new debts, which they may be pleased to contract! Good God! is this an entire surrender? My heart bursts with indignation and grief at the triumph which the English will obtain this day over a fierce and warlike nation which has struggled to maintain its independence so long!

" But, if England should offer us our own conditions, never will I consent to the surrender of our sovereignty, without which, unless the contracting parties remain independent, there is no security different from his who stipulates for the preservation of his property when he becomes a slave!"

Patriotism breathes in every line of that appeal, which was concluded thus:

" I see our ancient mother Caledonia, like Cæsar, sitting in the midst of our Senate, looking mournfully around, covering herself with her royal garments, and breathing out her last words, '*And thou, too, my son!*' while she attends the fatal blow from our hands."

Lord Belhaven was thrown into prison for making that speech, but was soon liberated. An attempt to land the Chevalier was made by the French in 1708. Lord Belhaven was suspected of being in the plot. He was again arrested, and taken to London. The charge was never debated, and he died of a broken heart before he could say anything in his defence.

The Covenanting tradition lives on. The country folk are as pious as their forefathers, and on Sunday mornings they can be seen walking to the churches round which weather-worn stones tell their tales of the " Killing Time ".

My thoughts were of that period as I made my way to Garrion Bridge, where a prospect was revealed which drove the past from my mind—a landscape of woodland, river, and orchard. Garrion Tower, once the summer residence of the Archbishops of Glasgow, was behind me, and upstream I looked to the old mill which has been grinding corn for centuries.

I turned up the Clyde road, and entered the orchard country. I had not gone far when I saw a pretty group of houses round an odd-looking church with a curious belfry and outside stairs to the " laft ". This was Dalserf, a small village on a holm of the Clyde near the main road.

I entered the churchyard, and as I walked among the tomb-stones I found the grave of the " persecuting Raploch ", a man who distin-guished himself by his zeal against the Covenanters. Here also was buried the saintly John McMillan, the first minister

Dalserf

of the Cameronian Church, which adhered to the principles of Richard Cameron.

Hamiltons were numerous here at one time—Hamilton is still a common name in the district. A family of them had their home in Dalserf House, whose walls tower far above the lowly cottages clustered round the old church. One of their servants became Provost of Glasgow. He was Archibald Ingram.

Ingram became the friend and partner of the Virginians,

and the pioneer of calico-printing. He had to spin his
yarn and weave his cloth; he had to train his bleacher and
his colour mixer; *and he had to steal his patterns.*

He made a fortune, and nobody could take it from him,
not even the astute bankers in Edinburgh. He helped
to found a bank at a time when the Edinburgh people
thought banking should be their monopoly, and set about
destroying the credit of their rival in the west. They
sent a man from Edinburgh to gather all the notes he
could lay his hands on, and demand payment in coin for
them. Ingram and his friends were equal to the occasion.
The bank staff paid out in sixpences, and kept the Edinburgh fellow waiting for hours for his money.

The afternoon was already far advanced when I left
the village. A mist crept up from the south, and hid the
lights which were already glimmering through the twilight
as I approached Rosebank.

This village arose to supply the deficiency of houses in
Dalserf, and is one of the best-kept places in Clydesdale.
In summer the houses can hardly be seen for flowers. Their
occupants were long encouraged by the Newlands family
of Mauldslie Castle to take a pride in their gardens.

The red-tiled English-looking hostelry is a fitting place to
rest. It is, according to tradition, the scene of the tournament
described in *Old Mortality.* Its name recalls the favourite
sport of shooting the popinjay, and while you rest you can
picture the throng that came that day when they were
headed by the lovely Edith Bellenden. Or you can think
of the warlike Maxwells who once owned Mauldslie and
rode through this quiet countryside on their way to raid
the lands of their southern neighbours.

CHAPTER V

The Men of the Moss-hags

There are good reasons for the statement that Clydesdale was the cradle of Christianity in Scotland. St. Ninian and his disciples were the first to preach the Word in Strathclyde; St. Patrick was born within that old kingdom; and St. Kentigern founded churches there. These were pioneer missionaries in Scotland.

Clydesdale, which was the first of the early kingdoms to be converted to Christianity, also became later the seat of movements which transformed the Church.

Stonehouse claims to be the birthplace of Patrick Hamilton, the first Protestant martyr. His father was the laird of Stonehouse. The stoutest champions of the Covenant were the Lanarkshire men, and when, after the rout of Bothwell Brig, many were prepared to accept defeat, a remnant met in the moors above Lesmahagow and renewed the Covenants. That small body of rebels for the Kirk adhered to their principles, and were delivered from persecution at the Revolution in 1688.

Avondale, one of the most enchanting valleys in Clydesdale, runs westwards from Stonehouse to the moor-clad slopes on the Ayrshire border. The valley begins to open out at Stonehouse, where, on a site of commanding beauty, the old church dedicated to St. Ninian was built many

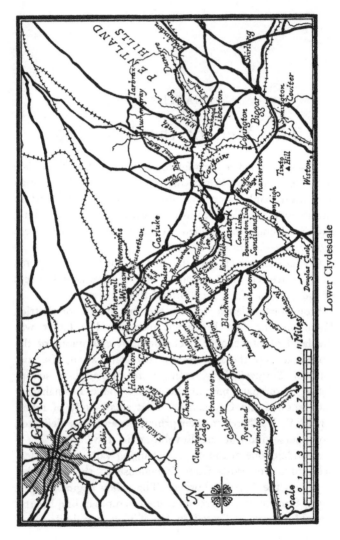

Lower Clydesdale

(Continuation on opposite page)

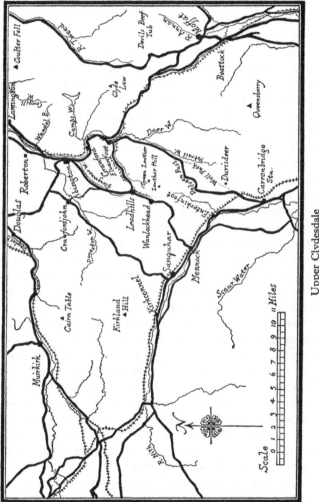

Upper Clydesdale

centuries ago. Little remains of that old building, but the beauty of its natural setting is unequalled by any other church in the county.

The village has left the old church and grown westwards. New churches have sprung up, and as the village is approached the spires of the modern buildings are seen high above the roofs. The long rows of oddly built houses have often provided an architectural puzzle to visitors who, in other places of the same size, have generally found the doors in the centre of the buildings. Here the doors have mostly two windows on one side and one on the other. House and workshop were once under one roof, and the odd window was in the weaving-shop.

But looms have disappeared, and most of the weavers with them. The whirr of the shuttle is a thing of the past, its click-clack is silenced, and the birr of the pirn-wheel is unknown to the younger generation. Instead of the blue-and-white aproned weaver, the grim and grimy collier is seen in the streets. Coal-mining is the village's compensation for the decay of weaving.

Glassford, which had its ancient church and castle, stands on the heights across the valley. This small village nurtured a pioneer missionary. The Rev. Francis Borland was one of the four ministers commissioned by the Church of Scotland to accompany the Scots colonists on the second expedition to Darien. He was one of the few who returned to Scotland. Two of his colleagues died, and the other became minister of a Puritan congregation in South Carolina, and founded the family from which President Roosevelt sprang.

Strathaven, which is about three miles west of Stonehouse, is a place of many memories. Her monument is her history book, and her crowning glory the ancient castle which stands majestically on the high ground on the left as you enter the town. Hardly a house in the old part of the town but has its story of centuries-long life, and has been the scene of supreme happiness and desolating sorrow.

The story of the castle has been one of changes and storms. In the first place it belonged to the Douglases, but on their forfeiture it was destroyed by James II. The position was too strong to remain long vacant, and three years after its destruction Sir Andrew Stewart, the first Lord of Avon-

Strathaven Castle

dale, rebuilt it. The Marquis of Hamilton bought it in 1611, and his family made it one of their principal seats. Its most famous occupant was the good Duchess Anne who befriended many of the pursued Covenanters on their flight from Bothwell Brig.

The road from Stonehouse is the best way to enter Strathaven, for you are at once in the old part of the town. Men and women whose names are famous in history have come this way before you. The compact buildings in the narrow streets at various angles to the highway seem older and more foreign to the twentieth century than anything I have seen in Lanarkshire, and I would like to have the power to take the woefully abused word " quaint ", and affix it to Old Strathaven, stopping its use elsewhere, so that it might belong alone to this place.

Todshill . . . what a name for a street! You expect to see a fox leave its lair and come to meet you. Strathaven knew its todlowries long after the fox had been driven farther into the country. At one time they were informers, at another agents provocateurs.

The people of Strathaven knew from experience what it was to have troops sent against them. In ordinary circumstances their arrival would not have troubled them, but when a party of dragoons arrived early on a Sunday in June, 1679, they were alarmed. These men had come not to fight against armed men, but to attack defenceless women and badly equipped rustics who had gone to the moors to worship. Quiet, homely people who refused to attend the services conducted by a curate in one of the churches were meeting that day under the shadow of Loudon Hill, a few miles beyond the town. News of the conventicle had reached Claverhouse, and he had come to stop it, and seize its promoters. The troops rested at an inn, and after breakfast set off for the moor.

The service had just begun when a shot was heard. It was the signal that the soldiers were in sight. A watchman ran from the hill-top with the news. The men who had gone to worship were partly prepared for any emergency. Some had muskets, a few carried swords, most of them had pitchforks and sickles.

The preacher stopped. Balfour of Burley, Hackston

of Rathillet, and Robert Hamilton, the leaders of the Covenanters, held a hurried consultation. They sent the women and children to a place of safety behind the meeting-place, and ordered the men to prepare for battle. They had a choice of positions, and when the dragoons arrived they found a morass between them and the rustics.

Claverhouse called on the Covenanters to surrender. They defied him, and retorted by singing a psalm.

" Their blood be on their own head. Be ' No quarter ' the word of this day!" roared Claverhouse.

His dragoons replied " ' No quarter ' ", and galloped down the hill-side. But they could not reach the Covenanters in consequence of the softness of the ground. Charge after charge was made, but the horses could not cross the morass. Claverhouse then ordered thirty of his men to alight and fire, but no one was hit. Then William Cleland, the poet, advanced alone from the other side of the bog, fired his musket, and brought down one of the dragoons. The horses of the soldiers became so entangled in the moss in the charge which followed that the ranks of Claverhouse's soldiers were broken and the squadron thrown into confusion.

" Out o'er the bog and at them, lads!" shouted John Nisbet of Hardhill at that moment — an order the Covenanters jumped to obey. The soldiers could not withstand the charge, and they fled from the field in confusion. Burley at the head of the horse and Cleland in command of the infantry pursued the dragoons. They splashed through the swamp, and engaged in hand-to-hand fights with the troopers who had become fast in the bog.

Claverhouse succeeded in the end in rallying his men for another charge. They turned on the Covenanters who were waiting for them. A sharp encounter followed, but the soldiers could not gain the upper hand. Hamilton grasped the Covenanters' standard, and went to the front. The brave countrymen, with three rousing cheers, then rushed once more on the dragoons. Then Claverhouse sounded the signal to retreat. Swordless and helmetless he left the field at the head of his troopers, whom he led back to Strathaven. The result of this battle of Loudon Hill (or Drumclog) was a sore blow to his pride.

The people of Strathaven were relieved when they saw the soldiers go down the Glasgow road. A welcome was prepared for the victorious Covenanters. Claverhouse never forgave the townspeople for that rejoicing, and had he had his way after the rout of Bothwell Brig three weeks later, he would have sacked the town.

Strathaven became a base for operations during the " Killing Time ". Informers were everywhere, but the Covenanters were not so easily caught. Many had to take to the dens and caves of the earth. Life at home was impossible. Those who survived the persecution went to Edinburgh at the Revolution to make sure of their liberty.

These hillmen were equally ready for preaching and fighting, and equally ardent in both. They went to Edinburgh well armed with " lang-hafted gullies to kill Cavaliers ". The Presbyterian leaders of the time thought they were too dangerous a set to be out of discipline, and so, by a happy device which anticipated Pitt's treatment of the Highlanders half a century later, they were formed into a regiment and given King William's uniform to wear. They became the Cameronian Regiment, and were mustered by the young Earl of Angus at Douglas.

William Cleland, who distinguished himself at Drumclog, was made lieutenant-colonel. He was killed in their first battle, at Dunkeld, where the twelve hundred rustics from the western counties defended themselves against five thousand Highlanders, firing on until their bullets were exhausted, and then stripping the lead from the roofs.

The discipline and morals of this regiment were those of Cromwell's soldiers—prayers night and morning, no card-playing, and no drinking. Their regimental chaplain was the Rev. Alexander Shields, the author of that delectable pamphlet *The Hind Let Loose*. Yet even their rigid discipline was not enough to satisfy the chaplain, who lamented the dangers to their morals and orthodoxy which they ran in foreign parts.

Strathaven was also the centre of a later rising. Its population of weavers were keen politicians a century ago. Nearly all of them were Radicals and strong advocates of reform. They spoke out, and acted up to their convictions at a time when the Government was passing repressive measures to counteract the growth of the popular movement. Troops were massed at Glasgow and Hamilton, and the yeomanry were held in readiness for service. Spies were employed to watch the movements of the Strathaven weavers, and in the spring of 1820 one of these informers, who had won the confidence of the Avondale men, brought news of a rising in Glasgow, and a call to the weavers to join their fellows at Cathkin. In great excitement the weavers left their looms. Meetings were hurriedly called, and plans made. They prepared for battle.

For twenty years the men of Avondale had looked to James Wilson, one of their number, for guidance. Now he faltered. He was suspicious, and did not hesitate to say that he would have liked more evidence of their fellows' intentions than the verbal message of the stranger who had brought the call to mobilize. His hesitation was misunderstood. He was accused of cowardice in the hour for which he had worked, when the weavers were to fight for emancipation. He could not bear the taunts of the younger men, and reluctantly agreed to accompany them to Cathkin.

Wilson's fears had been well founded, for when they reached Cathkin they found nobody waiting. He realized that they had taken up arms against the Government, and had rendered themselves liable to severe penalties. They made for home. Wilson knew he was a marked man. He decided to seek the shelter of the moors where his Covenanting forefathers had found safety, but he was seized before he could leave the town, taken to Glasgow, and tried for treason. He was sentenced to death, and executed in Jail Square.

We are prone to take our freedom as our birthright, and apt to forget that our political liberty was won by men like this trusting weaver. Twelve years after he suffered martyrdom the first step in parliamentary reform was taken. It is hard for us sometimes to realize that these elementary rights of democracy were won over the bodies of our great-grandfathers.

Wilson was buried in the common burying-ground in Glasgow, but as soon as night fell his daughter and niece went to the graveyard, and removed the coffin to Strathaven. A monument under the cemetery wall commemorates his stand for political freedom.

The town is no longer the home of weavers. Only three remain at work. When they have finished the web of life, the looms will be silenced for ever.

Strathaven silks were once world-famous. Now silk-

weaving is a thing of the past. The survivors are making
tartans.

It does not date a person as being Victorian if he con-
fesses to a memory that is pre-petrol. That being so, I
recall, without feeling ashamed, the day when I first
entered Strathaven. The Common-green was then a large
empty square, quiet and eminently suitable as a sun-
parlour for a cat, which might sit and bask there the live-
long day without fear of being disturbed except by a dog.
Many changes have taken place in the interval. They
have been chiefly changes of movement.

No cat could sit now in the Common-green undisturbed
by the traffic. Instead of the old fly standing outside the
hotel with passengers for the railway station more than
a mile away, a number of motor-omnibuses wait to carry
passengers long distances east and west and north and
south. Instead of an occasional old wagonette or farmer's
cart appearing from the outlying districts, a regular stream
of motor-cars hurries through the town in all directions.
That is the most striking difference between the appearance
of the town to-day and at the beginning of the century.

There is an old saying, " See Naples and die ", but you
have only to look at Strathaven and live. There is a wealth
of beauty in every corner. The old town is picturesque,
and the modern portion with fine houses in well-kept roads
and avenues is a fitting complement.

CHAPTER VI

The Haunts of Prehistoric Man

The early governors of Strathaven were the monks of Kelso. They were also the superiors of Lesmahagow. It is a pleasant walk from the one to the other, leaving Strathaven by Todshill, with the old castle on the left across the Pomillion Burn.

Open country lies ahead—a landscape rich in curving lines of hill and valley. It is downhill to the bridge across the Avon. The road is pleasant, especially on a day when the sun shines brilliantly and a freshening breeze stirs the leaves into a soft continuous murmur, and as main roads go nowadays, it does not carry a great deal of traffic. It is an old road, too, one of the great roads of the Middle Ages, along which, " armed in all the panoply of war ", the mighty Douglases, with their retainers, marched in the days of strife and chivalry. Along it Covenanters and Royalists marched and counter-marched; along it Claverhouse and his dragoons rode in search of their foes.

Away up the river is Loudon Hill, where Bruce defeated the English, and under whose shadow the Covenanters routed Claverhouse's troopers.

Whatever may be said of the splendour of cornfields, the glory of the countryside is its grass. Those who have travelled far distinguish a Scottish landscape by its verdure. The pastures and meadows in the valley of the Avon make you experience fresh gladness in this green and pleasant land.

At the last bend on the road above the bridge I halted to look across the fields to a waterfall over which Kype Water leaps to join the Avon. Its name is Spectacle E'e. There was once a mill at that point. The miller was prosperous and wealthy. He was also stubborn and proud. He had a daughter who was in love with a neighbouring farmer's son. The miller did not, however, favour the suit.

One day about noon workers in the fields saw smoke and flames leap through the roof of the mill. Soon nothing but the walls remained. Nobody knows whether the miller was burned alive, but he was never seen again. Some time after, his daughter and her lover were married.

The fire was planned by the young farmer. He fixed the lens of spectacles in the thatched roof of the mill by night, and the lens caught the rays of the sun at its brightest. The dry straw became hot, and burst into flames—hence the name. At least, that is the derivation assigned to it by local tradition.

Sandford, which is, perhaps, the least-known and least-frequented place in this part of the country, stands on the bank of the Kype a short distance above the waterfall. No one, except the inveterate wayfarer, would dream of coming here. It is " off the map ". It possesses none of the customary appurtenances of most small villages—the school and post-office excepted; the letter-box is cleared once daily. It does not even have an inn. Little wonder, one feels, that remote places such as this show a dwindling census return each succeeding decade. The towns offer prospects of more money, greater recreational facilities, better education for the children; in fact, all those resources of modern civilization which have not yet penetrated to rural Scotland.

I left this quiet village behind, and went along the road

Sandford

that follows the course of the Kype to Deadwaters Bridge, where I took up the right bank of the river. Half a mile upstream I left the water's edge, climbed the hill to a farmhouse, circled the buildings, and made for the moorland round Brackenridge.

This is a lonely road, steering its way across the moors. It obviously has some definite end in view, and presses on. A few farmsteads front it, and at wide intervals in the heather-clad slopes which extend to Nutberry Hill and Tod Law are places with fascinating names. The road is much as it must have been when the Prior of Lesmahagow used it on his trips to his moorland home at Priorhill. It has escaped the straightening and widening processes to which other roads have been subjected. It winds pleasantly, has a diversified surface, and is delightfully narrow.

I shall never forget my visit to this countryside. The sun was bright, and as I walked downhill from Brackenridge I gazed across a region capped by flying clouds which cast an endless variety of shadows over the ridges. Tender green changed to purple grey, and then again to blue in quick succession. Past farm and steading, across tinted woods varying in shade from the dark green of the fir to the delicate tone of the birch, the changing shadows flew, and I revelled in a vision of loveliness.

I turned up the road to Auchrobert, passing the farm on the side of the hill, and making for Dunside. Half a mile beyond a gate which wayfarers should close behind them, I climbed through the heather to the summit, where the remains of a prehistoric settlement are found. This settlement is shaped like a figure 8, and inside one of the sections are two smaller circles. On the hill-side around are innumerable cairns where the settlers were buried under mounds so vast as to have survived to this day.

From this hill-top the eye can sweep from Tinto and Coulter Fell to the smoky regions down the Clyde. Logan House, where the Cameronians renewed the Covenant, lies a few miles to the south, and in the hollow Dunside reservoirs sparkle like diamonds in the sunshine.

As I went from the summit to the road below, stories of the dim past came to my mind. They all begin with the time-honoured " Once upon a time ", and they are all interesting.

Once upon a time, runs one of them, in the days before

the Romans came, this moorland was a place of fame, for, here on this hill, sun-worshippers had their home. To this place on the eve of the summer solstice came priests and Druids, chiefs and kings, tribesmen and tribeswomen clad in skins, armed with spears, adorned with necklaces, to witness the sacrifice that was to propitiate the gods and ensure a bountiful harvest and a year of peace and prosperity. From here, too, they could watch the fires rising from Tinto, the chief temple of the Druids in Clydesdale.

Once upon a time, so runs another, when the Roman cohorts came striding across the country, and the Roman engineers forced the enslaved Celts to make the road which runs westwards from Cleghorn to Loudon Hill, the fugitive inhabitants set watch and ward on this round peak to guard their families against surprise attacks by invading legions, and to watch for the sign of fires from neighbouring heights.

Once upon a time, runs still another, these friendly hills provided a refuge for fugitive Covenanters who were driven from their homes by the persecutors, and who made their beds among the heather. Not far away is the hag where the daughter of one of the fugitives was born after her mother and brothers had been turned out of their home down Logan Water.

I left this spot, and made my way down the right bank of Logan Water, from which I had a good view of the wonderful rock formation. This has been the happy hunting-ground of three generations of geologists whose discoveries have won a place for the district in the annals of the science.

Waterhead Farm is an interesting place. Its tenant is more interesting still. John Steel has lived on Logan

Waterhead Farm

Water all his days, and his family have been here for more than three hundred years. All the Steels were Covenanters. Two of them were diehard Cameronians who were at Drumclog and Bothwell Brig, and who, after the rout, had a price placed on their heads. Their goods were seized, and their wives, who remained on the farms, were harassed by visits from soldiers anxious to gain rewards. These visits were so frequent that the fugitives ran great risks when they came to see their families.

David Steel was surprised at Skellyhill on 20th December, 1686, by Lieutenant Crichton and a party of soldiers. He seized a musket, escaped by a back window, and made for the moors. He ran a good distance, hotly pursued by the dragoons, whom he kept at bay with his musket, but his strength failed, and he surrendered on the promise of a fair trial. He was carried back to his home, where, in a field before his house, Crichton, in spite of his promise, ordered the dragoons to fire on his captive. They refused, reminding him of the condition. The infantry, however, obeyed, and then the party left.

Captain John Steel, who was then tenant of Waterhead, was more fortunate. He was a fugitive, and for a time his wife shared his privations. The only shelter Mrs. Steel and her young family could find was a turf hut in the moors. Their food consisted of berries and " guddled " trout. This rude hut had to be abandoned, and the brave family party found shelter in a gully, where a daughter was born. Some time later, Mrs. Steel and her three children were allowed to return to Waterhead, but the farmer had to remain in hiding.

Stone at Waterhead

He was never far away, and paid frequent visits to his home, having a number of hairbreadth escapes from the soldiers who came across from Hell's Bike, a garrison near Lesmahagow, at all hours of the day and night. He resumed the cultivation of his lands after the Revolution in 1688.

A small part of the farmhouse of those days remains, and in one of the walls is the stone of which there is a drawing on this page.

The present tenant of Waterhead, which is owned by his father, who lives at Skellyhill, is not an ordinary farmer. His views are as broad as the country horizon, and after a short conversation no one can fail to be impressed by the breadth of his vision and his scientific knowledge.

He is modest and thoughtful, and for a minute or two you can hardly believe that a man of power is speaking, but as he proceeds it is found that a mind of real insight, that has been at work for itself, is setting forth with true force earnest and firmly held convictions.

John Steel is a geologist of fame and an enthusiastic biologist. He was associated with those geologists who had the good fortune to discover in the silurian deposits in this district fossil remains which previously were not known to exist in Scotland. In consequence, he gained the friendship of many leading scientists, and secured a place for his own name in the records of geological science.

John Steel told me his story. Like all of his race, he was a keen theologian and sermon-taster. One Sunday, when he was in his twenties, he heard the parish minister of Lesmahagow, who had seldom a hard word to say against anybody, denounce, with great vehemence, Darwin's *Origin of Species*. Surely, thought this young farmer, this must be a terrible book. He bought it, and became so interested that he secured the *Descent of Man*, and began to understand what Darwin was driving at.

" I wondered if I could find anything on Logan Water to illustrate Darwin's theory," said this farmer-scientist. " I began digging. Then one day I found a nodule which showed the remains of a fish. I knew my discovery was important, because I had read somewhere that such remains had not been previously found in Scotland.

" Naturally, I was excited. I sent my specimen to experts, and immediately Logan Water was thronged with geologists and archæologists from every part of the country. Further specimens were found, and it turned out I was right. This discovery was said to be the biggest geological discovery of last century."

John Steel has since numbered among his friends and correspondents the leading scientists of the world.

Before I left the farm he showed me some of the things he has found on Logan Water, and a number of cherished relics, each of them associated with stirring events in Scotland's history.

At the end of the farm road I turned down Logan Water, and as I walked I thought of the anxious times when keen eyes watched this roadway for the dragoons. In a few minutes I had reached Waterside School, behind which stood the old schoolhouse in which Alexander Muir, the author of *The Maple Leaf*, Canada's national anthem, was born in 1830. Broken walls and a heap of stones are all that remain of this old " side-school " of Skellyhill.

John Muir, the poet's father, came from Crawfordjohn to Skellyhill. He was a typical dominie, and his salary was thirty shillings a month. He met and fell in love with a Mrs. MacDiarmid, a widow with some means, then living on the neighbouring estate of Stockbriggs. They were married in 1829. Alexander was born in the following year, and in 1833 John Muir took his little family to Canada, and settled in a township near Toronto. He taught at different schools in that district, and died in 1865.

Alexander Muir was also a teacher. He graduated from Queen's University, Kingston, Ontario, in 1851, and two years later took charge of a school in Scarboro' township. He remained there a few years, and then became headmaster of a school near Toronto. He was principal of Gladstone Avenue School there from 1888 until his death in 1906. *The Maple Leaf* was composed in 1867, while he was living in a log-cabin on the outskirts of Toronto.

Through an opening a few yards beyond the school you can look uphill to Skellyhill, where a monument was raised in the middle of last century to commemorate David Steel's martyrdom.

The road crosses Logan Water, and for a mile runs along the right bank of the stream, which joins the Nethan below Stockbriggs. Few bits of scenery could surpass in charm the countryside round the confluence of these two rivers. Trees of all descriptions clothe their banks, and all is so peaceful that it seems hard to realize that within a few miles is one of the most important coal-fields in Lanarkshire, whence supplies have gone to all parts of the world for more than a century.

I decided to follow the Nethan, and chose the road which passes Auchlochan. For a short distance I was walking between high beech trees whose branches form an arch high overhead, and whose foliage excludes the sun. As I emerged from the shade I knew summer had really come. The birds had mustered, and I heard the notes of the cuckoo. I was delighted to hear him, for he is one of the prominent harbingers of better and warmer days.

The countryside would be unimaginable without its bird life. The scarcity of birds, caused by the ruthless war waged on them, strikes the Scots visitor to the Continent with a sense of something missing. Most of our birds are sober in their plumage, but if they lack the feathered beauty of the tropics, they more than make up in song for their lesser splendour. Their music was in my ears as I walked uphill to New Trows and down the path that skirts the policies of Birkwood to the old village of Lesmahagow.

CHAPTER VII

Where Nethan Flows

Lesmahagow was a place of considerable importance in the Middle Ages. Monks settled in the priory founded by King David I and given by him to the Abbey of Kelso. The haze which enshrouded the early history of the district is henceforth lifted by the monastic hands which kept a record of Lesmahagow in the copious cartularies of that great Border monastery.

Tyronensian monks settled in the priory. They were masters of various handicrafts, and were the masons and builders of their time. Examples of their craftsmanship are to be found in Clydesdale, although not a part of the old priory has survived. Many of the priors and monks stand out prominently in the records. At least one of them in the thirteenth century was a member of Parliament.

The priory had its ups and downs. It was burned in 1335 by the English troops under the Earl of Cornwall, the penalty, no doubt, for the monks' adherence to the cause of Wallace and Bruce. The church was soon rebuilt, but was again destroyed by the Reformers. It was raised again. This building was demolished to make room for the present parish church in 1803.

The villagers were stout champions of Presbyterianism,

and, consequently, strong supporters of the Hanoverian dynasty. They incurred the wrath of the Highlanders for their capture of young Donald MacDonald of Kinlochmoidart when he was on his way south with dispatches for his prince. So, when the army retreated with Prince Charles from Derby, the Highlanders threatened to destroy the village, which was only saved by a ruse. One of the inhabitants, seeing how angry the Highlanders were, left the village unnoticed, and rushed back with the news that the Duke of Cumberland's army was on its way from Douglas. The Highlanders, unprepared for battle, left hurriedly for Hamilton before they had time to carry out their threat of destruction.

Time did what the Highlanders meant to do. The old landmarks have disappeared, and a new village has risen from the ruins of the old.

Lesmahagow is the capital of Nethanvale. The district has never enjoyed the popularity of the neighbouring valley of the Avon, yet it possesses great charm. The invigorating air, the unusual variety of scenery, the vast spaces of open country round it, the revelations of changing colour—all these unite in happy harmony.

The Nethan fascinates me. I like to roam by its banks, and on my last visit I made straight for Kersegill, a lovely glen below Kerse House, about a mile north of Lesmahagow. The stream at this point flows through a charming glade, and in its waters are mirrored the high trees on its banks. The floor of the woods is carpeted in their season by hyacinths, primroses, and buttercups.

Raging floods have left their mark on the banks. Large slices have been gouged out by the angry river in winter. Yet the valley was a quiet haunt of peace on a day when

spring and summer merged, and I could hardly imagine
from the slumber song softly heard above the day-dream
stillness that the waters could have wrought the havoc
disclosed by the broken banks. Cattle grazed peacefully
where the risen waters have at times lipped the edge of
daisy-strewn pastures, over which butterflies danced. The
whole countryside, except the butterflies that dipped and
rose, and dipped again above the fields, slept in the afternoon sunshine.

The Nethan has a singular charm and beauty viewed
from the " rainbow " bridge at this point. Whether the
view is upstream or downstream the river makes a beautiful
picture. Upstream the channel is wide and the water shallow; downstream the bed is deep and the channel narrow,
with trees overhanging from both banks.

The path below the bridge soon becomes little more
than a ledge midway down a steep wooded bank, where a
mass of bramble bushes and trailing plants grow in great
profusion. The river then makes a wide sweep from the
Hawk's Nest, a cottage built on a promontory many feet
above the water, and circles a holm where fruit has been
grown for many years.

The road to Lanark is joined at Burnfoot, a hamlet
clustered round the confluence of the Birkwood Burn
and the Nethan. The village is one-sided, but why it
should be labelled one-eyed I do not know. The adjective,
first used by a pedlar who said the villagers could not
appreciate a bargain when he offered them one, certainly
does not apply to its present inhabitants, who possess the
usual number of eyes, and use them as effectively as do
their fellows. And it certainly did not apply to the man
who designed the three-storey house at the foot of the hill,

each storey of which can be entered from the ground level without a stair!

Kirkmuirhill is about a mile from Burnfoot, and stands on high ground near the main Glasgow-Carlisle road; its modern neighbour, Blackwood, is on the main road.

Kirkmuirhill was a place of considerable importance half a century ago, but the coal-seams have been worked out, and it has fewer inhabitants to-day than at any time in its history. Its future is problematical; at the moment it looks as if the dwindling process must continue.

The old manor house of Blackwood lies across the fields in the heart of a peaceful countryside. It was not always so quiet, and as I looked towards it the story of the fight for Catherine Weir's hand flashed through my mind.

Clydesdale is famous for its old country homes and long lines of lairds who have in succession rendered eminent services to the country. Blackwood House and its owners have been no exception. The Weirs have lived here for more than five centuries, and have left a deep impression in the county history.

One of them in the sixteenth century had two daughters. His wife died the day the younger was born. The elder daughter married, but her sister, who had inherited her mother's good looks, elected to remain with her father. She had accomplishments more valuable and more lasting than beauty; she was amiable and kind-hearted, and, in consequence, had many admirers.

The Weirs were friendly with their neighbours, the Hamiltons of Cander. The Hamilton family consisted of two sons, Cuthbert and Henry, both of whom loved Catherine, but dreaded the consequences of their rivalry. The friendship of the families gave the young men frequent opportunities of visiting Blackwood and spending time with the laird's daughter. Catherine, however, saw the impropriety of showing more regard for one than the other. Henry, in spite of her efforts to be impartial, won her heart, and they contrived to meet secretly in the mazes of the beautiful surroundings.

Cuthbert chanced to find the lovers together one day. Jealousy seized him. He was friendly with the governor of Craignethan Castle, a kinsman of his own, and to him he hurried with the story of his brother's perfidy. They agreed to keep a careful watch on Henry, and to kidnap the fair Catherine when they found her waiting for her lover.

Henry was intercepted on his way to Blackwood and delayed, while a body of armed ruffians went in search of Catherine, whom they seized and carried to Craignethan, where she was confined in one of the gloomy apartments of the castle.

Although Cuthbert did not visit her at once, she suspected that he was behind her abduction. When he did appear, he offered to repair the insult by an immediate marriage. With all the indignation of an injured woman, she rejected every proposal, and demanded her freedom with a firmness which at once awed and astonished him. She reproached him with the meanness of thus seizing a defenceless woman, and stung him by the most solemn affirmations that she loved his brother with a regard which only equalled her contempt of himself. That brother, she warned Cuthbert, would end or avenge her wrongs.

Cuthbert, who saw he could not win her hand by persuasion, tried threats. His words were, however, interrupted. From below rose the sound of men arming, and he dashed from the room, locking the door behind him.

Catherine had been traced to the castle, and her lover, with some friends, had arrived before the gate, determined to rescue her or die in the attempt. They forced an entrance after heavy fighting, and in the courtyard hand-to-hand battles took place.

Henry, above the noise, could be heard asking his brother to be reasonable, and release Catherine, but Cuthbert was too angry to listen. He disclaimed kinship, and madly impeached the honour of their dead mother. Henry could not bear to hear his mother's name slandered, and rushed at Cuthbert, whom he brought down with his sword.

" 'Tis well!" Cuthbert cried, " thou hast proved thyself a Hamilton, and nobly vindicated our mother's virtue. Oh, my brother, I am justly punished."

These were the last words of Cuthbert Hamilton as he died in his brother's arms. The contest for Catherine's hand was over, but some years elapsed before the marriage took place.

One hundred years after the fight for a daughter of this house, William Lawrie, the tutor of Blackwood, was captured and thrust into prison for associating with the Covenanters, many of them farmers hereabouts, who took part in the Pentland Rising. He was fined, condemned to death, and respited a number of times. Eventually he was pardoned. John Brown, his servant, was shot before his home in the woods near the mansion, where his martyrdom is commemorated by a simple stone.

The modern village of Blackwood owes its origin to the establishment of a sawmill on the fringe of the " black wood " little more than half a century ago. The mill has gone, but the village has grown, and is one of the most pleasant in Clydesdale.

It is an easy walk from Blackwood to Tillietudlem. Shades of *Old Mortality*! This is the way by which Sir Walter Scott made his characters go to the old castle of Craignethan, which he chose as the original of his Tillietudlem. The castle, famous alike for its romantic interest and picturesque beauty, is situated on a high rock overlooking the Nethan. It was built, at least reconstructed, by Sir James Hamilton of Finnart, who became the owner of the lands of Craignethan in 1529. An earlier fortress stood on the site, which was first gifted by the Prior of Lesmahagow to Lambyn Asa soon after the founding of the priory by King David I.

Sir James Hamilton was an architect of great ability. He also designed the palaces of Holyroodhouse and Falkland, and remodelled the castles of Edinburgh, Stirling, and Rothesay.

Craignethan Castle is surrounded by a high wall which is flanked by massive towers. The courtyard was at one time intersected by a deep moat, over which was thrown a drawbridge defended by two parallel vaults now buried in the debris with which the moat has been filled. The skill and craftsmanship of the designer are revealed at every part of the building. The bartisaned corners, corbelled parapet, and the panel above the main doorway are attractive, while the lofty banqueting hall and the other apartments seem to suggest that the castle was meant for a palace rather than a fortress.

Craignethan Castle has played but a small part in the history of Scotland. It was never the centre of any great battle, although its owners were involved in every struggle in their country's history. Parliament ordered its destruction after the battle of Langside, in consequence of the Hamiltons' stand for Queen Mary. The artillery were successful in rendering it uninhabitable, but another owner arose who used the stones for building a house for himself in another part of the courtyard. This house was offered to Sir Walter Scott as a summer residence, but he reluctantly refused. What a loss to the west! Craignethan might have become a Clydesdale Abbotsford.

I tarried in this old castle, and gave my imagination a little rein. First of all, I saw Sir James Hamilton arrive from France, and begin the reconstruction of the building. He was a proud man and wealthy. He was the king's favourite, and his rival in pomp. He would have a palace to equal anything his master had. He achieved it.

Then one day the King arrived with his courtiers for the wedding of Hamilton's daughter, whose husband was the son and heir of Lord Somerville of Couthally Castle. There had never been a wedding feast like it in Scotland before. The castle was filled with the merry laughter of a happy gathering.

The scene changed rapidly to mourning. Within a few months of his daughter's marriage, Sir James Hamilton died on the headsman's block. He was denounced by his cousin as a traitor, and he claimed trial by ordeal of combat with his accuser, the brother of Patrick Hamilton, the martyr. The two cousins fought. Finnart was defeated, and then ordered to be executed.

King James and his Queen returned to the castle. This time the King stole the chapel plate. He died soon after, leaving an infant daughter as heiress to the throne.

Another Hamilton, the Earl of Arran, became lord of Craignethan. He wanted to marry the Queen, but she refused to have anything to do with him. Still, I could see great preparations for Queen Mary's reception. She came not as a bride but as a fugitive.

A day or two after her escape from Lochleven Castle, she was brought here for safety. Arran, whose suit she rejected, could not entertain her, for a double failure in love-making had unhinged his mind, and he was a prisoner in another part of his own castle. His brothers, Lord John and Lord Claud Hamilton, did all they could for their unfortunate guest. They mobilized their retainers and followed her to Langside.

Queen Mary remembered their kindness in her darkest moments at Fotheringay. While under sentence of death she took a ring from her finger and gave orders that it was to be delivered to Lord John Hamilton as a token of her great sense of his family's fidelity to her.

But far more interesting than any historic association is the story which Sir Walter Scott wove round these old walls. His wizardry is responsible for the visits of thousands to Tillietudlem every year. They come anxious to identify the scene of every act recorded in *Old Mortality*. To them Jenny Dennison, Cuddie Headrigg, Tam Halliday, and Edith Bellenden are living characters, and of greater importance than the Hamiltons or the Douglases.

Tradition has set its seal on one of the apartments as being the room occupied by Queen Mary. The visitors are more anxious to see the spot from which Jenny Dennison discharged the pot of boiling brose which scalded Cuddie Headrigg.

Craignethan Castle stands at the top of a lovely glen.

I have been there many times; in midsummer, when the trees are clad in beautiful foliage and the woodland surface covered with luxuriant and varied undergrowth, and when the whole place throbs with the song of birds; in the dead of winter, when the trees are naked, but when the scenes have, nevertheless, their own attraction.

On my last visit the birds greeted me with song as I descended the slope from the castle to the opening of the glen where a stream, which falls into the Nethan at the base of the castle rock, is crossed. A greater volume of water was running in the burn than I had ever seen before, and as it tumbled over the rocks the music was sweet. Its course was accompanied by the loud piping calls of thrushes and the mellow notes of a blackbird. There were love calls and harsh notes in plenty.

The path which follows the windings of the river is dangerous, and no liberties should be taken with the fence along its edge. Sandstone rocks rise almost perpendicular on the left, and on the opposite bank are the Blair heights. Dislodged boulders lie at intervals in the bed of the river, and masses of rock by the path. All the way down both sides of the ravine trees tower far above the rocks, and when the sun is at its height in summer its brilliance cannot be seen.

Crossford, in the heart of the orchard country, is at the foot of the glen.

CHAPTER VIII

Scotland's Garden of Eden

History records one instance of a man coming to grief through eating fruit. It was not, however, the eating of the apple that landed Adam in trouble, but allowing his wife to get into conversation with a strange serpent.

That old story from the Book of Genesis was uppermost in my mind when I entered Crossford. It seemed as if I had stepped into Paradise. Traces of insecticide on the fruit trees provided the only hint that there is a Satan in this Garden of Eden.

How fine it is to be here in spring when fresh fragrant breezes are wafted down the valley of the Clyde, and when the fruit-grower is wondering whether the promise of blossom-time will be fulfilled at harvest! To watch the cloud shadows chase each other across the sloping lands on either side of the river is to experience something that is peculiarly restful and soothing to jaded nerves. How invigorating, too, are the fragrant odours of the orchards!

Crossford is in the heart of Scotland's Garden of Eden. Dotted at frequent intervals on the slopes on both banks are the homes of those who own the orchards and strawberry plantations, and on the main street are the cottages where the workers live and in their spare time make their gardens lovely.

The village is in its highest glory in May and June. It is

then decked in colours of every hue—the variegation of the orchards, the pure white of the hawthorn, and the freshest green of the grass and growing corn. Blossom-time is an anxious time for the fruit-grower. By relying on fruit-growing for his livelihood he is courting trouble. The Scottish climate is capable of producing the finest fruit in the world, but it is equally capable of destroying it. The man who stakes money on fruit-growing is gambling with spring in this country. A night's frost can make the difference between a good harvest and failure.

If ever there was a place to which townspeople should make a pilgrimage it is here. Most of us are so divorced from Nature, and have so cruelly cut off our children from her presence, that the reminder of her beauty and bounty provided by blossom-time in these Clydeside orchards is a spiritual prophylactic.

Fruit has been grown here from early times. Strawberries and apples were both undoubtedly cultivated by the early Britons. " Apple ", indeed, is a British word, and Avalon, whither King Arthur was translated, means " apple orchard ". If history does not record that the Romans planted orchards in the Clyde valley, it is probably an oversight. Merlin, in the sixth century, sang with feelings of pride of the orchards of Clyde, and the Venerable Bede, two centuries later, wrote of the " appleyards of Lanark ".

The Romans brought to this country finer varieties of apples than the early Britons knew, some of which, no doubt, are still cultivated in an improved form. The Romans brought these fruit trees partly for the sake of the apples themselves, but equally as the staple food of the edible snails which they devoured in large quantities.

The raspberry was not cultivated before the fifteenth

century. It was known, but was apparently regarded as a sort of inferior blackberry. The gooseberry, too, is a comparative newcomer. It has been the favourite fruit of the cottager for nearly four centuries.

The Golden Age of fruit-growing on the Clyde opened about the middle of the nineteenth century. A Hamilton merchant brought some strawberry plants from France, and experimented with them. Two years later he planted two acres. His neighbours thought him foolish to plant so much of his land. They watched him carefully, and most of them visited his farm, convinced beforehand that he had made a mistake. Many came to scoff, but they remained to profit by his courageous experiment.

Then the rush began. Everybody was planting strawberries. The price of land soared. Good returns were obtained for the novelty. Landowners, growers, merchants, shopkeepers, and the consumers of the greatly improved strawberries were happy. The fame and fortunes of Clydeside fruit-growing were tied up in strawberries for the next thirty years. The market was only twenty miles away. No long hauls were necessary, no picking of immature fruit. The consumers could eat the fruit, picked the day before, in the most desirable condition of ripeness.

But these boasted advantages were in some ways a hindrance. The ease of growing and selling fruit made the growers careless, and loose production methods soon followed. Then came a series of bad seasons, poor crops, and worse prices. On top of everything, the stock of plants had degenerated, and overcropping had worked out the soil. Fortunes had been made, but bank balances began to vanish. For a time nobody seemed to know where to turn. Then, somebody whispered " Tomatoes ".

Main of Bowling and Findlay of Baillieston had built glass-houses in the 'eighties. They were growing tomatoes, and doing well. One man went to Baillieston, and was so impressed by what he saw that he returned to the valley and built some houses for himself. Others followed, and in a few years ranges of glass were sparkling among the fruit trees. Now there are more than two hundred tomato-growers in Lanarkshire.

There is one feature of this district which is especially charming—charming not merely because it adds to the beauty of the place, but because it indicates the innate honesty of the villagers. In summer and in autumn fruit clusters overhang the roadway. Every schoolboy, as he passes, could tear them from the branches by handfuls, and every villager, casting envious eyes on them, could purloin whatever he chose. Yet none are touched, although all are admired. That would not be possible in other places where barbed wire is not sufficient protection from garden raiding. I have watched the Clydeside children play, and they seem to be no more angelic than those of other places. That makes the thing all the more unaccountable.

Stay-at-home Scots always think with pleasure and pride of their adventurous brothers carrying on the traditions of their race in other lands, often forgetting the hard work of those on their doorsteps. The one man whose claim for encouragement is usually overlooked is the fruit-grower. Those who know him, I am sure, feel privileged, those who have not yet met him should cherish the desire to have a talk with him. He is a big man with a big heart, an energetic man with an active brain, a hard worker, a deep thinker—in short, a Scot to be proud of.

I like to meet these men of the orchards. They have always something interesting to say.

One day I was looking over a hedge into one of the best-kept fruit farms in the valley, when a middle-aged man appeared among the apple trees. He began to talk, and saw I was interested in his crops. He invited me into the orchard. I accompanied him from tree to tree as he explained the formation of the fruit clusters and the differences in varieties. He talked of Grenadiers, Bramley's Seedling, and Cambusnethan Pippins, the last being introduced by a leading Clydeside grower. Then he astonished me by an account of the superstitious beliefs and interesting customs which have been associated with fruit, and which his fathers held and practised until recent times.

It was considered unlucky, he told me, to pick any apples that might be found after the full crop had been gathered. They were the property of the pixies, and on no account were these creatures to be robbed of their due.

At one time care was taken to leave a few apples on the trees for the use of these elves, as it was supposed that they would exert their influence on behalf of a good crop the following year.

The Devil was usually regarded as an enemy. There was a common belief that if an apple or pear tree blossomed twice in the same season death would follow, and if the trees were blighted on 17th, 18th, or 19th May, it was due to an arrangement between the Devil and St. Dunstan, who was thus able to sell at a big profit a brew of barley beer he had bought. When it rained on 15th July, St. Swithin was said to be christening the apples.

" There was more than we are prepared to admit in some of these old beliefs," said my companion. " There was an old proverb hereabouts: ' In the year when plums flourish all else fails.' I have had that experience over and over again.

" My mother used to say that if the sun shone through the apple trees on Christmas Day there would be an abundant crop in the following year. She was right. I have seen that too."

By this time we had reached a shed in the heart of the orchard. We sat down. Then my friend showed that he was a classical student. He knew the mythical history of the various fruits, and as I listened I was carried back down the years to the time when I sat at the feet of a worthy headmaster not many miles from this spot, and did my best to struggle through Latin and Greek prose and poetry. Those lessons were never so interesting as this rustic scholar made them.

He started off with the account of the golden apples which grew on the tree in the sequestered garden of the Hesperides, and were sacred to Hera. Guarded by the ever-watchful dragon, it was thought to be impossible to secure them, but Heracles, who had been told by the Nymphs where the garden lay, brought back the apples to Argos. These golden apples were regarded as the symbol of love and fruitfulness.

When he had finished, I agreed with him that the apple had the widest and most fabulous history, and that myths concerning it were to be found in every age and country.

This man, steeped in classical knowledge and folk-lore, was also a skilful entomologist. He had to be, for an orchardist cannot afford to work in the dark. Should his trees be attacked by pests—and their number is legion— he must be able to detect what they are. In addition, he must be a chemist, for he must know what measures are necessary to subdue the pests.

He gave me a lesson.

Insect pests, he told me, may be divided into two classes —chewing insects and sucking insects. The first chew leaves, fruit, and flowers, and may be poisoned thereby. For this reason growers use a poison such as arsenate of lead against the grubs of codlin moth, caterpillars, and slugs.

Sucking insects extract the plant juices, and may be killed by contact sprays, including oils, benzole emulsion, and lime sulphur wash, and nicotine, which are either caustic or penetrating in their effect, and kill by suffocation or irritation. The various aphis, scale insects, plant bugs, and mites are the principal pests of this type. These suck their food from beneath the surface of the leaf, fruit, or bark. Thus no poisonous spray can be applied against them.

Fungus diseases are another source of worry. Fungi are destructive parasites which deprive the host plant of its nourishment, and cause fungus diseases. These include mildew, black spot, brown rot, leaf curl, and scabs. As the majority of the fungi live within the host plant, it is impossible to destroy them after the plant has become infected. Spraying, therefore, with fungicides is to prevent more than to cure the diseases.

Spraying, however, is only one of the various methods necessary to keep an orchard clean and in good bearing condition. There are other operations, such as pruning, manuring, draining, and irrigation, all of which must receive adequate attention at the correct time.

Now you know why a fruit-grower must be an alert man.

Perhaps you will think of all the worry and care attached to their production the next time you buy Clydeside fruits.

These men of the orchards are the best type of land-workers I know. The day will probably come soon when their struggles will be lessened, when the work they are doing will be better appreciated.

" Man," said my friend, as he escorted me to the roadside, " was meant by Nature to be an eater of fruit. Age-long efforts to turn him into a carnivore are responsible for most of his troubles. When he eats more fruit he will be healthier, wealthier, and wiser."

CHAPTER IX

The Lockhart Country

An Ordnance Survey map is a pleasant companion. History, romance, geography, geology, and many other things are found on every sheet. Few spots of interest are omitted. The survey has been thorough. Those responsible for it deserve our thanks.

I was studying the map of Clydesdale when the train in which I was travelling steamed into Carluke. How many of the thousands who pass through this quiet upland station are aware that the pioneer of the Ordnance Survey Department was born in this township? The foundations of the Government map-making service were laid by Major-General William Roy, the son of a Carluke gardener. He was born in 1726, joined the army at an early age, and took part in the " Forty-Five ". In 1746 he was appointed assistant to the deputy-quartermaster who had been commissioned to carry out an extension of Marshal Wade's plan for the subjection of the Highlands by opening up new roads. A year later he was superintending this work.

Wars on the Continent later claimed Roy's attention, and when he returned to Britain in 1763 he was asked to undertake a survey of the British Isles. That plan miscarried, and in the following year he came north and collected material for his work on the military antiquities of his native land. The work he did became the basis of later attempts at cartography.

It was a fine crisp day as I stepped from the train at Carluke for a leisurely walk through the countryside roamed by this soldier map-maker when he was a boy. The sky was a steel-blue, flecked with fleecy clouds driven by a brisk north-westerly wind. Overhead the crows were flying lazily, from every coppice came the chuckle of a multitude of starlings, while the fields were speckled with the mottled plumage of the peewits. The air was filled with the strong scents of spring. As I walked downhill towards the gully through which Jock's Burn has cleft its course, I thought of another soldier born in this region. Like Roy, he won fame, but he is remembered not by his deeds but by his misdeeds.

Thomas Weir was born in 1607. He was a son of a farmer, but work on the land was too quiet for him. He had inherited some of the fighting spirit of the Lockharts, and he joined the army that went from Scotland to Ireland about 1639. Promotion was rapid, and he soon held a commission, but eventually he returned to Scotland and settled in Edinburgh.

He was a zealous Covenanter, and as major of the Edinburgh City Guard he became active in rounding up Cavaliers. He was noted for his prayers. Many came fifty miles to hear him pray at the clandestine kitchen meetings which became necessary after the persecution of the Covenanters had begun. His fluency and enthusiasm amazed the simple worshippers, who presumed he was controlled by the Unseen.

He reported the defeat at Preston a few days before the news reached the capital. This prediction did much to increase the belief that he had a spirit of prophecy as well as a power of prayer. His friends believed he was another Moses.

Then he dropped a bombshell. He confessed he was in league with the Devil, and that his religious fervour was a cloak for his sins. News of his confession travelled through the city like wildfire. Fantastic stories of his powers were carried from ear to ear. It was said that he had cast a powerful spell on the stair leading to his house, by which those who were ascending felt as if they were going down. His incantations, it was added, were mainly effected by means of a black staff with a curiously shaped head, which had been given to him by the Devil. This staff could be sent by him on errands, and on dark nights might be seen going before him carrying a lantern.

Weir and his sister, who also confessed to association with the Evil One, were arrested, tried, and condemned to death. They were burned at the stake.

The sufferings of the pair, who were condemned on their own ravings after their minds had become unhinged, were forgotten as I began the descent to the Clyde through the Lockhart country, in the heart of which Wallace was chosen Guardian of Scotland. This region was once the property of Sir Simon Lockhart, the hero of many battles, who brought back from Spain the casket containing the heart of Bruce, after the trusted Douglas had been slain by the Moors. Waygateshaw, one of the family's early seats, is among the trees on the right at the point where the road enters an orchard.

The road from Waygateshaw is especially attractive. It runs through seemingly endless orchards, and emerges on the Crossford-Braidwood road a few yards above the Clyde bridge.

There is no link between fruit-growing and sculpture, yet two of Scotland's greatest sculptors began their work among these fruit trees.

Robert Forrest was born at Orchard. He was apprenticed to a mason in the district, and later took Edinburgh by storm. He executed the statues of Wallace in Lanark, John Knox in Glasgow, and many more.

John Greenshields, although born in Lesmahagow, was a colleague of Forrest, and also lived hereabouts. He was a friend of Scott, who visited his workshop in the same year as he chose the site for Milton-Lockhart, a short distance down the river.

The Tower of Hallbar is about a mile up the hill on the road to Braidwood. It is an admirable example of the square baronial keep, and dates from the eleventh century. It is well preserved, but little is known of its history or owners.

I did not climb to Braidwood, however. I preferred to follow the old road which rises from the orchard country to Nemphlar and Lanark. Neither in width nor surface does it compare with the modern Clyde road, but it has its compensating advantages. You are right off the beaten track here. Ask any motorist who boasts that he " has done " Clydesdale what he thinks of the Crossford-Nemphlar road, and he will almost certainly confess that he has not been there. In truth, he may be forgiven. The road was never meant for motor-cars, and pedestrians can go leisurely along, undisturbed by hurrying traffic.

The climb between orchards and the wooded policies of Carfin House is exhilarating. Up and up you go, up from the valley where Crossford and its neighbouring hamlets nestle; up until the valley stretches away at your feet, its dwellings like tiny models of toy houses shaped out of cardboard and set on a multi-coloured carpet; up until, on the far horizon, the purple hills of Douglasdale and Avondale show clear-cut against the cloud-flecked sky.

The lovely Fiddler's Gill rises gently on the left to the

The Tower of Hallbar

well-wooded slopes round the site of old St. Oswald's Chapel, with the red-tiled bungalows of modern Braid-wood, in striking contrast to the lowly cottages of the old hamlet, a little higher up.

The woodman's axe has cleared Blackhill, whose bare summit rises behind the thickly wooded policies of Stonebyres, for centuries the home of a branch of the Weirs of Blackwood. The last of his house was Daniel Vere, who died in the middle of last century. Stonebyres has had a number of tenants since his time.

There is little " village " at Nemphlar. A few houses cluster round the white-washed school, while not far away are a number of farms. It was not always so quiet. Knights Templar had a settlement here, but no traces of their occupation remain. Their most gallant member was, no doubt, Sir Simon Lockhart, whose home was in the valley below.

A path runs from the Crossford road to the lands of Lee Castle, descending rapidly between bramble-clad banks, past a cottage, to a wicket-gate which opens on the policies. The ancestral home of the Lockharts lies away up the valley. It is a castellated two-storey building, with many round corner turrets. The grounds are beautifully laid out with terraces and wooded slopes. Many of the trees in the large park which surrounds the house are very old; some of them, indeed, are said to be survivors of the Caledonian Forest. Their branches are gnarled and twisted into fantastic shapes, and under them cattle graze peacefully.

One oak, the famous " Pease Tree ", is nearly seventy feet high, almost fifty feet in girth at the ground, and forty-six below the branches. Twelve men could easily hide in its hollow trunk. Cromwell, with a party of his followers, is said to have dined under its branches. " Pease " is probably a corruption of " Peace ", the name indicating the signing of some treaty under its spreading foliage.

Sir Walter Scott, in *The Talisman*, cast the glow of romance over the house of Lockhart. In 1329 the young

Sir Simon accompanied Sir James Douglas when he set
out to carry the heart of Bruce to the Holy Land. It is
this Sir Simon whom tradition identifies as the Lockhart
who brought home the " Lee Penny ", a small triangular
dark-red stone set in a silver coin. It is this talisman which
Scott used with such dramatic effect in his novel.

During the fight with the Moors in Spain, in which
Douglas fell, Lockhart captured a Moorish chief, whose
wife or mother offered a ransom for his release. Part of
the ransom was an amulet which, it was said, had wonderful

The Lee Penny

medicinal properties. Sir Simon brought it home, and,
according to tradition, it bore out its Moorish reputation,
and was found to possess great medicinal virtue. Its fame
spread far and wide, and many wondrous cures were
attributed to it. At a time when the Church of Scotland
impeached many other " cures ", the " Lee Penny " was
excepted. It was described as " an amulet to which it
has pleased God to annex certain healing virtues which
the Church did not presume to condemn ".

A path which enters the wood beyond the avenue of
Lee Castle twines luringly up the steep bank, and joins

the highway opposite Cartland Mains. Cartland Bridge is less than a mile to the south. It was built in 1822, to the plan and design of Thomas Telford. It consists of three arches, and the height from the bed of the Mouse, which it spans, is more than one hundred and twenty feet. Below the bridge is the confluence of the Mouse and the Clyde, with Kirkfieldbank beyond.

A path on the north side of the bridge leads up to Cartland Crags. It runs along the brink of a deep glen of romantic interest. At points the Mouse is four hundred feet below the ridge of the precipitous rocks which bound it on either side. Natural wood clothes the face of the rocks, and for most of the way the bed of the river cannot be seen, but a deep murmur rises from below.

It is easy to understand how a fugitive could feel safe in this region. The most illustrious one to find shelter in the dark recesses of the ravine was Wallace, after he had slain the son of the English governor of Lanark.

A castle once stood on the edge of this precipice, nearly opposite Baronald. A green mound is all that marks its site. History is silent concerning Castle Qua.

A track which is not so well defined continues upstream from the old bridge over the Mouse. Trees of many varieties grow to a great height on the other bank. The river is wider here, and at intervals the water leaps over small ledges of rock. The right bank, along which the path runs, becomes steep beyond the ruin of an old mill, and stones, dislodged from the heights above, lie across the path. Craiglockhart Castle, another early seat of the Lockharts, stood at this point. It is not now easy to trace its foundations. On the opposite bank is Jerviswood, once the home of Robert Baillie.

Robert Baillie lived in the seventeenth century, when Scotland was fighting for liberty. In June, 1676, he rescued his brother-in-law, a minister, who had been arrested in Edinburgh. Baillie was fined, and was to be kept in prison until the fine was paid, but after four months' detention he was released on payment of half the amount.

Seven years later, having given up hope of relief from the tyranny of the Government at home, Baillie and some others decided to found a Scots colony in South Carolina. They opened negotiations with English Protestant malcontents and Scots exiles in Holland, but their attempt was frustrated. Baillie and five others were arrested, and accused of complicity in the Rye House Plot, with which they had no connexion. They were sent to Edinburgh for trial, and Baillie was fined six thousand pounds. But his persecutors were not satisfied with this. They kept him in prison, where his health gave way, and on 23rd December, 1684, he was brought before the High Court in a dying condition, and accused of treason.

Baillie denied the charge. He said he had never taken part in any conspiracy against the King or the Duke of York. He was condemned to death, the sentence to be carried out the same day.

When he heard the sentence he said: " My lords, the time is short, the sentence is sharp, but I thank God who hath made me as fit to die as you are to live."

He was so weak that he had to be helped to the scaffold, and as soon as he was there he said: " My faint zeal for the Protestant religion hath brought me to this."

He was not allowed to say more. The drums interrupted him. The speech he had prepared was undelivered.

The family were ruined by his forfeiture, and his son,

George, escaped to Holland, whence he came with the Prince of Orange at the Revolution. The family lands were soon restored.

A footbridge spans the Mouse at Jerviswood. The path on the opposite bank runs up to that house and the road to Lanark. The glen is, however, too attractive to be left at this point. Near the bridge is a beautiful waterfall.

The path now rises from the water's edge, and winds through the woods. Suddenly you reach a bend, from which one of the finest sights in the country is seen. The Mouse is emerging from a cañon whose receding walls almost meet up the glen. The deep murmur of the water as it leaps over the narrow rocky channel pleases the ear. This spot possesses a charm in the exquisite untrodden freshness of all around, and the air of extreme seclusion which prevails. It is only a short distance from a main road, but few seem to know of it. I have gone over this path a number of times, but I have never met anyone.

A few yards above this spot the path skirts the wall which surrounds Cleghorn House, still another seat of the Lockharts. There is a rich luxuriance about the fragrant climbing plants and wild fruit bushes that ramble over the banks and wall, and wreathe themselves about the bases of the trees, adding fresh graces to their green old age.

Below the bridge, where the path emerges on the highway at Cleghorn Mill, is a weir to catch the water to generate power in a little power-house on the opposite bank. That is the only sign of modernity along the whole route. It does not obtrude itself, and is soon forgotten in the memories you carry away from this delightful glen.

CHAPTER X

The Cradle of Liberty

Lanark is a quieter-looking place than its history would warrant. It is old. It was the seat of a Roman garrison, and it was the cradle of Scottish democracy and national independence. It has been asserted that the first Parliament was held here in 978, and Wallace struck one of his first blows for independence in its High Street. Kings and courtiers lived in the old castle, and at the Cross the Covenanters renounced their allegiance to Charles II.

Lanark is little more than twenty miles from Glasgow, yet from Glasgow to Lanark is a far cry. Lanark, stubborn in its history, refuses to be jogged by its powerful and progressive neighbour. The march of Progress has halted at Wishaw, and has made few breaches in this stronghold.

Lanark is the capital of the wealthiest and most prosperous county in Scotland, but it retains its sleepy, old-world character. It is a typical country market town. The country folk, with their leisurely habits of life, dominate the hustling spirit of the age, and refuse to bow the knee to the modern gods.

I arrived in the town on the morning of a market day. In the distance I could hear the bellow of cattle and the plaintive bleat of sheep. As I walked up High Street, men were standing in groups exchanging the gossip of the countryside. Then all made their way uphill to the cattle market. Thick heavy boots clattered on the hard streets. Hoarse, deep voices rose and fell. A babel of sound from the market was wafted on the breeze, and the narrow thoroughfare at the top of the High Street acted as an amplifier to the pleasant discord. Farmers elbowed their way to the ring, picking a passage among the pens of animals. All were keen to get on with the job, to hear the auctioneer's voice.

I followed the stream, and found myself in the heart of a cheery lot of men from various parts of the country. There was the old farmer, white-haired and red-faced, who had not missed a sale for half a century, and who came from a neighbouring parish in a two-seater gig badly in need of a coat of paint, with an old and faithful horse between the shafts. Beside him was the young man who came in a smart two-seater motor-car from a farm fifty miles away. They belonged to different ages. The one farmed as his fathers had done for generations, and farmed successfully. The other had adopted the modern methods of the college instructors, and had been equally successful. Both were shrewd business men and expert judges of stock. Every animal was examined thoroughly, but speedily, to keep pace with the auctioneer, who had to work quickly to overtake all he had to do.

Bids came from various parts of the building without a word being spoken. Animal after animal was knocked down on a movement of the head or an eyelid. Inadvertently I nodded my head to show my agreement with a remark made by a neighbour, only to find myself the owner of an Ayrshire cow.

I left the building as quietly and as quickly as I could, lest I should find myself the owner of enough stock to start a farm. Everybody I encountered on my way out was in a hurry. Cattle were whisked past me in motor-lorries, and drovers ran to take the next lots to the ring. This activity was the expression of a great agricultural community.

I walked about one hundred yards. And then . . . I stood still, and marvelled. I was in another world. Only a minute before I had been in hustle and bustle and noise. That was all across the way still . . . yet here I was centuries away from crowds and commerce. I was standing in the ruined Kirk of St. Kentigern on the knoll opposite the cattle market. The atmosphere was one of peace and beauty. The babel of tongues and the common sounds of the market-place were near enough, but they were unheard.

St. Kentigern's Church is the town's most cherished possession. Its finely proportioned arches and the south wall with its beautiful doorway are treasured as the glory and gem of Scottish architecture of the early Middle Ages. It is a typical Scottish ruin, blackened with time and lacking in colour, but steeped in old associations of its bygone grandeur and traditions.

To this wind-swept eminence came monks from Dryburgh in the middle of the twelfth century, and rebuilt on the site of an earlier church one which they dedicated to St. Kentigern.

Here, Blind Harry tells us, Wallace fell in love with Marion Bradfute at first sight, and here, at midnight, they were secretly married, lest the English governor of the town, whose son was a rival suitor, might forbid the marriage. They kept their secret, and Wallace visited his wife in disguise. It was generally in the evening that he entered the town. One night as he passed a tavern he was insulted by an Englishman who sat with some friends before the door. None of them, however, penetrated his disguise as a shepherd. Wallace at once drew his sword, which had been concealed in the folds of his plaid, and killed the spokesman of the party, who was the governor's son.

The Englishmen, enraged by the death of their leader, rushed on Wallace, and some of them shared their leader's fate. Wallace would soon have been overcome had not some of his friends come to his aid. The English withdrew, and Wallace passed on to his house. Explaining to Marion what had happened, he left immediately by a back door, and was soon lost in the depths of Cartland Crags.

Haselrig, the governor, was not the man to accept this blow without seeking revenge. He hurried to the house with troops, but Wallace could not be found. Marion boldly refused to say where her husband was, and, mad with passion, Haselrig thrust his dagger into her bosom. She died immediately.

Anna Dickson, her maid, who had been one of the witnesses of their marriage, stole away to her master's hiding-place with news of his wife's murder. Wallace swore he would not rest until he had avenged Marion's death. Next night he fulfilled his threat. He stole into the governor's house, and killed him.

" So perish all the enemies of poor afflicted Scotland, and so likewise perish every monster who can imbrue his hands in a woman's blood!" exclaimed Wallace when he rejoined his friends.

The inhabitants of Lanark now openly identified themselves with Wallace, and flocked in great numbers to his standard. From that time he took the field openly against the English, and soon after had his first battle with them.

Is there any need to wonder why these old stones of St. Kentigern's Kirk have a powerful effect on the people of Lanark? I felt something of it as I stood among them and looked down the centuries. I could appreciate the wave of indignation that swept the countryside when the inhabitants heard of the cold-blooded assassination of the lovely heiress of Lamington, and I could see the townsmen coming to church to ask the blessing of the priests before they left to join the bereaved champion.

Love-making in Lanark always seems to have been a risky business. William Lithgow found it so. He had his ears lopped off by his sweetheart's brothers.

William Lithgow, alas, is almost forgotten, though he was the first Scot to leave a record of foreign travel. He was buried somewhere in St. Kentigern's kirkyard, but no stone marks his grave. His townsmen did not think it worth while to raise a memorial. To them he remained " Lugless Willie ".

Lithgow was born in Lanark about 1580. His father was a merchant. William fell in love with the daughter of the laird of Bonnington, and the young lovers met secretly in a house in the town, where, on one occasion, they were surprised by the girl's two brothers, who were so indignant that they cut off Lithgow's ears. The ill-treated lover's vexation increased when news of the outrage leaked out. The townspeople, so far from sympathizing with him, ridiculed him as " Lugless Willie ". He left the town and went abroad.

He travelled across Europe, tramping more than thirty-six thousand miles. During these wanderings he was attacked by robbers, and was shipwrecked; he helped a

French galley slave to escape, and redeemed from bondage a Dalmatian widow; he was arrested as a spy at Malaga, robbed by the governor, placed in irons, and tortured on the rack for six and a half hours. At last he returned to London more dead than alive, and was carried to the Court on a feather bed. King James sympathized with him, twice sending him to Bath to recuperate, and later on advising him to apply to the Spanish Ambassador for the recovery of his money and reparation for his injuries. Fair promises were made, but nothing was done.

Lithgow and the Ambassador met at a levee, and the Scot, exasperated beyond endurance, rushed at the Spaniard, and rained blows on his head. Of course, this was an offence which could not be overlooked. Although his boldness was generally commended, he was cast into prison, and kept there nine weeks. On his release he left London for home. In Lanark he wrote accounts of his experiences at home and abroad. He died in 1660.

It is a pity that a memorial has not been raised to his memory. It would have become the shrine of the globe-trotters of the present age. He blazed the trail which they have taken up and popularized.

The forenoon had passed by the time I had finished my tour among the tombstones. I left the churchyard, and shaped my course in the wake of more knowledgeable men. I soon found myself in a comfortable room. A fire blazed in the grate, and three men were slowly grilling themselves before it.

There was a distinct old-world flavour about this inn. News of the countryside is spilled under its roof every sale day. I sat back and listened.

History may take count of more stirring times in this

old town, but no chronicle could fill me with half the whimsy I feel at the rich and commonplace records of the Clydeside farmers. I like the zest with which they speak of their ailing bodies, their descriptions of symptoms, and their direct location of their aches.

A subtle odour of cooking sent me in search of food. With the food I found a magistrate, one of the best-known men in the county, where his family have been prominent for nearly three centuries. Our conversation drifted from one thing to another until, finally, my companion began to compare life in Lanark to-day with conditions a century ago, when the townspeople had two interests—work and politics.

The men of Lanark in olden times, I gathered, were weavers—and rebels. Weaving and Radicalism, like whisky and freedom, used to " gang thegither ". But in the good old days, when elections were often won by the deepest purse, few were above " turning an honest penny ". Every vote had its price, although one douce burgess, Ritchie Lyon, in the middle of the nineteenth century, refused twenty pounds for his. His claim to be above corruption was, however, greatly damaged when he said he could not lippen the man who made the offer.

Election contests were often real battles. For example, in the election of 1832 one candidate for the county challenged another to a duel, and instead of meeting to fight with pistols, the challenger was bound over in £200 to keep the peace. This did not improve feeling, and at the hustings a few days later the challenger was kicked by the man who had refused to fight, and sent to the rails. The two closed instantly, and the hustings became a boxing-ring, with proposers and seconders as seconds.

The election before that was even livelier. The free-holders met in the parish church, and while one candidate was speaking he was hit on the head with a stone. The proceedings in the church were followed by a riot outside. Carriage windows were broken, the Riot Act was read, and cavalry were summoned to clear the streets.

The greatest enemy the early political reformers had was a Lanark man, Lord Braxfield, " the Jeffreys of Scotland ".

Robert Macqueen was born at Braxfield on the side of Clyde not far from Lanark. He was trained for the Bar, where he made rapid strides, eventually being raised to the Bench and becoming Lord Justice-Clerk.

The reformers who were active in the years following the French Revolution were tried by him. His court at that time was said to be the best show in the country, and Braxfield the actor-manager.

" Come awa'," he whispered to a juror in the lobby of the court one morning, " come awa', an' help us tae hang ane o' thae damned scoundrels."

His language was always coarse and brutal, and he was one of the last judges to adhere rigidly to the Scots dialect.

" Ha'e ye ony counsel, mon?" he asked one of the re-formers when he was standing trial for sedition.

" No!" was the reply.

" Dae ye want tae ha'e ony appointit?"

" No!" the man replied. " I only want an interpreter to make me understand what your lordship says."

In one case when Lord Newton was an advocate, he happened to be pleading before Braxfield after a night of hard drinking. The opposing counsel had also had a con-vivial night. The judge, seeing how matters stood, ad-dressed them in his usual manner: " Gentlemen," he said,

" ye may just pack up your papers, and gang hame; the
tane o' ye's riftin' punch, and the ither's belchin' claret,
an' there'll be nae guid got oot o' ye the day!"

Braxfield spent all his vacations by the Clyde, where he
farmed successfully, and enjoyed the rude pleasures of the
old Scots laird. He had a hard head for drinking as well as
for thinking. Being one day at Douglas Castle, where port
was the only kind of wine produced after dinner, he,
with his usual frankness, asked if there was no claret
in the castle.

" I believe there is," said his host, " but my butler tells
me it is not good."

" Let's pree't," said Braxfield.

A bottle was produced, and circulated. All pronounced
it excellent.

" I propose," said the facetious old judge to the parish
minister of Douglas, " as a *fama clamosa* has gone forth
against this wine, that you absolve it."

" I know," replied the clergyman, at once perceiving
the allusion to Church court phraseology, " that you are
a good judge in cases of civil and criminal law, but I see
you do not understand the law of the Church. We never
absolve till after three several appearances."

Nobody relished better than Braxfield the wit or the
condition of the absolution.

The best thing Braxfield ever did was to encourage
David Dale to build his first cotton mill on Braxfield
estate. A short distance above the house is New Lanark,
the village founded by Dale and developed later by his
son-in-law, Robert Owen. Dale and Arkwright chose this
site for their factory, but they quarrelled, and, after they
parted, Dale was joined by Robert Owen, who, when he

became sole proprietor, made New Lanark one of the show-places of Europe. Here he sought to establish Communism; instead of men working each for himself, everyone was to co-operate with all for all. By dint of annihilating property, selfishness and injustice were to be annihilated also.

The business was successful. The results at first were as remarkable as the rapidity of Owen's commercial success. That success fired him with the ambition to reform the world, and he went forth to preach his Socialist gospel.

But the community at New Lanark fell on evil times, and the communal element broke down. The barrack-like tenements terraced on the side of the steep slopes, and the mill, are monuments to Owen's enterprise and memorials of the idealism of a well-meaning and benevolent man who was an unpractical economist. His experiments with child labour, however, prepared the way for the Factory Acts and other industrial reforms.

When I returned from New Lanark the streets of the old town were quiet, almost deserted. The farmers had gone home. Lanark would have gone to sleep for another week but for the omnibuses which make the town their terminus. They make slumber impossible.

A battle is going on between the ancient and the modern, but the Lanark of an earlier day is an easy winner. Modernity is penned into a small area; modern entertainments and places of entertainment there are, but they are unobtrusive.

Lanark cannot forget its past.

CHAPTER XI

The Niagara of Scotland

The Falls of Clyde, despite the hand of man, remain Lanark's greatest glory. Hydro-electric stations have been built by the river bank, and have robbed the Clyde of much of its charm in summer and autumn, but in spring and winter after heavy rain there is enough water to impress you with the grandeur of the waterfalls.

I left Lanark by High Street, passing on my way to the open country the parish church with its statue of Wallace looking down from a niche in the front of the building. The names of the streets at this end of the town are a link with the Middle Ages, when kings and courtiers lived in the castle, which stood on an eminence down one of these side streets. The castle was cleared many generations ago to make way for a bowling-green.

We are apt to sigh for the time when men travelled on horseback, but the drawbacks to that apparently idyllic period must have been considerable when horsemen had roads like this one to travel. The descent to the Clyde at Kirkfieldbank is rapid and dangerous, and had many terrors for a horseman by night.

One story is told of a worthy minister of a neighbouring parish who went to Lanark to collect six firlots of beans from a merchant. He met some friends in the town, and spent a few convivial hours with them. It was dark before he thought of turning towards home. The landlord of the inn where the party had been regaling themselves helped the minister into the saddle, and placed the bag of beans across the horse's back in front of its rider. So off he rode almost at the gallop.

Unluckily, however, at the sharp bend below Steel's Cross, down came minister, beans, and all. The whisky he had consumed earlier had so deranged his powers of perception that he mounted the bean sack instead of his horse, which was standing a few yards away, no doubt well pleased to hear its master belabouring the bean sack instead of its flanks. One of the minister's parishioners arrived on the scene later, and in the moonlight saw a man riding on a sack in the middle of the road. He halted, and, after listening for a few minutes, recognized the voice of the minister. Venturing a little nearer, he exclaimed: " Preserve us, what are you doing there?"

" What am I doing here?" asked the minister. " I've been fechtin' this twa 'oors with this stupid horse, an' de'il ae fit he'll lift!"

There was no bridge at Kirkfieldbank until the end of the seventeenth century. Before that time there was a ferry.

The river above the bridge is divided into three currents by small islands, and as it approaches the bridge the water glitters in the sunlight, bearing on its breast the pictures of overhanging trees or the dusky shadows of the milky clouds. From the bridge, which is old and narrow, with its angled buttresses sticking out like elbows, and which, by the way, was built from church collections, you look downstream to the spot where the Mouse adds its dark waters to the Clyde, and across to Nemphlar Braes.

Kirkfieldbank

The road to Cora Linn lies up the river from the west side of the bridge. On either hand are the ruins of some of the early villagers' homes. There are, however, ruins and ruins. It is easy to stand in the ruins of St. Kentigern's Church, and picture the townsmen of the thirteenth century coming to worship. It is easy to stand before the ruin of Cora Castle higher up the river, and people it with the warlike Bannatynes, and see the drawbridge lowered to allow the passage of a cavalcade of knights and men-at-arms. But the crumbling cottages on the braeside at Kirkfieldbank conjure up no visions. This may be partly due to the fact that nothing is known of their occupants' history, and partly because they have not been associated with any great historical event. Yet they were the homes of an industrious and patient race. The stones were not dressed, but had been gathered from the fields and river bed. Yet every one dovetailed into its neighbour—a testimonial to the industry and patience of the builders.

Still, the villagers must have been witnesses of stirring incidents. They would see the flight of King Henry VI of England, his wife, Margaret of Anjou, and their son, who passed this way from Kirkcudbright to Linlithgow Palace in 1461. And they would see the Covenanters cross the river on their way to Rullion Green, and would probably help to destroy the ferry-boat after these rebels for the Kirk had passed, so that the force which pursued them might be delayed.

The highway to Lesmahagow swings to the right through an avenue a short distance beyond Byretown; a private road to Corehouse runs to a cottage where a card admitting the bearer to the Falls of Clyde is obtained for sixpence. Signposts point the way to the riverside.

The ruins of Cora Castle and the modern mansion of Corehouse stand on the bank above Cora Linn. The banks at this point ascend like lofty walls, through which the Clyde has cleft its way for centuries. The asperity of the scene is softened by the trees which rise from either slope. All that is left of Cora Castle stands on the verge of the high cliff, which, before the introduction of artillery, formed an impregnable front. The building seems to have been no less unassailable from behind, for vestiges of a moat are still visible. The passage of centuries and the falling of stones from the decaying walls have not been able to obliterate this defence.

A path leads past the spot where the drawbridge was once thrown, and from a point a few yards below the ruin you have an inspiring view of Cora Linn. The volume of water after a heavy rain is great, and the thunder of the cataract shakes the ground. In spring and summer, if the sluice above Bonnington is open, the sun lights up the whirling platform of white foam above the final plunge, and provides a picture that is not often seen and not readily forgotten.

A power-station is built into the opposite bank—a reminder that man has controlled this mighty force.

Cora Castle was the home of the Bannatynes, of Martha Bannatyne who captured the heart of young James Somerville of Cambusnethan. Love-making had, however, to wait until the clash of arms had ceased, and then followed the greatest wedding that ever took place in the old church of Lesmahagow, and a feast by the Clyde that lasted five days.

Young Cambusnethan was an ardent wooer. He arrived at Cora Castle one night after a hawking expedition. He met Martha, and proposed to her after supper. It was the time of the Civil War, and Martha's father was at Perth with his regiment after the battle of Dunbar. The young lover rode there, interviewed Major Bannatyne, received his consent to his suit, and returned to Clydesdale to wait for more peaceful times for the marriage celebrations. But he wished to prove his manhood, so he announced his intention of joining King Charles II, who was preparing to advance on England. His father was against this step, and did his best to dissuade his son. But he would go.

His lover at Cora Castle adopted another course. The young man came to bid her good-bye. She welcomed him, and then gave orders that the drawbridge was not to be lowered to allow him out. Few men in those days had so happy imprisonment. He soon decided that life in the castle of his betrothed was sweeter than an uncertain shelter during a campaign in a hostile country. He had every reason for congratulating himself, for many who crossed the Border never returned.

The marriage took place in 1651, and from that date Martha was master in the Somerville household. The fortunes of the family were then at a low ebb. Her skilful management saved her husband from bankruptcy.

As I walked past the ruined stronghold I thought of the lines of John Wilson, who was born on Corehouse estate in 1720:

> Where ancient Corehouse hangs above the stream
> And far beneath the tumbling surges gleam,
> Engulphed in crags, the fretting river raves,
> Chafed into foam resound his tortured waves.
> With giddy heads we view the dreadful deep,
> And cattle snort and tremble at the steep,

Where down at once the foaming waters pour,
And tottering rocks repel the deafening roar.
Viewed from below, it seems from Heaven they fell,
Seen from above, they seem to sink to Hell;
But when the deluge pours from every hill,
And Clyde's wide bed ten thousand torrents fill,
His rage the murmuring mountain streams augment,
Redoubled rage in rocks so closely pent,
Then shattered woods with ragged roots uptorn,
And herds and harvests down the waves are borne,
Huge stones heaved upward thro' the boiling deep,
And rocks enormous thundering down the steep
In swift descent, fixed rocks encountering, roar,
Crash as from slings discharged, and shake the shore.

Poor John Wilson! His life was a tragedy. His father
died when he was only fourteen, and the boy had to be
taken from school, where he was making great headway.
He was later appointed schoolmaster of his native parish,
and while there wrote *The Clyde*. After a short spell in
Rutherglen he was appointed to the Grammar School at
Greenock. One of the conditions of that appointment was
that he would abandon " the profane and unprofitable art
of poem-making ". That was a hard blow to the young
poet, but, having a wife and family to support, he was
obliged to comply.

The distant view of Bonnington Linn, which is higher
up the river, is, perhaps, best from the left bank, which,
however, does not offer the same facilities for approaching
the waterfalls. The suspension bridge to the island is cut
off.

Still, the view from the leafy path among the trees is

striking: a double fall thunders down the rocky ledge, sends up pillars of foam, and drapes the dark cliffs with the fleecy veil of drifting mist. The island itself, crowned with trees, reminded me of Humboldt's picture of the palm-topped rocks that divide the cataracts on the Orinoco.

A rustic bridge carries the path across a little stream which comes down the hill-side and leaps over its own waterfall to the foaming river. From this point you command a full view of the weir and bridge built above the Falls by the proprietors of the hydro-electric station.

A road continues upstream to Tulliford, and passes from a wood beside a raging torrent to a peaceful meadow through which the river flows quietly.

There was once a ford at Tulliford. It was used by the monks as they passed between the old Priory of Lesmahagow and the parent Abbey at Kelso. The brethren from Lesmahagow made the road from the ford, which skirts the policies of Harperfield House, once the Scottish home of Chinese Gordon.

This road rises slowly from the river-side, and from the summit, looking backwards, you can see the spires and roofs of Lanark. Green fields and heather-clad hill-sides stretch away to Ayrshire. Douglas Water, which rises fifteen hundred feet above the level of the sea, joins the Clyde below Harperfield. The wayside station of Sandilands is on the rising ground on the other side of this sluggish tributary.

Douglasdale, over which Tinto stands guard, has had a stirring history. Away up the valley is Douglas Castle, on the site of which stood the early home of the formidable Douglases, and round which Sir Walter Scott wrote *Castle Dangerous*, the last of the Waverley Novels.

CHAPTER XII

A Race of Restless Knights

Palm Sunday, as far as Douglas is concerned, is one of the most memorable days in the year. It matters not whether it falls in March or April; it is the day that brings back to the memory the Douglas Larder.

On that day, in 1307, the Good Sir James Douglas surprised and slew the English garrison who held his castle while they were at worship in the old Church of St. Bride, recaptured and destroyed his ancestral home, and by his success counterbalanced the grievous disaster which had overtaken Bruce, who had been forced to shelter in the rocky fastnesses of Galloway.

Douglas was the faithful comrade of Bruce. The cupidity of Edward I, who had portioned out the best part of Scotland to his own vassals, had driven this young man into the ranks of Bruce's followers. It was well for the Scots that Edward did not yield to the prayers of Douglas, or one of the brightest chapters in our history might never have been written.

Douglas's father died a prisoner in the Tower of London for his support of Wallace. His lands were forfeited by Edward I, and gifted to one of his followers. The prospects of the Douglas heir, who was still young when his father died, were, therefore, not bright. He took his courage in his hands, and appealed to Edward for the restoration of his patrimony.

"What lands doth he claim?" asked Edward when the youth was presented to him at Stirling.

"The lordship of Douglas, under your pleasure, sire, whereof his father was lord," replied the Bishop of St. Andrews, who had introduced Douglas.

"Sir bishop!" exclaimed the King angrily, "you cannot by your fealty speak of this to me. His father was a traitor; let him seek lands where he may; he shall not have these, for Clifford, who holds them, has ever served me loyally."

Douglas hurried from the King's tent, in his breast that deep hatred of the English which nerved his strong arm to many desperate deeds in years to come.

It was a memory of that rebuff that made him ask Bruce's permission to visit Douglasdale in the spring of 1307. He arrived with two companions, and visited a trusted retainer who occupied a house little more than a mile from Douglas Castle. This man, Thomas Dickson, had been the faithful friend of his father. Douglas was concealed in his house for a few days, during which Dickson mustered the leading adherents of the family. All pledged themselves to help their young leader to recover his inheritance.

Dressed as landworkers, and with their swords concealed under their frocks, they took their places in the old Church of St. Bride on Palm Sunday, after the English garrison from the castle had been accommodated. The English, knowing that Bruce and his handful of followers had been driven to the hills in the south, and believing that an attack was impossible, had become careless. They were, in consequence, taken by surprise when, during the service, the war-cry which was to turn the tide in a number of battles rang through the church.

" A Douglas! A Douglas!" That was the signal for action.

Swords were drawn by the Scots. The English made for the door. They were not fast enough. Dickson was there before them. He allowed no one out.

The English were easily overcome. Most of them were slain. The doughty Dickson fell.

The few who had been left behind at the castle to prepare the dinner were soon overpowered. All were killed, including those who had not been cut down in the church, after which the victors sat down to the meal prepared for the garrison.

Douglas knew he could not keep the castle at that moment, but if he could not have it, no other would be left to enjoy it. Accordingly, he collected all the valuables that could be carried off, killed every animal in the place, staved the wine-casks, and placed all in a heap, to which were added the bodies of the Englishmen. A light was put to the pile, and the castle burned. This incident is known as the " Douglas Larder ".

The castle was rebuilt, but no sooner was it finished than it was again attacked, and the governor and many of his men killed.

In consequence of Douglas's exploits, the castle became known among the English as " Castle Dangerous ". Men were afraid to accept the governorship when it became known that Douglas had vowed to be revenged on anyone who dared to occupy his home. An Englishwoman who had many suitors promised to marry the knight who should hold the castle for a year and a day. Sir John de Wanton accepted the conditions, and was placed in command of a stronger garrison than any of his predecessors had had.

Douglas, however, was not to be beaten. He concealed many of his men on the Lanark road, and instructed fourteen more to fill sacks with grass, throw them over their horses' backs, and ride past the castle as if they were on their way to Lanark market. The men were seen by the garrison, who thought the sacks contained grain. Sir John and his men went after them. Nearly all the garrison, including their commander, were killed in the ambush which had been laid for them. The castle was once more taken, and again destroyed.

Douglas shared the command of a division at Bannockburn, where he was knighted by Bruce on the morning of the battle. The King, remembering his debt to his comrade, also bestowed many lands on him.

After the English had been driven from Scotland, this restless knight began a series of raids on the north of England. In these, as in pitched battles, he was successful. Of seventy engagements fought by him he lost only thirteen.

Bruce, dying of leprosy, asked his friend and comrade in arms to bear his heart to the Holy Land. Douglas accepted the commission, but he never reached Palestine. He fell fighting against the Moors in Spain, where he had offered his lance to help the King of Castile against his enemies.

" Forward, brave heart, as thou wert ever wont! Douglas will follow thee or die!" were his last words as he threw the casket with Bruce's heart ahead of him, and plunged headlong amongst the Moors.

Two of his companions brought back Bruce's heart, and it was buried in Melrose Abbey. The heart of Douglas was brought to St. Bride's Church in Douglas, where it may still be seen.

Another Douglas was the hero of Otterburn. He fell in the charge, but his cry turned the tide of battle, and Percy, the leader of the English, was captured.

After he had fallen, Douglas was asked how he felt. " Indifferently, but blessed be God, my ancestors have died in fields of battle, not on down beds," he replied. " I sink fast, but let them still raise my war-cry, and conceal my death from my followers. There was a tradition in our family that a dead Douglas should win a field, and I trust it will be this day accomplished."

It was.

His successors were equally skilled in arms, and increased the power and influence of their house. Territorial influence, however, was not enough for some of them. They aimed higher. They came nearer the throne by marriage, and as they advanced they became a menace to the Crown. Weak kings were as clay in their hands, and they exercised in their territories power equal to, if not greater than, that of a king. When they went from home they were followed by a retinue which became the envy of their sovereigns.

At one time they were the favourites of the King, and no honour was too great for them. At another they were the object of royal suspicion, and plots were hatched to rid Scotland of a family so dangerous to the peace of the realm.

One Earl of Douglas and his brother were seized while at dinner with King James II in Edinburgh Castle, and beheaded in the courtyard. This broke the power of the family—but only temporarily. Another arose who restored it. He maintained an army of 40,000 men, and was no less ready to defy than to appropriate the royal authority. No word but his was law in Douglasdale.

He entered into a pact with his neighbour, the Earl of Crawford. This combination scared the King, who asked Douglas to meet him at Stirling. He went under a safe conduct. The King remonstrated with him against the bond, and said he must break it. Douglas refused.

" If you will not, I shall," said the King, as he thrust his dagger into the bosom of the earl. Thus ended the career of the most powerful and most unbridled of the nine Earls of Douglas.

The murdered earl left no son, but five brothers. One of them was a priest, and kept out of fighting. The other four rushed to arms to avenge his death, and with them went half of Scotland. James II quailed, and was on the point of flight. He opened negotiations, however, and succeeded in detaching their allies one by one from the Douglases. Peace was declared. It was, indeed, only a truce. The King was determined to break the House of Douglas.

The end came in 1455. The King collected his forces, and marched against the Douglases, whose resistance was feeble. They were routed at Arkinholme.

The Black Douglases—as the direct descendants of Bruce's comrade in arms were called—were beaten. Three great houses shared the spoils. The lands were divided among the Hamiltons, the Scotts of Buccleuch, and the Red Douglases, who were the Angus family.

The Earl of Angus, who had been induced to become an

ally of the King, became the new lord of Douglasdale, and was soon as formidable as his kinsmen had been. His son, the fifth Earl of Angus, was Archibald " Bell the Cat ", who hanged the King's five favourites over Lauder Bridge.

His grandson, the sixth earl, married Margaret Tudor, the widow of King James IV and sister of Henry VIII of England. The Countess of Lennox, the mother of Darnley and grandmother of James VI, was the only child of the marriage. Thus the House of Douglas gave the United Kingdom its first king.

In striking contrast to the sturdy chiefs of his house was the first Marquis of Douglas. He lived during the Covenanting struggles, but remained aloof. At one time he seemed to favour the King, at another he sympathized with the Kirk. If he was not being reprimanded by the King for having intercourse with the Covenanters, he was being rebuked by the Presbytery of Lanark for condoning practices which they disliked.

The third Marquis of Douglas was a recluse. He shut himself up in Douglas Castle, and refused to have anything to do with the outside world. He was the last of his line, and when a boy of nine was created Duke of Douglas. It was after his death that one of the most famous succession claims in Scottish history arose. The dukedom became extinct as there was no son to follow. The title of marquis went to the Duke of Hamilton, while the estates became the property of a son of the Duke of Douglas's only sister, Lady Jane Douglas.

Lady Jane was one of the most accomplished women of her time. She was engaged to the heir of another dukedom, but the engagement was broken off in 1721. In consequence of that disappointment she refused to listen to the appeals made by other suitors until she was forty-eight, when she married Colonel John Stewart, the penniless heir to a baronetcy. Her brother declined to have anything to do with her after this match. He stopped her allowance, and she and her husband lived in poverty. They settled in Paris, where twins were born in 1748, Lady Jane being at this time fifty-one! She came to Scotland in 1752, hoping to make friends with her brother, but he refused to see her. Another attempt was equally fruitless.

The younger of the twin boys died in 1753, his mother following him to the grave the next year. To the last she adhered to the statement that the boys were her sons.

Meanwhile the Duke of Douglas married when sixty years of age. He had no family, but made a number of wills, in all of which he excluded his sister's son from the succession. Finally, however, a week before he died, he cancelled all these deeds, and settled his estates on the heirs of his father, and appointed trustees to look after his sister's child, who was to succeed him. The trustees took the necessary steps on the death of the duke, but Stewart's right to the Douglas property was challenged by the guardians of the Duke of Hamilton, who was a minor. They claimed that the children alleged to have been the sons of Lady Jane Douglas were impostors whom she had procured in order to secure the family inheritance.

An action was raised in the Court of Session. It dragged on year after year for eight years. Family and national records were produced either to support or rebut the claim. Trips were made to France to search for evidence to support the theory that the twins had been kidnapped. For a long time the issue was in doubt, and the excitement in Scotland while it was pending was unprecedented. The question was argued by the people with as much keenness as if the fate of the kingdom depended on the result.

Fifteen judges took eight days to deliver their opinions. A majority declared against young Stewart. That decision was reversed by the House of Lords, and Archibald Stewart, in whose favour public feeling had run strongly throughout the proceedings, became laird of Douglasdale.

Archibald Stewart left a large family, but all his sons died without issue. His daughter, Jane, carried the estates to the Buccleuch family, and her daughter married the eleventh Earl of Home, whose descendant is now lord of Douglasdale.

You are reminded of these stirring events as soon as you enter Douglas. The town can have altered little since the time when this race of warriors rode down its narrow streets. Houses have been planted down at all angles, some of them projecting farther into the street than others. A network of alleys and courtyards lies behind the buildings fronting the streets. As you go down the main thoroughfare you see the old Church of St. Bride above the houses, which cluster round it like grapes round the stem of a bunch.

The shops of Douglas provide customers with all they require, but as an afternoon's entertainment their fascination is soon exhausted. The real Douglas is to be seen behind the scenes. Long narrow yards, some of them with innumerable doors and outbuildings, are hidden behind the shops and houses. I dived down one of these wynds, and at once felt that I had gone back a century. I saw a man with left arm outstretched and carrying a bucket of water in his right hand. There was a dog-cart with

Main Street and Church of St. Bride, Douglas

shafts on the ground, as if the horse had recently been unharnessed. There was no sign of petrol, not even a motor-bicycle.

The scene was so restful and reminiscent that I lingered. Then I passed to another scene, from which I saw windows of all sorts and sizes, giving a look of passages and rooms at surprisingly different levels. I was told it was an inn. It looked more like a tolbooth. It happened to be both! Douglas Jail is now an inn. Instead of a jailer you find a publican. The jailer locked people in its apartments. The law has changed all that. The present occupier locks people out when closing-time comes round. Instead of the rattling of chains, there is the clinking of glasses.

I have seen many strange inns and hotels, but this is, indeed, the strangest of them all. The bar is in a vaulted chamber, dark as all prisons used to be. A small window throws shadows on the walls, and provides hardly sufficient light to see the faces of your companions.

Burns visited this inn. Claverhouse and his dragoons were often here. Some of them were never far away from Douglas. They were as troublesome to the Covenanters as wasps are to all of us. No wonder their billet came to be known in the neighbourhood as Hell's Bike.

Douglas people talk with pride of their fathers who

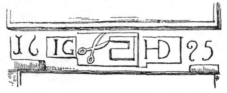

Lintel of James Gavin's House, Douglas

received these unwelcome attentions. Every one of them will tell you of James Gavin, a tailor, who had his ears cut off with his own scissors. They will show you his house in the main street, where on a lintel are carved the symbols of his trade, scissors and goose. An inscription informs you that Gavin was banished, but returned to Douglasdale and built this house, carving the lintel stone himself.

One party of visitors to the old inn were the victorious dragoons after the defeat of the Cameronians at Aird's Moss. Captain James Bruce of Earlshall and his men halted here the night after the battle in which Richard Cameron, the Lion of the Covenant, was slain. Five thousand marks had been offered for Cameron's head. One of the soldiers had the hero's head and hands in a bag, which he tossed into a corner of the room above the bar. The place where these gruesome relics of victory lay is pointed out to visitors.

A round stone near the fireplace was the spot on which criminals stood during their trial in the court of the baron-bailie.

"This room, with its stone floor, is almost exactly as it was when Richard Cameron's head lay in that corner," the landlord told me.

The large open fire in the kitchen shows that the jailer enjoyed the good things of life, whether his charges were fed or not.

The inn is a building of secrets, and many fanciful people think that some of the prisoners of long ago return now and again to watch the revels in the room in which they stood their trial, and to listen to the arguments which take place in the vaulted chamber which was their prison.

Across the road from the inn is St. Bride's Church. High above all towers the restored chapel, the mausoleum of the Douglases. This is not the building made memorable by the Douglas Larder, but part of one built a century later. The chancel of the church was restored by the Earl of Home. An oak roof was placed over it, broken arches were repaired, and the walls were strengthened. Monuments to the Douglases are round the walls; in fact, in this little building you have the history of Scotland at a glance.

The Black Douglas who fell in Spain is buried here. The figure of a Crusader lies under a Gothic canopy, and beside it is the casket with the warrior's heart. A similar casket holds the heart of Archibald " Bell the Cat ". Another monument shows James the Gross with the

effigies of his six sons and four daughters, the last of the
race of the Black Douglases. The names of all the Douglases
who rest in the vault appear on a slab on the wall.

Round the ruined walls of the south aisle outside are the
tombstones of the Inglis family, a race who claimed the
right to be buried beside the Douglases. The north aisle,
of which no trace remains, was known as the Dickson
Aisle, for here were buried the descendants of Thomas
Dickson of Haselside, who held the door of the church
on the fateful Palm Sunday.

The church stands on a knoll overlooking the valley of
Douglas Water. Higher up the stream is the spot where
the Cameronians were first mustered by the young Earl of
Angus, whose statue looks up the valley. Downstream is
Douglas Castle, the seat of the Earl of Home. It was built
by the Duke of Douglas after his wife had burned down
the earlier building. The duchess was fond of society, but
could not persuade her husband to take a house in Edinburgh. She decided to force his hand, so she applied a
torch to their home, as the famous ancestor of her husband
had done. The duke immediately rebuilt it. Adam, the
famous architect, designed it.

CHAPTER XIII

A Cooper-historian of a Baronial House

The thousands who pass through Carstairs every week think it a most unromantic place. To them it is no more than a necessary railway junction. Yet centuries before the railway was made it was the most important centre in Scotland. It was the clearing-house for the Roman legions. Agricola had his camp in the neighbourhood—at Cleghorn —whence marched the legionaries who sought to subdue the stubborn Britons. Traces of that early occupation are found in the heart of Carstairs and in the surrounding countryside.

Long after the Romans came the Bishops of Glasgow, who had a castle in the village. That castle was built by Bishop Wishart under licence from King Edward I of England when he was attempting the conquest of Scotland.

Wishart, by the way, was not a friend of the English. He was an ardent supporter of Wallace and Bruce, and was reprimanded by Edward for starting the castle without his permission. The King, however, allowed him to continue, thinking, no doubt, that it would be a convenient resting-place on his journeys north and south. He even provided some of the material for finishing it. The castle stood in the glebe, but nothing remains to mark the site. The stones were used to build farms and other houses in the neighbourhood.

Carnwath, on the other hand, has links with those early times, although most people only associate it with freak vegetables. " A Carnwath Cabbage " is regarded as a subtly humorous phrase. It is unfortunate that it should be so, and the inhabitants may be forgiven if at times they fail to appreciate the humour of the phrase.

St. Mary's Aisle, Carnwath

I like Carnwath. I like its old church. I particularly like the five-light traceried window in the centre of the gable, the arched stone roof, and the coats-of-arms of the St. Clairs, the Somervilles, the Edmondstones, and the Campbells worked on the outside walls. More than anything else, I think, I should like to have met the great craftsman whose skilful hands worked these stones for St. Mary's Aisle, which is older than Roslin Chapel. I wonder if he was a monk. He may have been one of those travelling masons of the Middle Ages who spent their lives in building the churches which the mistaken zeal of the Reformers destroyed.

The story of Carnwath is a long one. It was founded by
one of the most powerful Scots families, and kings and
princes have often passed along its solitary street. Men
and women who have played a prominent part in history
have tarried in its houses, and quaffed ale in its hostelries.

I approached the village by the path that runs from the
station through the wood. When I emerged from the
plantation, the cairn in the wood which may have given
the village its name was on my left. This artificial defence
was probably erected by the Somervilles, whose stronghold, Couthally Castle, occupied a site in the middle of
the moss a mile north of the village.

The green slopes of the mound are covered with trees,
and nearby is Carnwath House, the home of the Lockharts for two and a half centuries. The road enters the
village between this old house and St. Mary's Aisle, which
adjoins the parish church. The aisle is all that remains of
the church built by Thomas, Lord Somerville, in 1424. His
wife was Lady Marie St. Clair, a daughter of the first Earl
of Orkney of Roslin Castle. The famous Roslin Chapel
is dated 1446, so that St. Mary's Aisle is older.

As I stood admiring the window in the gable, which is
considered one of the finest specimens of Gothic architecture in Scotland, I was joined by a sturdy man, with a
sandyish moustache, luxuriant, but kept firmly in check,
who had seen me approach, and who looked quizzingly at
me over a pair of pince-nez. He indicated and described
the various coats-of-arms on the walls, and then asked me
to accompany him round the church. As we passed among
the tombstones he pointed out the resting-places of prominent families in the district.

" The aisle is used now as a mausoleum for the Lockharts," he said, " and nobody is allowed inside. It's a pity! It's a pity!"

This was no ordinary workman—he was wearing a canvas apron—whom I had met. He knew the history of Carnwath and its families, and seemed to be on more than nodding acquaintance with the Somervilles, the Dalziels, and the Lockharts from the days of Bannockburn.

" Come in," he said, after we had left the churchyard, and had reached a door a few yards beyond the church. He led me to a workshop crammed with lathes, stones, iron hoops, rings, shavings, tools of all shapes and sizes, tubs and barrels at different stages of manufacture. My newly found friend was a cooper—" about the last of my race in the county," he said.

" Times are changing," he added, as he saw me looking at the unfinished tubs on the floor. " Most of my work was in connexion with dairy farming. I made wooden pails, tubs, and barrels. But now all these hygienic regulations have put me out of business! Milk has to go into glass containers to keep it clean."

My friend, one of the last Somervilles in Carnwath, thought a moment, and then smiled his peculiarly fascinating smile:

" I really ought to have compensation. *If* I belonged to some powerful organization——"

He shook his head, and his pince-nez rocked gently on the bridge of his nose. With a sigh he turned to a book he had taken from a shelf. It was a record of the Somervilles which he had written. This village cooper was the historian of that baronial house.

This book took James Somerville ten years to compile. Its title is *An Abridged Account of the Principal Branches*

of the Baronial House of Somerville: Compiled, collated, and
arranged in Chronological Order by James Somerville.

Here we have condensed ten years (and more) of hard
work, done by lamplight, after a different hard day's work
was finished. The arduousness of it even James Somerville admitted.

" It was," he said, " a laborious business. Still—it was
a labour of love.

" It took a great deal of time—ay, and money, too. It
didna pay me financially. . . . Of course, I didna mean it
to! I didna mean to have it published at all."

But others thought differently.

Influential members of the Somerville family in different
parts of the country came along, and the book was published. Two hundred and fifty copies were printed, and
they are now rare. James Somerville keeps one by
him. He promised to do this, because descendants of the
Somervilles sometimes call at his workshop to refer to the
book.

James Somerville decided to start on this valuable book
because he was left some notes on the family by a friend.
After he had worked on his subject for years, during which
he made many visits to Edinburgh to consult records, it
reached " the dimensions of a considerable manuscript ".
So he happened to show it to friends, and they strongly
urged him to publish this labour of love.

" And that's the reason for the appearance of the work
in book form," said this modest historian.

His modesty is everywhere apparent in the book. In
his Introduction he writes that " there is no attempt at or
claim to literary merit on the part of the writer ". He is
solely " moved by an earnest desire to give a plain and

accurate account of a family which has held a place in the affairs of the nation for nearly eight centuries ".

But, although he would be the last ever to suggest or admit it, this cooper-historian has a simple and pleasing style. At the end of his Introduction he writes:

" Having said enough by way of introduction, we now stand aside and allow the impatient reader to pass through the arched and turreted gateway into this old-world garden of family history and romance."

I encouraged this man who merged sympathetically into his grey and wholesome background, to tell me of old Carnwath and its families.

" Carnwath," he said, " was founded by William Somerville about 1185, and the family remained here until 1602. They fought with Wallace and Bruce, and were the friends of successive kings of Scotland."

He then described some of the royal parties which came down the Lang Whang from Edinburgh to be entertained at Couthally in the heart of an extensive hunting district. Here James III and four hundred guests were frequently accommodated; here James IV was present at the home-coming feast of Sir John of Quothquan and his bride, when the feast consisted of " fifty kine, two hundred sheep, forty boles of malt, sixteen boles of meal, twenty stones of butter, besides fishes, tame and wild fowl in such abundance that both the King and the nobility declared they had not seen the like in any house within the kingdom ".

Here, too, King James V fell in love with the sixteen-year-old daughter of Sir John Carmichael, Captain of Crawford, whom he carried off after a twelve months' courtship to a house he built for her at Crawfordjohn.

" The Earl of Mar," resumed my companion, " bought

the lands of Carnwath in 1602. He sold them thirty-two years later to Robert, Lord Dalziel, who was created Earl of Carnwath in 1639. Less than half a century later the estate was bought by Sir George Lockhart, a son of the laird of Lee, and Lord President of the Court of Session.

" Sir George was murdered on his doorstep in Edinburgh by an unsuccessful litigant, against whom he had given a decree.

" Carnwath, in the days of Sir George's son, became the centre of Jacobitism. The second George Lockhart led the Jacobites against the Treaty of Union in 1707, and then became involved in the plotting which led to the ' Fifteen '. He was too old to take an active part in the ' Forty-Five ', but members of his house were ' out '.

" Some say Prince Charles Edward rested there," my companion concluded, pointing towards the picturesque crow-stepped gabled house, now a golf clubhouse, " but I ha'e my doots."

From the last page of the cooper-historian's book I read the motto of the House of Somerville—" Fear God in Life!"

" Ay—and it's no' a bad motto either," said James Somerville, as I prepared to leave him so that he might resume his work of violin-making, with which he occupies his time now that his tubs and barrels are not wanted.

Carnwath was an important stage in the journey by coach from Edinburgh to Lanark. The coach came swinging down the Lang Whang, and halted at one of the old inns, the centre round which most events of the time revolved. But the long ringing gallop down the moorland road, the echoing bugle of the mail-guard, the welcome pleasures of the wayside inn, and the hurried cordial at the bar, all vanished, with the more questionable delights of the robbery on the desolate moor, and the snow-wreath in the windy valley, when the railway was constructed between Carstairs and Edinburgh.

Carnwath still has its inns. The motto of one of them, in bold letters on the gable, " BETTER A WEE BUSS THAN NAE BIELD ", must have attracted weary pedestrians when driving against a blinding storm, glad of the shelter and cheer to be found within its lowly walls.

The villagers have retained one interesting link with the past. Every year in August the historic race for the Red Hose, the oldest foot-race in Scotland, is run in terms of an old charter, in which it was stipulated that the Carnwath estate was to be held as a gift from the Crown so long as the Baron of Carnwath paid each year to the King " the price of one pair of red hose containing half a yard of English cloth, to be given on the feast of St. John at mid-summer, to whoever, on the ground of the Barony of Carnwath, should run *fasted* from the east end of the town of Carnwath to the Cross called the Calla Cross ".

For a long time after the grant of the charter a certificate of the performance of the condition was sent by special messenger to Edinburgh, and at one time the result was proclaimed from the Mercat Cross there. The reasons for this condition in the charter are not known. It is possible that in an age when Border forays were common the encouragement of foot-racing ensured an adequate supply of messengers to carry the warning of approaching invaders and instructions to meet impending dangers.

The Mercat Cross, erected by the fifth Lord Somerville in 1516, stands in the heart of the village. The coat-of-arms has disappeared, but on the shaft are still seen lists of stages between Edinburgh and Ayr, and Peebles and Glasgow.

A few stones and a mound in the moor mark the position of Couthally Castle. A mile farther west is another old family seat, the manor house of Westshield, which stands in the angle formed by the meeting of the River Mouse and Dippool Water. It was formerly the home of the Denhams and the Stewarts.

Robert Lockhart of Birkhill, a son of the Cleghorn family, was tended by a daughter of this house during the troublous times of the Covenant. He was at the battle of Bothwell Brig with the Covenanters. His horse was shot under him, but he escaped, and took refuge with others in the upper reaches of the Mouse. While in hiding someone suggested a psalm of praise. Lockhart, knowing that the dragoons were not far away, tried to dissuade them. His advice was not heeded. He left the party, and took refuge in a tree. The soldiers discovered his friends. He saw them pass under the tree in the branches of which he was hiding. Soon after, the captives were executed in Edinburgh.

Lockhart found a friend in a daughter of Westshield. She carried food to him while he lurked in Cranley Moss. Worn out by fatigue and privations, he was found dead in the moss one morning. His body was removed by his family, and secretly buried after nightfall within the church of Carluke.

Westshield is now occupied by a farmer. I was told when I was there that at one time it was haunted. The ghost used to walk in the old dining-room round about midnight. Noises were heard nearly every night at that hour, but no one ever could see the apparition. Watch was kept for years without result. The only noise that comes from that room now is the sound of merriment. In winter the room is used by farm servants for carpet bowling matches.

CHAPTER XIV

The Early Home of the Gladstones

The name of Gladstone was so long associated in the public mind with Hawarden that few are aware that the land round Carnwath was the part of the country from which the family of Gladstone sprang. Viscount Gladstone, the youngest son of the Victorian statesman, took his title from the county of Lanark.

The early home of this family was in the parish of Libberton, and in the little God's-acre round the parish church the name Gledstanes is a common one on the tombstones. These mark the resting-place of farmers who cultivated the land which was once held by the Gledstanes of Gledstane.

Libberton is less than four miles from Carnwath, and as I approached this little hamlet from Carnwath the green Law of Quothquan was straight ahead, and Tinto on the right. I crossed the sluggish Medwin not far from its junction with the Clyde. The stillness of the day was only disturbed by the noise of quarrying operations far across the valley and the occasional rumble of a train on the main line. The dimpling pasture land is broken with belts of trees and here and there an open drain or a small stream brattling on its way to swell the waters of the Clyde.

The parish church of Libberton sits squarely on a

height. It is a plain, barn-like building which has served many generations of farmers. A few houses are clustered round the gate. The deserted smithy tells its own tale of man's adoption of modern equipment for work on the land. I went into the churchyard and walked among the tombstones. The last Gladstone to be buried here was William Gledstanes, the son of the last laird of Arthurshiel, who died in 1728. He was the link in the passage of the family from the landowning to the burgher class. He became a maltman in Biggar, and his son was the first to change the name to Gladstone. His descendants are still in business in Biggar.

The next few hours I spent going round the farms this race once held. From the height above Whitecastle I was able to survey the early Gladstone domain, and, incidentally, stood in full view of a panorama which would be hard to match in the south of Scotland. The village of Thankerton lay at the western extremity of the valley, and about a mile behind Whitecastle was Arthurshiel. Tinto, the monarch of Clydesdale, rose majestically on the south-west, and round its shoulder was Coulter Fell. Dotted here and there in the valley were the houses of the owners of small estates, surrounded by noble trees of every hue, and a road to Quothquan in the hollow was flanked by a pleasant wood.

Although the woods were not the cosy places they ought to have been, the great transformation had begun. Some of the trees had boldly decked themselves in " gaudy green ". The poplar and the weary willow had cast their catkins, and the long silvery leaves were coming out. The outline of the spreading beech was like a picture to which the artist has just begun to add the colouring, and although the sunshine still poured through, there was ample promise of effectual covering. The palmate leaves of the plane tree, like little fans, faced the breeze, and the casual warmth had justified the chestnut in throwing off the resinous gloves of his many fingers which were hanging limp and listless.

On the floor of the woods those flowers of spring, the primrose and the cowslip, bloomed in all their humble beauty, but the rising silky whorl of the bracken gave promise of a ranker undergrowth. Hedges were brilliant. The hawthorn boughs were hid in freshest green, but the blossom was waiting to add to the wealth of June.

The birds do not wait for the weather. The blackbird had mated a month before, and in many a still bare bush his rough nest was seen with speckled blue eggs, inviting the attention of the curious.

The rookery was no longer a nesting-place, but a nursery, and great was the hubbub. The young rooks had left the twig platforms of their birth, and sat on the swaying boughs, wondering what sort of world it was. They looked round and cawed; they looked at each other and cawed.

The jackdaw was also betimes with his family affairs, and from odd corners let the world know, in tones remarkable for their curtness, that something supremely interesting was growing up within. The starling was chattering inside the worn-out boles of isolated trees, or rushing about in search of grubs to satisfy the cravings of the hungry brood just emerged from the pale-green eggs.

The smaller birds, however, had not taken time by the forelock. The chaffinch had sought out his fork, and was studying resemblances in moss and lichens, but only in rare cases had he begun housekeeping. The song of the lark was still the song of love; he rose with joy to greet the sun, and his mate went with him.

The most summer-like sound of any heard that day, more so than the twitter of the swallow, was the mysterious grate of the corn-crake. I always think of the lazy crake as issuing from the scented clover on days when the sun is high, the air is calm, and a warm haze hangs on the horizon. The crake had begun his tune, however, but his voice did not sound with proper summer vagueness.

Can you wonder that I was loth to leave this spot where I had come so close to Nature, and strike into an open and almost treeless stretch?

Two roads come in on the left at the foot of the hill beyond Whitecastle. I chose the first, and climbed the hill-side. I halted at the summit, and looked around. Tinto was now well behind. The region was dominated by the Black Mount. Beyond it was the Hill of Dunsyre, and between the two peaks was the village of Dunsyre, through which the River Medwin flows. East Gladstone, a farm built on the site of the Gladstone castle of early times, was across the fields on the right.

East Gladstone was built with stones from the old castle, and some relics of an earlier structure are preserved in the walls of the steading, notably two lintels, one showing a quaintly carved monogram, " I. M.", and the date 1619. The other bears the letters " G. P. K. M." and the date 1778. These inscriptions have nothing to do with the Gladstones. The initials are those of members of a family who occupied the old stronghold after it passed from the Gladstones.

The course of an old avenue may be traced in a howe

near the Gill Burn, which rises on the height above the farm, and there are mounds concealing early masonry, which doubtless mark the line of the ancient buildings. Near the burn is a well-defined square which I was told had been the castle garden.

The Gledstanes were a powerful family for four centuries. Besides the lands of Gledstane, Cocklaw, and Arthurshiel in this neighbourhood, they held property in Teviotdale, but by the end of the sixteenth century, by some stroke of ill-fortune, they were left with nothing but Arthurshiel. The Biggar descendants of the early maltman recovered part of the fortunes of the house, and from them sprang the " Grand Old Man ".

Newbigging is about three miles from East Gladstone. It is nearer Carnwath, and is set in the heart of a pleasant district in the southern uplands. It enjoys a view across the valley of the Medwin towards the setting sun. It is a place where, notwithstanding motor-cars and wireless, you feel remote from your fellows, and where the flavour of bygone centuries lingers provokingly; a place where, in spring, the grass is greener and the birds more songful; where, in summer, the sun shines more warmly; where, in autumn, the harvest fields have a ruddier tint; and where, in winter, the moon sheds a more silvery radiance, and the air is clearer than elsewhere.

There are old people in this part of the country who have never taken kindly to " new-fangled " ideas. I know there is at least one in the neighbourhood who has never been in a train. I should not be surprised to hear there are others like her. After all, there is no reason why a countryman or a countrywoman who derives a living from the soil should want to leave this place. Many were forced to leave it long ago, because there was no living for them. They drifted into the towns and the mining villages of Lanarkshire, but their hearts remained in Newbigging. Roofless ruins tell their own tale of desolation.

On a grassy knoll beside the school stands the Mercat Cross. The village's right to it has been challenged. Some say it was originally at Dolphinton, and followed the market when it was transferred to Dunsyre. In time Dunsyre market fell on evil days, and the meeting at Skirling took its place. The cross, it was thought, should follow the market, and arrangements were made to remove it. A band of stalwart yokels were commissioned to go from Skirling to Dunsyre and carry the cross to its proposed resting-place. They were caught in a snowstorm at Newbigging, and further progress became impossible. They went home without the cross, meaning to collect it when the snow had cleared. When they returned, the weavers of Newbigging are said to have claimed the cross, and refused to part with it. At Newbigging it has since remained.

Carnwath people have another version. They assert that this cross was erected at Newbigging by Sir Gaulter Somerville in the thirteenth century.

If you want to create a discussion which will keep things lively in any of these hamlets, all you need do is to advance the right of another to the cross. I have done it, and enjoyed the result.

Whatever the truth, the cross is one of which any village might be proud. On its back are cut the date 1693 and the letters " G. L."—which were the initials of George Lockhart, the laird of Carnwath at that time.

The road from Newbigging to Dunsyre skirts the
fringe of Carnwath Moor. It rises and falls, passing on
the way spots where fortalices once stood, and where a
few stones or a cairn on the hill-side are the only reminders
of that early period.

Dunsyre is a small but by no means uninteresting
place, with a tiny church and an eventful history. It was
once a thriving community, but now there are not a dozen
houses round the church. Its old castle, which stood by
the Medwin, has also disappeared, but the records of the
early inhabitants remain.

The villagers were stern Covenanters. They were
denied the church for their services, but there were many
friendly cleuchs behind the village where conventicles
were held. Donald Cargill preached his last sermon
on the common here, and was afterwards seized by Irving
of Bonshaw at Covington Mill, taken to Edinburgh, and
executed.

Many of the farmers round about had to shelter among
the hills during the persecution. Surprise visits from the
dragoons made life at home unsafe. One notable fugitive
was William Veitch, the tenant of Westhills. One night
he sought refuge in a barn at Dunsyre, about a mile from
his home. He heard the soldiers were searching Anston
House for him. He emerged from his hiding-place and
went to Anston. No one penetrated his disguise, and
he helped the soldiers to look for himself!

Veitch made one slip, however, and was captured. He
was tried in Edinburgh, and was defended by Sir Gilbert
Elliot, whose eloquent pleadings secured his release.

By the side of the Medwin beyond the village is Newholm
House. Its history is of greater interest than might be

expected—it is not always the largest and most flourishing places which have the longest history, or can claim association with the most famous people. Its occupier during the Stewart period was Major Learmonth. He raised a troop of horsemen, and commanded them at the battle of Rullion Green. He was a capable leader and a staunch Covenanter. He had to take to the cleuchs of the Pentlands after that abortive attempt against the King and his ministers. Soldiers came to the house often, but they never succeeded in capturing him. Sometimes they traced him to the house, but when they reached it they never could find him. At other times they saw him enter. Still they could not lay their hands on him.

They never solved the mystery of his disappearances. Nor could they wrest the secret from his faithful valet, whom they led from the house four times under the threat of being shot if he did not disclose his master's whereabouts.

There was a secret chamber behind the fireplace in the hall. It could be entered by a panel in the wall or from the bank of the Medwin, where a large stone covered the entrance to the passage which led to it.

Major Learmonth survived the persecution, and died at Newholm four years after the Revolution.

An interesting relic of the days of severe Church discipline hangs near the door of Dunsyre Church. The jougs which were used to punish troublesome women are exhibited in a case.

Geographically speaking, Dunsyre is a place of trifling consequence. But it is delightfully situated at the base of the Pentlands. I did not have time to go up the hills behind the houses, but I am going back.

CHAPTER XV

Queen Mary's Playground

There is a little town in Clydesdale where I would like to live all the year round. There is no smoke to spoil its beauty. It is never crowded. There is something life-like in the tonic quality of the breeze which sweeps the valley in which it is situated. Brain and body respond to it with delight. In the morning it blows fresh, laden with the scents of field and hedgerow. Then it is refreshing and stimulating. During the afternoon it cools the warm streets. In the evening, when it dies down to a faint zephyr, it whispers of the romance and fascination of the Clydesdale hills and moors.

That little town is Biggar.

Biggar is the dormitory of the professional men of Glasgow and Edinburgh. Its recent history is a tale of two cities. Breeding with a capital B presses down on every side. Its dignity hypnotizes me. There are many fine shops in the town, but you have to know where they are before you can find them. They do not obtrude them-selves. There is no attempt at advertising. Shopkeepers are content to remain far back from the highway.

Everybody in the place is happy. There are many smiles, but little laughter. Hilarity is unknown. Motor-

cars and omnibuses move quietly up and down the main
street. All seem to be affected and softened by the Sabbath
calm which has settled on the town. There are, of course,
occasional streaks of throbbing modern life. In the evenings and at the week-ends, young bloods on motor-cycles
run to and fro to the accompaniment of exhaust noises
which give the impression of great speed. Their behaviour
is more amusing than terrifying.

The town was not always so peaceful. Armies have
mustered here, and battles have been fought on its
boundaries. It has welcomed kings and courtiers, and it
has been forced to quarter invaders. It has known the
joys of victory and experienced the sorrows of defeat.

For centuries Biggar was the home of the Flemings,
the most progressive of the Continental families to settle
in Scotland, a family conspicuous for their loyalty and
devotion. Their home at Boghall, on the outskirts of the
town, was the playground of Scotland's tragic Queen. Her
best friends were Lord Fleming and his kinswoman, Mary,
one of the five Marys celebrated in ballad and legend.

What happy times the Marys must have had at Boghall!
They loved hawking. Here was a spot in the moors where
they had plenty of sport. The old castle must have rung
with their merry laughter, for, despite the difficulties of
the time, they were happy together.

Mary Fleming seldom left Queen Mary's side. She was
the Queen's favourite, and the only attendant at her secret
marriage with Darnley in Castle Wemyss.

Queen Mary did not lack courage. The Lords of the
Congregation rebelled against her marriage with Darnley.
They wanted her to marry a Protestant. They took arms,
and mobilized in the west of Scotland. The Queen sum-

moned her faithful subjects, and at the head of five thousand men marched against the rebels. She expected to meet them in Clydesdale, but they eluded her and made for Edinburgh. No support for their stand was forthcoming, and they withdrew to Lanark, whence they went to Dumfries, so that, if necessity arose, they might retire across the Border.

The Queen called on them to lay down their arms, and appear before her at St. Andrews in six days to explain their conduct. None appeared. They were denounced as rebels, and outlawed. She then called her friends to arms once more, asking them to assemble at Biggar.

The royal party left Edinburgh, Mary and Darnley in the van. The Queen was armed as well as any of her adherents. She rode a stately charger, and had a pair of pistols in holsters at her saddle-bows. Under her scarlet riding-dress she wore a coat of mail, and under her hood a steel helmet.

No chivalrous knight could refuse to follow such a gallant sovereign. Eighteen thousand men were waiting for her at Biggar when she halted at Boghall. She herself was the life and soul of the army. She took command, gave orders like an experienced general, and outlined the plan of campaign against her foes. Her youth and beauty won every heart.

There was great stir in Biggar the morning the army left. Women and children came to cheer their brave Queen on her way. Many of the women would willingly have gone with her. It was the finest demonstration of loyalty the unfortunate Queen ever had. She was as proud of her subjects as they were of her.

The army passed through Coulter and Lamington to

Crawford and Dumfries. The rebels fled at her approach and took refuge in England, so her army was disbanded, and she and her friends returned to Edinburgh.

Less than three years later she was in flight from Langside. One of her companions was Lord Fleming, who was sent from Dundrennan Abbey to the English Court to be his Queen's advocate.

Then followed the Raid of Biggar. Parliament sent Regent Moray into Clydesdale to destroy the homes of the adherents of the Queen. He came to Biggar, besieged the castle of Boghall, and demolished part of it. Other houses in the district were also destroyed. Biggar, which had been a town of joy a short time before, was now a place of weeping and desolation.

Boghall was again besieged about one hundred years later, when Cromwell sent a force against it. The castle could not withstand an attack by artillery, and the garrison yielded after one shot had been fired.

Another unwelcome visitor to Boghall was Claverhouse. The castle was for long a haven for fugitive Covenanters. A number of conventicles were held within its walls, the chatelaine, herself a devout Covenanter, defying persecution. She was haled before the Lords Commissioners, fined, and warned to hold no more meetings in her castle. But she never wavered in her faith. She saw her friends and many whom she had helped sent to the plantations across the seas, and she saw her home garrisoned by a force sent into Clydesdale to overawe those who dared to take a stand for freedom of conscience, but through it all she remained true to the Covenant.

Biggar also had a part in the Jacobite risings. Philip Lockhart of Carnwath mustered the sympathizers of the

Old Chevalier here in 1715, and a detachment of Prince Charles's men was quartered here thirty years later. Soon after that, Boghall was deserted by the Flemings, who preferred to live at Cumbernauld.

Biggar had been the seat of the family for nearly six hundred years.   Baldwin Fleming had settled in the district in the reign of David I, and from that time the family had been prominent in every outstanding struggle in history. A Fleming was with Bruce in Dumfries when he slew Comyn. He went into the church with Kirkpatrick and Lindsay, who wanted to "mak siccar" that Comyn was dead. When they emerged, and Bruce asked if his enemy would trouble him more, Fleming held up Comyn's head and cried, "Let the deed shaw!", which henceforth became the family motto.

Another member of the house fought with Douglas at Otterburn.

Although the lands of Biggar have long since passed from the family, there is one important link with that house of warriors and courtiers. The parish church, which sits on a hill like a broody hen watching over her chickens, was built by the father of Queen Mary's devoted servant, and is one of the few pre-Reformation churches left in Scotland.

I climbed the tower, and from the roof had a fine view of the surrounding countryside. Tinto and Coulter Fell dominated the picture. The ruined home of the Flemings was seen beyond the railway, and away down the valley were the hamlets which owed their origin to the Flemings.

As I stood on the roof of the tower looking towards Tinto, I remembered the words of a rhyme I was taught at my grandmother's knee:

On Tintock tap there is a mist,
And in that mist there is a kist,
And in that kist there is a caup,
And in that caup there is a drap.
Tak' up that caup, drink aff the drap,
And set the caup on Tintock tap.

The mist was lifting from the summit, and as it cleared
I saw the cairn which has capped it for centuries. The
stones which form this cairn are said to have been placed
there a long time ago as an act of penance. The kist of
the rhyme is a large stone in which there is a hole, in most
seasons full of water. According to legend, the hole is
the thumb-mark of Wallace, who threw the stone at some
unknown enemy.

Research has destroyed many traditions. One of the
best of those associated with Wallace is brought to my
mind every time I see the Cadger's Brig in Biggar. There
is no ground for it other than Blind Harry's romance,
but I must tell it.

The Scots army was stationed at Tinto, when it
learned that the English were approaching from the south.
Wallace, eager to know how many were in that force and
to discover something of their preparations for battle,
decided to do a bit of spying for himself. He left his camp
secretly, and went towards Biggar. On the way he met a
cadger who was travelling the countryside with crockery.
He bought this man's stock-in-trade, and bargained with
him to exchange clothes also.

Wallace passed the English outposts, who did not
penetrate his disguise, and was soon in the English camp,
where he sold his dishes, at the same time making note
of all he saw and heard. One soldier declared that if the

hawker had not been blind of an eye and lame, he would have taken him for Wallace himself. It is also said that Wallace was followed out of the camp by a number of the English who suspected he was not the harmless cadger he represented himself to be. He did not like having his steps dogged, and when he reached the small narrow bridge at the foot of the town he suddenly turned on his pursuers and beat them off. Thus the bridge which spans Biggar Burn received its name, the Cadger's Brig.

Biggar people are proud of the old bridge, which has been celebrated in a number of local rhymes. Here is one addressed to a Cockney:

> Ye may boast o' yer brigs ower the horrible Thames,
> The Hungerford, Vauxhall, an' siccan like names,
> But we ha'e a brig worth a score o' them a',
> The Auld Cadger's Brig at the fit o' the Raw.
> Yer Edward ance heard o't when sair to his loss
> His bowmen, like vermin, we drowned in the moss,
> The cruel invader, the crafty intriguer,
> He thocht himsel' big, but he found us still Biggar.

One name which the townspeople remember with pride is that of Dr. John Brown, the author of *Rab and his Friends*, who was born in the old United Presbyterian manse. His father was minister here for a number of years.

Dr. John Brown, "the Charles Lamb of Scottish literature", won the hearts of his countrymen by his charming descriptions of the simple everyday things of life. *Rab* was given to the public for the first time as a lecture in the parish school of Biggar. It was a description of incidents noted by the young doctor more than twenty years before.

The Cadger's Brig, Biggar

Biggar was also the home of the designer of the Scott Monument in Edinburgh, while Henry Scott Riddell, who is best remembered for his song *Scotland Yet*, received part of his education here while he was a herd-laddie.

The town is a place where you would expect letters to thrive. There is inspiration for the poet and ample material for the novelist. Her sons and daughters are living up to the traditions of John Brown.

A number of novelists have come from the surrounding countryside. It is the region combed by John Buchan, his sister, O. Douglas, Gilbert Rae, and Amy McLaren for their romances. They are peopling the town and district between the Clyde and the Tweed with the courtiers and warriors of a bygone day. They are making the past live.

CHAPTER XVI

The Last of the Dandies

A grey crumbling ruin stands on the right bank of the Clyde a few miles above Carstairs. That is all that is left of the home of the Lindsays of Covington. This old stronghold dates from the fifteenth century, when the Lindsays were one of the most powerful families in the Lowlands. They have no seat in the district now, but they have left a tradition.

The lairds of Covington were notorious reivers. They were continually at war with the Armstrongs, the Johnstones, and the Jardines. They were happiest when driving stolen cattle over growing crops, and putting their neighbours in fear of their lives. An old couplet places them in the same category as the Devil:

> Who rides so fast down Coulter Brae,
> The Devil or a Lindsay?

The twelfth laird of Covington, who succeeded his father in 1646, was distinguished not for his fighting but for his beard, which was long and picturesque, but not fashionable. He had a serious illness, and it was at last believed that he was dead. The family had gathered to see the body placed in the coffin for burial, when a granddaughter of the dead chief whispered to her mother that the beard was moving.

" The beard is wagging! The beard is wagging!" exclaimed the child.

It was. The old man was not dead. He had only been unconscious. The room was cleared, and he was soon talking to his family, who explained that they thought he was dead, and had made arrangements for his funeral.

" Have the folks been warned?" he asked.

He was told that the family had been called to the funeral, and an ox killed to feed the mourners.

" All is as it should be," he replied. " Keep it a secret that I am in life, and let the folks come."

The company assembled for the funeral, but the clergyman who was to take the service did not appear. The mourners grew restive. Suddenly the door of an apartment leading to the hall where the mourners had gathered opened, and to the surprise and terror of all in came the " dead " knight, pale and dressed in black, leaning on the arm of the parish minister. Explanations were given by the old man himself, and, after a prayer of thanksgiving for his recovery and escape from being buried alive, the day was given over to merrymaking. The old knight himself presided over the carousals.

This Lindsay chief escaped premature burial by minutes. He was more fortunate than another of his house. This young man had a sweetheart whom his father considered beneath his station. The parent asked his son to have nothing more to do with her. The youth refused, whereupon his father shut him in a secret room to reflect on his folly. None other knew of his imprisonment.

The laird had a stroke soon after the stormy interview,

and died without regaining his speech. The absence of the heir at such a time could not be understood, and it was not till long after that his body was discovered in the prison, in which he had been starved.

In its day Covington Castle was an imposing stronghold. Its walls were eleven feet thick, and there are traces of a moat which surrounded it. A large dovecot stands on the edge of the extensive courtyard, a relic of the times when our rude forefathers had to keep a large supply of pigeons for food during a siege.

Covington Mains Farm, beside the castle, provides a link with Burns. The poet rested here for a night on his way to Edinburgh. A monument near at hand recalls the capture by Irving of Bonshaw of Donald Cargill, the famous martyr of the Covenant, at Covington Mill.

The parish church, a few yards south of the old peel, is a pre-Reformation building to which additions have been made. The windows date from that early period, and above the door is a panel with the arms of the Lindsays.

Thankerton village is less than two miles higher up the river. It is a quiet little hamlet, picturesquely situated on the green banks of the Clyde, enjoying a view across the valley to the treeless grassy slopes of Quothquan Law and upstream to the great back of Tinto, whose summit may be reached by the path which winds up the slope from the main road at the end of the village.

The valley of the Clyde at this point is guarded by Tinto and Coulter Fell. These peaks are almost of equal height, Coulter Fell being the higher. They are linked in this old couplet:

> Between Tintock Tap and Coulter Fell
> But scarce three handbreadths and an ell.

The bases of these two hills are about four miles apart, but the walk between them is a pleasant one. Coulter village, which nestles at the foot of Coulter Fell, is worth finding. It is not on the main road to the south, and, consequently, those who are intent on reaching their destination in the shortest possible time do not come this way.

There is another reason why I like Coulter. It stands at the end of the best way to approach Lamington. As I walked along the road from Coulter I thought I had been transported to Lochaber. I was shut in on one side by the high hills whose grandeur awed me. I felt close to Nature, and I imagined I heard her speaking to me.

Greater splendour lay ahead.

No more charming picture can be imagined than the peaceful village of Lamington, with its rustic cottages set in gardens, and the green slopes of the Lowthers beyond. To the west is spread a rich green carpet of pasture, wood, and meadowland, through which the Clyde winds its way. Here is a corner of Sussex in the heart of Clydesdale. It recalls one of the most interesting chapters in land reclamation in the history of Scottish agriculture, and the name of one of the most brilliant men of his day.

Lamington was not always the model village it is to-day, nor the inhabitants the industrious, tidy people they are now. It is less than a century since this region was a desolate moor. Farmhouses were hovels with manure heaps built against the walls to keep out the cold. There were no trees. The land was so sodden that it could not be cropped, and nobody had ever attempted to drain it.

Then a magician arrived. He waved his wand, and the scene was changed.

For a long time nobody knew who the owner of the land was. Then, in 1837, the uncertainty was removed when Alexander Dundas Ross Wishart Baillie-Cochrane, the young laird, arrived to claim his heritage. He was only twenty, but he could trace his descent from Wallace, whose daughter married a Baillie of Hoprig in East Lothian.

The dilapidated state of his property would have disheartened most men. Here is what his sister had to say about his arrival:

" The intelligence of the arrival of the young laird produced a great sensation. A few miles from Lanark some of the tenants met him, and, after changing horses at Chesterhall Inn, on the Stirling road, two miles from Lamington, which was the only place to stop at (now a farmhouse), the Clyde was forded, for at that time there was no bridge, and, as the river was high, it was not without a great deal of splashing and flogging that a landing was effected—with some risk of being carried down the river.

" On the arrival of the carriage at the inn, the whole population poured forth like rabbits from a warren. They had probably never seen a carriage before, for they touched the panels and the harness, and gazed with mute astonishment.

" It cannot be said that the appearance of the Lamingtonians was prepossessing; they were as wretched and dirty as their abode, and no wonder. For a century they had never had a day's work; the children were in rags, and enjoyed themselves on the dung heaps, which stood before every door. Savage, hopeless, melancholy, bleak was the prospect, moral as well as natural."

There was no house for the laird. The old inn on the road between Abington and Coulter was little better than the hovels of the village. The old home of the Baillies was in ruins, its decay having been helped fifty years before by a factor, who carted off the stones to build houses elsewhere.

Tents were pitched in a glen above the inn. Then a shooting lodge sprang up. That was followed by a game-keeper's house. New farmhouses were next built. The land was drained, the river banks were raised to keep it from overflowing during a spate, the hovels were replaced by comfortable cottages, the highway was brought lower down the hill so that the lodge was no longer cut off from the glens and hills above it, and trees were planted on the hill-sides and in the glens. Bit by bit Lamington assumed the form we now know. The place is a monument to the skill, affection, and perseverance of the young idealist who planned and remodelled it.

These changes were not effected without a great deal of opposition. The villagers had never been used to dictation from their laird, and they would not stand it now. They tore down the dykes he made, because they restricted grazing; they resented his interference with their liberty. But that opposition was soon worn down, not by bullying, but by tact and sympathy.

The man who made this transformation was one of a group of clever and distinguished men. He came of sea-faring stock. He was a kinsman of the famous Earl of Dundonald. His father and grandfather were admirals who had served their country with credit. He was a leading member of the Young England party, who favoured a return to Mediævalism in Church and State, and who thought landworkers should be handled in a parental spirit. Nobody will deny that he fathered the tenants on his estate, and did it well.

When Baillie-Cochrane left Cambridge he had all the world at his feet. He might have attained high office in the State, as did some of his friends who had less ability. He might have done durable work in literature, for he had a nimble pen and a bright fancy. But he hesitated on the threshold of each, and lost his chances.

He was a novelist and poet. *Ernest Vane*, his best novel, is a clever piece of work, and might even now be readable if Lord Beaconsfield and Lord Lytton had not written with more artistic skill and with finer wit of the same society and of the same period.

Friend of Disraeli, who depicted him in *Coningsby* as Sir Charles Buckhurst, of Lord John Manners, and Lord Strangford, all members of an exclusive aristocratic set, he was made a peer in 1880. He chose his title from his Clydesdale estate, and took his seat in the House of Lords as Lord Lamington.

He died in 1890. He was the last of the Dandies.

There is much of interest in Lamington House and grounds. A number of additions have been made to the house since 1837, and above the entrance is a panel with the Latin inscription: " Pax intrantibus, salus exeuntibus, benedictio habitantibus "—Peace to those coming in, safety to those going out, a blessing to those living within.

Lamington Burn flows through the glen on which the house stands. Its banks are clad with the trees the designer planted. It is a fairyland among the hills. There are tiny waterfalls, rustic bridges, a duckpond, trees and plants of many varieties—in fact, everything that one would like to see.

Away up among the hills, in Cowgill, are the remains of Windgate Hall. Tradition gives it a romantic origin.

Fatlips Castle, traces of which remain on the slopes of Tinto, was owned by the laird of Symington, and overlooked Lamington Tower across the river. The two lairds were not on friendly terms. Symington sent Lamington a message couched in no delicate terms, that he could see everything that went on outside his tower. That annoyed Lamington, who, the story goes, said he would build a home which would be out of sight from Fatlips. He chose the site up Cowgill, and built the hall where he was overlooked by nobody, and where, on looking out, he was able to call everything he saw his own.

The Village Pump, Lamington

No doubt, that retreat was useful as a storehouse for stolen cattle during the reiving days. It was to the Baillies what the Devil's Beef Tub beyond the hills was to the lords of Annandale.

Burns halted at Lamington once when going to Edinburgh. He spent a night at the old inn, and went to church on the Sunday. He has left us a picture of the place then:

As cauld a wind as ever blew,
A caulder kirk and in't but few;
As cauld a minister's e'er spak,
Ye'se a' be het ere I come back.

The parish church is a little to the south of the village. It was built in 1828 on the site of an earlier one which was dedicated to St. Ninian. Its outstanding feature is a beautiful Norman doorway, on the north side, which was in use until 1828.

I passed from the village with its small cottages, latticed windows, and village pump, with its rustic pillars and pavilion roof, to the side of the Clyde, anxious to visit the early home of Marion Bradfute, the wife of Wallace, from whom the House of Lamington claims descent. The northwest angle is all that is left of the old tower, and it is some distance from the river, though the Clyde used to wash its walls.

The story is told that Hugh de Bradfute and his son fell defending Lamington Tower against Haselrig, the English governor of Lanark, who carried off Marion, the daughter of his foe. He insisted that she must marry either himself or his son, so that his right to the lands would not be challenged by his master. Marion was unwilling to accept the condition. Her plight was explained to Wallace, who, after seeing her in the church at Lanark, fell in love with her, and delivered her from the fear of an alliance with the Englishmen by marrying her himself.

A child of that marriage was taken to Lamington for safety, and from that girl the Baillies claim descent.

The difficulties of Lord Lamington's first journey to his estate, and the description given by his sister of the passage across the Clyde, were brought back to my mind a few minutes after I had left the ruin of the tower to make for Symington on the other side of the river. My map indicated a ford less than a mile downstream. I made for it.

There were no stepping-stones, and no indication that the ford had ever been used. But I had to reach the other side. I sat on the bank, took off my boots and socks, and prepared to wade across. The water was cold and fairly deep, but I went on. The farther I went from the bank, the deeper it became, and by the time I was in midstream the water was well over my knees. A strong current was flowing, and I nearly lost my balance. A moment's hesitation and I would have been swept off my feet. I became reckless, went forward unmindful of the depth of the water, and emerged on the other bank after being waist-deep in Father Clyde. I was soaking, but that did not matter. Symington was at hand, and my clothes would soon dry.

Every time I have passed that spot since I have felt the stones of the river-bed pressing hard against my soft feet!

CHAPTER XVII

A Royal Charmer

There were four of us. Outside, the rain was falling, a strong wind driving it against the windows with startling force. Somewhere a door which had not been fastened creaked on its hinges, and was banging against a wall. Those, with the occasional rumble of a train in a hurry to reach the Border, were the sounds from the outer world.

Inside, the fire glowed cheerily, and we sat cosily round the hearth of an old farmhouse at the foot of the Lowthers, not far from Crawford. The farmer sat in an easy chair, his elbows resting on the arms, and his legs stretched before the fire. The other two, besides myself, were a shepherd who had spent more than fifty years on the hills, and a doctor who was snatching a few days from a large city practice, and was spending them among the hills he had known since boyhood.

" It was on a night like this," the farmer was saying, " that the coach from Glasgow to Carlisle was dashed to pieces and some of the passengers killed at the Broken Brig."

Then he told the story of the disaster, and how an injured woman's shrieks saved the occupants of another coach from the south, which drew up a few inches from death.

The Evan Water was in flood after a heavy rain, and carried away the piers of the bridge which spans the river a short distance below Crawford. The coach, after a brief halt at Crawford Inn, came rattling down the road before a fierce gale. No sooner did the horses place their feet on the bridge than the whole structure collapsed.

It was after ten o'clock. The inside passengers had curled themselves up to sleep, and those outside had wrapped themselves in their rugs for protection against the storm. Without any warning they were hurled with the coach, coachman, horses, and guard into the torrent below.

There were two outside passengers, and both were killed. There were one woman and three men inside. They escaped with bruises. The coachman was so badly injured that he died soon after. The guard was knocked unconscious, but soon recovered. Three of the four horses were killed.

The woman scrambled from the water to a rock. While sitting there she saw the lamps of the north-bound coach coming through the darkness. She could not clamber up the steep bank to the road in time to stop the coach, but she screamed as loudly as she could. The coachman heard, and drew up on the edge of the hole where the bridge had stood. The guard, driver, and passengers descended from the coach and began rescue work. It was no easy task. The wind was strong, the rain was heavy, and the candle lamps did not provide much light.

The guard's first care was the woman who had warned them in time. He was a shy man, and was worried about the means he should adopt to raise her from the river-bed to the road above. Going down the bank with reins to draw her up, he asked doubtfully: "Whaur will I grip her?"

His caution exasperated the injured woman. "Grip me whaur ye like," she replied; "but grip me siccar." He tied the reins round her waist, and she was hoisted to the road above.

The coach from the south went back to Moffat, carrying the survivors and the bodies of the dead. The horse which had escaped was led behind.

The bridge at that point on the road between Crawford and Beattock is known to this day as the Broken Brig.

One of the interesting things described that night round the farmhouse fire was the early settlement of small-holders in the village. The colony was in existence long before a Government department took an interest in intensive cultivation of the soil. It was a thriving community in the Middle Ages. There were twenty-five small-holders, each with four or five acres of arable land, and the privilege of keeping a number of sheep, cattle, and horses on the hill or common pastures. They were called lairds, and their wives were *ladies*.

This community was really a little republic. It had its own Parliament, which met once a week. Each small-holder had a seat, and if he were unable to attend a sitting he could nominate a deputy. The " Birley Court ", as the assembly was called, regulated the number of animals each was to send to the grazings. It also tried to compose the differences of its members—not always an easy task. Its assemblies were noisier at times than a modern election meeting. Some members preferred to settle their disputes and assert their rights with their fists.

These bickerings seem to have been confined to the meetings on the Birley Knowe. There is no record of a renewal of the quarrels when " Parliament " adjourned and finished the sittings in an ale-house. The convivial gatherings lasted well into the morning. Nobody worried about paying for the refreshments at the time. Mine host kept a tally, and the bills were paid once or twice a year when a sheep or a cow had been killed and sold. Their credit was good. The system may have been crude, but it worked exceedingly well. All were satisfied.

The colony and its system of government were abolished after a long lawsuit in the middle of the eighteenth century. Traces of the early divisions between the holdings can still be seen. A golf-course occupies part of the site of the colony; the clubhouse is on the Birley Knowe.

Tradition also associates Wallace with the same ale-house. The Castle of Crawford was then held by the English. He wanted to seize it, so he went to the village to spy out the land. He came on a woman washing clothes in the Clyde, and from her learned that a dozen men of the garrison were in the inn. He decided to go there.

He was disguised as a beggar, with a patch over one eye. Having given instructions to Sir John de Graham to follow with the others under his command, Wallace made for the tavern. The soldiers welcomed the stranger, and plied him with questions, thinking that a vagrant would be able to tell them something of the man whose exploits were then the talk of the country. Wallace replied to their questions about himself without hesitation, none suspecting that they were talking to the national hero.

Some members of the party in their cups said they would like to meet this man and cross swords with him.

Their leader went so far as to offer a reward to the man who would bring Wallace and himself face to face. Wallace agreed to bring the hero before them for a trifle, and, rising as if to leave them, threw aside the countryman's cloak he was wearing, drew his sword, and overpowered the soldiers before they had recovered from the surprise. He sounded his horn, and his comrades came from their hiding-place. They then made for the castle.

The fortress was easily captured. The valuables were taken from it and divided among the Scots, who then burned the building.

Crawford Castle was held for centuries by the senior branch of the Lindsays. It was not safe for any family in Upper Clydesdale to be opponents of the Douglases. Consequently, the Lindsays of Crawford and the junior branches of the family were the allies of the Douglases. They were at Otterburn. Sir James Lindsay of Crawford, " Lyndsay light and gay ", was one of the heroes of the battle. He led the Scots in their pursuit of the defeated Percys.

Sir James could not be found when his followers returned from the chase. He had galloped after Sir Matthew Redman, the governor of Berwick and commander of one of the English divisions. The Englishman was overtaken.

" Ha! Sir Knight, turn ye!" exclaimed Lindsay. " 'Tis foul shame thus to flee! You have only me to cope with, and if you can discomfit me, then I am your prisoner. I am Sir James de Lindsay!"

Sir Matthew pulled in his horse, and, wheeling round, drew his sword and prepared for an attack. Sir James aimed at him with his lance, but Sir Matthew dodged the blow, and the point of the lance was buried in the ground.

Sir Matthew cut it in two with his sword before the Scots knight could recover it.

Sir James then seized his battleaxe and assailed his opponent, who defended himself with his sword. Thus they fought for a long time in the moonlight.

Sir James, in a pause in this encounter, asked: " Sir Knight, who art thou?"

The other replied: " I am Sir Matthew Redman."

" Well!" rejoined Sir James, " since we have met thus, I must conquer thee or thou me!" Then the battle began again.

At last Sir Matthew's sword flew from his hand, and he stood defenceless.

" Lindsay," said he, " I yield me."

" Rescue or no rescue?" asked Sir James.

" I consent. You will bear me good company?" anxiously asked the vanquished knight.

" I will," promised Sir James, " and for a beginning, since you are my prisoner, what shall I do for you?"

Sir Matthew asked permission to go to Newcastle, and promised to give himself up on St. Michael's Day. He was allowed to go on that promise.

Sir James, after the parting, lost his way in a thicket, in which he encountered the Bishop of Durham, who had been too late for the battle and was returning to New-castle. The bishop in the darkness called on him to stop. Sir James, in reply to the challenge, disclosed his identity.

" Ha! Sir Knight," cried the bishop, " you are wel-come. Render yourself my prisoner."

Sir James saw resistance was useless, since the bishop had five hundred men with him.

" Sith it must be so, God's will be done," he replied.

The journey to Newcastle was lightened by Sir James's description of his fight with the governor of Berwick.

" I cannot help it," he said, when he learned they were making for Newcastle. " I have taken, and I am taken. Such is the fate of arms. I had fixed St. Michael's Day for Sir Matthew's appearance in Edinburgh, but I think he need not trouble to take so long a journey."

The bishop agreed that it would hardly be necessary.

The Lindsays shared in the misfortunes of the Douglases after the battle of Arkinholme in the middle of the fifteenth century, but they soon recovered.

Crawford later became the property of the Hamiltons, from whom it passed to the King.

James V made Crawford Castle a hunting-box. He took his Queen there once, and on an earlier visit found a girl whom he carried away on the promise of marriage.

The King met Katherine Carmichael, the daughter of Sir John Carmichael of Meadowflat, the keeper of Crawford Castle, at a feast at Couthally, the home of the Somervilles of Carnwath. He fell in love with her at first sight, and prolonged his stay for four or five days.

He returned to Edinburgh, but he could not forget the charms of the girl he left behind. Then, suddenly, about two months after the feast at Couthally, he appeared once more before Lord Somerville's gate. He was made welcome, and soon after his arrival he asked Lady Somerville if she would send for the young daughter of Crawford, for he wanted to see her again.

" Sir, her father's house is much fitter, where your Majesty may expect kind welcome, being proprietor of the same, in honouring that family with your Royal presence," replied his hostess, who did not want to help the profligate young King in forcing his attentions on the innocent country-bred daughter of the keeper of Crawford Castle.

James laughed at this rebuff.

A messenger was sent to Crawford the next morning, informing the family there that the King would follow. All were happy at the prospect of the visit except Katherine. Her father and mother were pleased at the recognition, and considered their fortune would follow such attention from their royal master. But Katherine, poor child, thought of flight. Consideration for her parents alone prevented it.

The King arrived. He paid no heed to anyone but the girl whom he had come to see. He asked her to be his. For a year she refused his appeals, resisting great pressure from her family. In the end she surrendered, and became the mistress of Scotland's Merry Monarch.

She refused, however, to go to Edinburgh. If the King wanted her, he must come to her. James was willing. He built for her a castle at Crawfordjohn, one of the most remote parts of Clydesdale.

The next four years were the gayest in the history of the Upper Ward. James never went about without a large following of courtiers. Their laughter was often heard coming down the Lang Whang into Carnwath and on the road through Coulter and Lamington as they made their way to Crawford, which became the centre of hunting and hawking in Scotland.

Katherine Carmichael's reign as the King's favourite lasted four years. During that period she never left Boghouse Castle at Crawfordjohn, where she lived with her two children. Then the King found another charmer. Katherine was heart-broken for a time, but she soon recovered from the blow which followed her desertion and neglect. She went to another feast at Couthally, where she met Lord Somerville's nephew, John Somerville of Cambusnethan. The King was also there. No doubt, both recalled their first meeting. The King's heart was touched by the presence of his faded flower. He was sorry for her. He did not seek to comfort her himself, but arranged a marriage between her and the young man from Cambusnethan.

It was a happy marriage. She proved herself a good wife, and during the lifetime of the King she refused to go to Edinburgh. " She had honour enough in being Cambusnethan's lady without having to go to the King's Court," she said.

" Those were stirring times," said the doctor, after all of us had taken part in telling the story of Crawford.

" They were that," replied the farmer and the shepherd together.

The clock was preparing to chime the midnight hour, and the doctor and I had a bit to go to reach our hotel.

" Just one thing before you go," said the farmer to me. " Be sure you go down and have a look at the ruin of Tower Lindsay in the morning, and when you are there take a squint at Castlemains Farm. That was the home of the Welshes. Carlyle's mother-in-law was born there, and Carlyle has passed this way. He was a fine man was Carlyle!"

CHAPTER XVIII

God's Treasure House in Scotland

Few people would associate Upper Clydesdale with the stage, yet as I stood before the little church at Elvanfoot I recalled my first visit to a theatre. I had gone to see Wilson Barrett in *The Sign of the Cross*. From the stage he preached a more powerful sermon than many clergymen ever deliver from a pulpit.

Everything about the little church in this wind-swept valley at the foot of the Lowthers is linked in some way with that great actor's work. He selected the site for the building, the churchyard is the shape of a cross, and there is a memorial to the actor himself in the church. A stained-glass window commemorates his association with the church and district. This is the only memorial to an actor in a Scots Presbyterian church.

There is nothing extravagant about the church. In fact, inside everything is simple—whitewashed walls, stone floor, and plain oak pews. The sun, streaming through the stained-glass window, throws a crimson stain on the floor. On the window the Great Shepherd is shown pointing upwards to the Cross and " the Light beyond ". A small scroll in the corner of the pane reads: " Sacred to the memory of Wilson Barrett."

The parishioners speak lovingly of the man they could call friend. They recall with pride the names of the great actor-managers Irving and Toole, who became patrons of their dramatic club which, in recent times, has scored notable successes.

Travellers between Glasgow and Carlisle are familiar with the pastoral reaches of this part of the country, but the quiet valleys which separate the Clyde and the Nith are known only to a few. Pennant, the father of sight-seeing in Scotland, Daniel Defoe, Dorothy Wordsworth, and Dr. John Brown were all impressed by their rugged grandeur.

I decided to go up the valley of the Elvan Water. I turned on my tracks from the little church to the north end of the village, and took up the road that leads to Lead-hills. This is a wild and lonely road, steering its way unhesitatingly up the valley. It soon penetrates the bare brown hill country which is typical of the whole eastern slope of the Lowthers. The valley remains comparatively open, and affords fine glimpses of the central Lowther group. The road, the stream, and the light railway to Wanlockhead run side by side.

There are few inhabitants here, but, if the inscription on a tombstone in Leadhills cemetery is any criterion, they are a long-lived race. There you read that John Taylor, who lived in this valley, died " at the remarkable age of 137 years ". It is said that he started washing ore in a Cumberland mine at the age of four, and that he re-tired from the mines at Leadhills when he had completed his century, spending the protracted evening of his days in the rural seclusion of this glen. It is said that when he was 115 years old he was caught in a snowstorm while fishing among the hills. He thought the end had surely come, but resolved to fight for his life. He stuck his fishing-rod in the snow, and struggled on to the spot where a shepherd found him still alive. He was taken to the shepherd's house, and when he recovered he returned for his fishing-rod. He was a tough one!

Gold-digging was once the staple industry of this region. The great era of gold-finding lasted from 1511 to 1621. Nothing has since been done in the way of a systematic attempt to work the deposits, with, perhaps, the following exceptions:

Charles I had his coronation medals struck from Crawford gold, and Sir Hans Sloane, the founder of the British Museum, had a medal made of it. Early last century the working of the gold was attempted under the superintendence of the manager of the lead-mines, but it was hardly begun until it was abandoned. Still, an odd nugget may be picked up by the wayfarer. I have seen some recovered by the natives, but have not been lucky enough to find one for myself.

Three hundred persons maintained themselves by washing gold in the reign of James V. They supplied the gold for the finest Scottish coins ever minted—the " bonnet-pieces ", so called from the fact that they bore on one side the head of James V wearing a bonnet, probably the one he delighted to wear when he went about the country as the Gudeman of Ballengeich.

The King was proud of his gold-field, and he showed his pride in many ways. He took his Queen, Mary of Guise, to the district on one occasion, and conducted her over the mines. On another, he entertained the foreign ambassadors at Crawford. He apologized for the dinner,

which consisted of the game they had killed during the
hunting and hawking of the day, but he assured his guests
that the dessert would more than make up for the poor
quality of the other dishes. It would consist of the finest
fruits of his kingdom.

The foreigners looked at each other in surprise on
hearing the King talk of fruits being served in the heart
of a bleak moorland. Covered saucers were set before
each guest, and when they were examined they were
found to contain, not something for eating, but a number
of "bonnetpieces", which he asked them to accept as a
specimen of the fruit produced in Crawford Moor. No
doubt, all were pleased to accept the dish.

The crown of the Scottish kings was improved by
James, who had the arches made of Crawford gold, while
his Queen's crown was also prepared from the same
material. These crowns are still to be seen in the Crown
Room in Edinburgh Castle.

An early gold-finder on Crawford Moor called the
district "God's Treasure House in Scotland". It was,
indeed, a treasure house, for when gold-seeking became
unprofitable, the natives opened and developed lead-
mines. They are now anxiously looking for a substitute
for lead-mining, which has long been under a cloud.

The railway crosses the road a few yards below the
village of Leadhills, which lies in a shallow cavity among
the hills at the head of the Glengonar Valley.

The first thing you see on entering this village is the
monument erected in memory of William Symington,
a native, who was the first to apply steam power to navigation. The monument, which stands on high ground outside
the cemetery, recalls the fact that while his body was

laid in some hardly known corner of a London church-yard, his influence and work, established on the solid rock of the far-reaching benignant invention he gave the world, reach from London to this lonely glen, and then girdle the world.

Symington, as a youth, superintended the primitive steam-engine at one of the lead-mines. The task was a simple one, and he had plenty of time to plan things for himself. In 1786 he produced a locomotive for use on the roads. It was capable of doing the work of one horse, but the miserable state of the roads in Scotland at the time prevented him from following up the invention.

It does not seem to have occurred to him that "rail-roads" specially made for traction by steam were feasible. Were he to see the express train of to-day thundering down the "Summit", past Elvanfoot, or snorting up that steep defile, he would recognize in the magnificent loco-motive the bantling of his early genius, developed and burnished "as a bridegroom coming out of his chamber and rejoicing as a strong man to run a race".

Patrick Miller, of Dalswinton, on the other side of the Lowthers, was experimenting about the same time on paddle-boats driven by manual labour. He heard of Symington's locomotive, and wondered whether the young engineman could design and provide a boiler and steam-engine to drive the paddles. Symington agreed, and the first steamboat was launched on Dalswinton Loch, Dumfriesshire, on 14th October, 1788. It was a double boat, with the paddles in the middle. One boat contained the engine, boiler, and engineer; the passengers were in the other.

What excitement there must have been in Nithsdale

that October morning as the leaders in many walks of life took their places in the boat! Henry Brougham, then a young man, who subsequently became Lord Chancellor, was there; Alexander Nasmyth, one of Scotland's greatest artists, was another passenger; Patrick Miller and his friend Taylor were there. Doubt exists whether Robert Burns, then Miller's tenant at Ellisland, was present, but he must have known of the trial.

Symington was there, alert and hopeful. He was not disappointed.

Fired with success, Miller and Symington decided to experiment elsewhere. A boat fitted with machinery designed by Symington and made under his supervision at the Carron Ironworks, made a successful voyage on the Forth and Clyde Canal in 1789. It glided along at six miles an hour, and everyone aboard was delighted with the success of the experiment.

Miller, who had been Symington's friend and patron, ceased to experiment further, and little more was done until 1801, when Symington was employed to construct steam-vessels for the Forth and Clyde Canal.

The *Charlotte Dundas*, named after the daughter of Lord Dundas of Kerse, in 1802, against a head wind which kept every other vessel from sailing, steamed off with great ease, and arrived at Port Dundas, Glasgow, after a voyage of twenty miles.

A proposal was made by Lord Dundas to substitute steam for horse-power on the canal. This was vetoed by the canal proprietors, who were afraid that the wash from the paddles would injure the banks!

Symington was disappointed, but he did not have long to wait for another patron. The Duke of Bridgewater, who, in consequence of a disappointment in love, fore-swore the society of women when he was twenty-three, and devoted the rest of his life to engineering, proved his faith in the future of steam navigation by instructing Symington to build eight boats for his famous canal.

The duke's sudden death again dashed Symington's hopes. He confessed that he was unable to struggle against a sea of troubles. He had even difficulty in establishing his claim to the invention, and when that was settled the pittance he received from the Government fell far short of the amount it took to prove his case.

Symington died in London on 22nd March, 1831, and was buried in St. Botolph's Churchyard in Aldgate.

Many years elapsed before any memorial was raised to attest the high sense which Scotland entertained of William Symington and his work. The centenary of the successful trip on Dalswinton Loch was allowed to pass without anything being done to commemorate his con-tribution to progress. Subsequently his bust was placed in the Museum of Science and Art in Edinburgh. The inhabitants of Leadhills, however, desired something more. They erected the obelisk we now see on the site outside the village cemetery.

Leadhills was the birthplace of another famous Scot. Allan Ramsay, one of Scotland's most cherished poets, was born in the village in 1686.

Ramsay's father was an official at the mines. He died while Allan was an infant. His mother married again, but died when her son was fifteen. The boy, thus thrown on the world, was taken to Edinburgh, and apprenticed to a wigmaker. That flourishing profession did not, however, appeal to him, and he left it to become a bookseller.

The religious and civil wars which divided society into factions in the second half of the seventeenth century suppressed or absorbed its poetic fervour, and, in consequence, the names of few Scots poets of that time are written on the scroll of fame. When, however, in the beginning of the eighteenth century, the accomplishment of the Union of the Parliaments removed the gravitating centre of Scotland's political life, the poets, to whom political patronage was a necessity, followed their patrons over the Border. In this way the field was cleared for a new order of poets. Allan Ramsay was the first of them.

Ramsay restored native poetry to its original grace and beauty, and proved that the true patrons of the poets were the common people. He showed that the poetry of Scotland, instead of being a parasite deriving its sustenance from the Church and the nobility, was a healthy plant deeply rooted in the national soil, and fanned by the breezes of its native mountains.

He prepared the way for Burns.

The village which gave Scotland these two great men is a small one. Its neat white-washed cottages are built on both sides of the main street, with straggling houses here and there on the slopes. The combined parish church and manse in the hollow was once the mansion house of the Foulises and the shooting-lodge of the Hopetoun family. Its quaint panelled walls, circular stairs, and narrow passages fascinate the visitor. Not far away is the curious belfry from which the curfew is rung every night in winter.

I left the village by the road that runs down the valley of the Glengonar Water to Abington. The descent is gradual, and the road runs down an open valley, from which hills clothed with grass, with here and there a patch of heather, rise steeply to rounded tops.

A derelict smelting-mill and a few abandoned houses are the only blots on the landscape. A deep cleuch on the right leads over the hill to Bulmer Moss, where Sir Bevis Bulmer, an enterprising Yorkshireman, found £100,000 worth of gold in three years during the sixteenth century.

There is no lack of solitude here for those who seek it. Perhaps we owe some of our greatest men to this very fact. How the fresh breezes and the purple hills must have helped Carlyle at Ecclefechan on the one side of the Lowthers, and how Burns must have delighted in his various farms on the other side in those silences which allowed his thoughts to speak!

Three and a half miles from Leadhills a road leads over the hill to Crawfordjohn. From this point almost the whole valley of the Glengonar Water is visible, from the wooded slopes round Glengonar House at Abington to the old smelting-mill, an odd industrial intrusion in such a forsaken region.

I decided to go " out of the world and into Crawfordjohn ".

I was now walking between bare brown and green hills, with strong, treeless water-courses threading their way down the slopes to swell the Duneaton Water. I was energetic, and climbed the grassy Mill Scar, which rises from the roadside about a mile from Crawfordjohn. The effort was repaid, for from the summit I had a wide view of the countryside.

The sailor at the masthead at sea can see the crested

Crawfordjohn

waves for miles around striving to rise above their neighbours. That was my experience on this hill-top. I saw
a billowy sea of hills, each seeming to vie with its neighbour to reach the clouds first.

The hills above Symington and Biggar are dominated
by Coulter Fell, and have their gentlest slopes on the
north-east. The cairn-topped peak of Tinto stands on the
plain, and far north-eastwards may be seen the Pentlands.
Westwards, the hummocky country stretches away to
Cairntable and the heights above Muirkirk, and to the
south are the Lowthers. A silver streak in the valley
marks the course of Duneaton Water, with Crawfordjohn
on the opposite bank.

The village is not the place it was once. It is the Sweet
Auburn of the Upper Ward. Only a score of houses are
clustered round the parish church, and no one would
ever dream it was once the home of a king and his " Fair
Rosamond ".

Boghouse Farm, up the valley, is on the site of the bower
King James V built for Katherine Carmichael. Not a
trace of it remains.

There were other strongholds in the valley. Snar Castle was once the home of a notorious freebooter, Jock o' Snar. He and the men from Annandale were always at each other's throats.

On one occasion, a force of the Johnstones came up the valley, at a time when they knew Jock would be absent. The fare they found was so pleasant that they tarried too long, and Jock surprised them while they were draining his cellar. Few of them were able to stand to meet his onslaught, and he killed or maimed most of them.

One man, a priest, pleaded for mercy, but Jock was in no mood to listen to any appeal. He caught the man in his arms, carried him from the castle, and threw him into a deep pool behind the keep. The pool is still called the " Priest's Hole ".

The Duneaton is a delightful stream. It is said to be crammed with trout, and I certainly saw some speckled beauties as I stood on the bridge on my way from Crawfordjohn to Abington.

It is a wild and lonely road which links Crawfordjohn with Abington, which is five miles away, but I like its restfulness and solitude. It makes it easy to cover when you know there is a fine rest-house at the end of it.

Wayfarers were not always so fortunate. Prince Louis Napoleon carried away an unpleasant memory from Abington. After a day's shooting on Crawford Moor he arrived at the inn, tired, and drenched, and hungry. The sitting-room was occupied by engineers. He asked if he might join them. They refused his company. He sat before the kitchen fire, dried his clothes, and ate his supper. Then he went straight to bed, and left early next morning on foot before the other guests were down to breakfast.

CHAPTER XIX

The Lure of the Lowthers

Dr. John Brown's essay on Enterkin was the magnet which first attracted me to the Lowther Hills. Their soft, gentle outlines appealed to me, and I have returned as often as I could. I found in the heart of this region an unrivalled mental stimulant. There is nothing harsh in the landscape. A pleasing loneliness broods over it all. The plaintive murmur of the hill-side streams, the sough of the wind through the glens, the curlew's screams from the slopes are the only sounds that break the stillness.

Rough brown heather and coarse bent, the favourite material of the Clyde slopes, give place on the Green Lowther, Lowther Hill, Thirstane Hill, Stey Gail, and other heights on the Nithsdale slopes, to a mantle of smooth grass unbroken by bush or even a tuft of heather.

Here it is that the Lowthers attain their distinctive character, and here it is, winding between their large smooth flanks, that the remarkable gorges of Menock, Enterkin, Dalveen, and Well Path are to be found.

You come on the entrance to the Enterkin Pass suddenly, about two and a half miles from Leadhills. The pass starts high up on the shoulder of Lowther Hill, and sinks deeper and deeper. It is so steep at some points as to be almost precipitous. Eventually its course is turned aside by the massive form of Stey Gail, whose base is little more than a mile from the entrance to the glen, but which is seven hundred feet below the starting-point.

There is no room for a path at the bottom, where the Enterkin Burn has scooped for itself a still deeper gorge. The track is now a mere bridle path, and cuts its way along the face of the western slope of the hill. You are shut in on every side by smooth green walls, the only sound coming from the burn. A feeling of eeriness grows on you as you sit by the way, and you do not have to sit long before you understand why Harvey, the painter, while sketching in the still depths of Enterkin, felt constrained to break the overpowering spell from time to time by shouting at the pitch of his voice.

The charm of Enterkin is not its grandeur but its solitude.

A pleasant diversion is provided by scaling the slopes of Lowther Hill. From its summit you can see Ben Lomond, Goat Fell and the whole of Arran, Skiddaw and the heights of Cumberland, Hartfell, Broad Law and the other hills round Moffat. Near at hand is Green Lowther, the highest peak of the group.

The glen may be followed to Enterkinfoot, or the road which comes through Dalveen Pass may be joined and followed to Carronbridge.

The Menock Glen lacks the solitude of Enterkin. A road runs through it from Wanlockhead to Menock village on the Sanquhar road. Its features are diversified, and so it is less impressive than its neighbouring valley.

The descent is easy, and as Nithsdale is approached you have a foretaste of what you may expect in that well-wooded strath. The lower reaches of Menock Water are wooded, and the stream, swollen by the addition of many brooks from the hill-sides, flows for the last two miles of its course through an arch of overhanging branches.

Dalveen Pass is a deep, winding valley. Its steep slopes are covered with grass from base to summit. There are no trees and no heather. And yet, what enchantment lurks in this valley when the evening shadows creep out from their hiding-places, or when its dusky depths are made visible by the soft radiance of the moon! The imagination may even be beguiled into picturing fairies making merry on the broad, level sward at the foot of the pass beyond Laveran Bridge, where a brawling stream in a series of cascades leaps down the hill-side to join the narrow and silent Carron.

I like the Well Path, " the lang glen " which " Last May a braw wooer cam' down ". Burns knew it, and so did the Romans. In fact, it was chosen by the legionaries for their road from Nithsdale to Clydesdale.

The modern road from Elvanfoot still follows the general direction of that old highway for the first six or seven miles up the valley of the Powtrail, till it diverges into the Dalveen Pass.

The Well Path was for centuries the main road from Nithsdale, and along it marched the armies which kept the country in a state of turmoil. Now it is almost forsaken.

Durisdeer is at the other end of this path, and a mile from that hamlet, with its peculiarly shaped church, is a Roman camp. It is a perfect example. It has survived because it is on a remote hill-side, where no farmer can hope to cultivate the soil, and on a spot where it would have been difficult for the hand of vandals to work havoc. The site was well chosen. It was sheltered from above, and yet commanded the pass through which an army or war-like force must needs march.

The chief attraction of Durisdeer is the Queensberry Memorial in the parish church. This consists of an elaborate marble monument brought from Rome. It represents in effigy the second Duke of Queensberry reclining by the side of his dead duchess, with the figures of two weeping children on each side. Attendant cherubs are hovering cheerfully above. The vault below contains twelve Douglas coffins.

In the churchyard is the grave of a Covenanter who was shot in Dalveen, and beside it is a weeping ash said to have been planted by Peden, the Prophet of the Covenant. That tree is a link with a man who found refuge in these friendly hills. There is a Peden Burn between Dalveen and Enterkin, and a Peden tradition in every cot among the hills. Glendyne, which opens off Menock Pass, was one of his favourite hiding-places.

Every shepherd on the slopes of the Lowthers is pleased to go out of his way to show you spots where fugitive Covenanters found refuge during the days of the perse-cution, and where conventicles were held. I have trudged beside them from cleuch to cleuch as they told stories of hairbreadth escapes from the dragoons.

I liked best the story of Mary Hamilton.

Allan Hamilton and his daughter lived alone in a cot among the hills. He was religious, and sympathized with the measures adopted by the Covenanters, but never com-municated his views to anybody. Thus he escaped the attentions of the soldiers who patrolled the Lowther region. One August evening in 1683 the two were sitting by the peat fire in their kitchen, when a thunderstorm broke. Mary was terrified, and clung to her father. After a quick succession of flashes of lightning and peals of thunder, rain began to pour down with great violence. Later, gusts of wind swept tumultuously through the glen, and the little stream which flowed past the house became a torrent. In a lull in the storm a knock was heard at the door. Allan opened it, wondering who his visitor might be. It was one of the most distinguished preachers of the Covenant. He was an old man, and seemed overcome with hunger and fatigue, while his clothes were drenched with rain.

Allan had never turned anyone from his door, but on this occasion he was unwilling to admit the visitor. The minister was included in the number of proscribed persons, and persecution then ran so high that it amounted to a capital crime to have intercourse with a fugitive.

" I see, Mr. Hamilton," said the minister, " that you do not wish me to enter your house, that you refuse to give me shelter on a night like this. If you give me protection, I shall pray for you and yours; if you refuse it, I can only depart, perhaps to die on the hills."

Allan was saying it was as much as his life was worth to allow him to enter, when the minister interrupted him:

" Yes, I know your position," he said. " You are one of those faint-hearted believers who, for the sake of ease and worldly gain, have deserted that glorious cause for which your fathers bled.

" You have failed in the hour of need, and when a humble soldier of Christ seeks the shelter of your roof from the storm, you refuse him admittance. I leave God to judge of your iniquity. Good-bye."

Mary, who had heard the conversation at the door, rushed past her father, and caught the aged minister by the arm as he was moving away.

" Father, you will not turn away this poor man," she said. " Indeed, you will not. Surely you were not in earnest. Come in," and she led the man to the fire.

" Thank you, my young friend," said the visitor. " The Lord, for this good deed, will aid you in your trials. You have shown that the old may be taught by the young, and I pray that this example of charity may not turn to your scaith or your father's."

The father relented. He was ashamed of his earlier denial. Now his only concern was the comfort of their guest.

That night the preacher had a softer couch than he had had for a long time. His slumbers were deep, but they were not long, for no sooner had the morning light begun to peep through the window of his room than he was up and at his prayers. Then he went to Allan Hamilton's room, thanked him for his hospitality, and said he must go before anyone saw him in that house or found him leaving it.

Next day at noon half a dozen soldiers arrived at the cottage in the glen. Their leader demanded an interview with Allan.

" So, Mr. Hamilton," he began, " you have taken up with the pious remnant; you have turned a psalm-singer, eh? Come, don't stare at me as if I were an owl. Answer me the question—yes or no."

Allan said he would answer any question that was put to him. Then, in reply to a number of queries, he said he had never attended a conventicle, and denied that he was an associate of the Covenanters.

The soldier next accused him of having spoken to the minister for whom Claverhouse was searching.

" I have spoken to him," Allan admitted. " I do not deny he has been in my house."

" Then, Allan Hamilton, you have harboured a traitor, and unless you deliver him up, or tell where he may be found, I shall hold you guilty of treason, and punish you accordingly."

" The Lord's will be done," answered Allan. " I did no more than an act of common charity. The old man called on me in his distress, and it would have been cruel had I closed the door on him. Wreak your will on me as it pleases you. Where he is now I know not; and though I did know I would hardly consider myself justified in telling you."

The officer in charge of the soldiers then threatened to take Allan's life.

" Give him ten minutes to say his prayers," he said to his comrades, " and then bind up his eyes. It is a waste of time to palaver with him."

Mary uttered a scream when she heard these words, and fell on her knees before the soldiers.

" Do not slay my father," she pleaded. " Take my life. It was my fault alone that the old minister was in this house. My father refused to allow him to enter. I brought him into the house."

The officer shook her off as she clasped his legs, and she fell speechless at his feet.

He was about to lay hands on her, when a trooper stepped forward, and, raising her gently up, placed her on a seat.

" Captain," said the trooper, " I do not see the use of shooting this old fool. Besides, if what the girl says is true, there is no great matter of treason in the case. Whatever you think, I would vote to leave the business to the Justiciary."

The officer became angrier than ever, and threatened to report the soldier for insubordination. Hamilton was then blindfolded, and led to the green patch before his door. The soldier who had opposed this course did not join his fellows, but remained with Mary.

Throwing herself before her companion, Mary cried: "Young man—young man, save my father's life! Oh, try at least to save him! I will love you, and work for you, and be your slave for ever! Blessings on your kind heart; you will do it! Yes, you will do it!"

He could not resist the appeal of this beautiful young woman whose father was about to be shot before her eyes. He rushed from her side, and, without saying a word, unslung his carbine and shot his officer. The troopers, who had raised their weapons ready for the order to shoot the kneeling man, were confounded by this turn of events. They lowered their carbines, and discussed what they should do. One of them then took command.

"Get up," said the self-appointed commander to Allan Hamilton, "and bless your stars. It is not every day that you will find a young fellow to shoot your executioner and save your life.

"As for you," he added, turning to the soldier, "I hold you prisoner. You must come to head-quarters, and there take your trial for this business."

Mary's champion was immediately disarmed and pinioned by the four troopers.

"Farewell, young woman," said the bound man as the party made to leave. "Farewell, I have saved your father's life and forfeited my own. Don't forget Jack Graham."

With that the troopers departed. Mary then began to wonder whether any scheme could be devised to rescue her father's deliverer. She discussed the position with her father.

" Yes, there is a chance," said Mary. " Gallop over to our neighbours on the other side of the hills, tell them what has happened, and ask them to help us."

That wild gallop down the glen was not in vain. Allan told the story of the morning's events. A small force, who were preparing to go to a conventicle to be conducted by the minister the Hamiltons had befriended, was mobilized, and they set off to rescue the young soldier.

Thirty men took up their position at the entrance to a glen through which the soldiers had to pass on their way to Lanark, and which they reached by a more direct route. When the soldiers arrived, they were surprised to find a formidable force opposing their passage.

The Covenanters demanded the release of the captive soldier. They refused to listen to any reason for his retention. The troopers, realizing that resistance against such odds would be madness, freed their prisoner.

Mary Hamilton, who had followed the men on a pony, sprang forward and embraced her father's rescuer.

" Good-bye, Graham!" cried the leader of his former friends, with a sneer. " You have the better of us now, but we shall return soon, and you can expect a severe punishment. The gallows is waiting for you in the Grassmarket. Take my defiance for a knave, as you are."

Graham unsheathed his sword, and sprang at the man who had insulted him. " You have challenged me, and you shall abide by it or withdraw it," he said.

Peacemakers intervened to no purpose. The two men fell to with their swords. The combat was desperate. It was ended by a blow which Graham dealt at his opponent's head. The man fell to the ground, and his conqueror disarmed him. A full-throated shout of victory went up from the crowd.

The defeated trooper admitted he had been overcome by a better man, and withdrew what he had said. Graham handed him back his sword, and the troopers were allowed to go.

" Take this advice in return for my weapon," said the trooper. " Shift your quarters as soon as you choose. Good-bye!"

Allan Hamilton and his daughter left their home, and settled in Avondale, while Graham found a haven in Argyll. They emerged from their hiding-places after the Revolution, and returned to the slopes of the Lowthers. Mary married her champion. They lived long in the glen, and their children grew up in comfort around them.

Quite a different type of battle took place over the hills from Nunnery Farm, near the head of Evandale, ninety years before. It was one of the last clan battles on the Borders.

The Johnstones, who lived on the eastern slopes of the Lowthers, were notorious freebooters, lifting everything that came in their way. In fact, it is told of one of them that, passing a haystack, he said: " Wae's me, if ye had but four feet, ye wadna stand lang there!"

William Johnstone, a laird of Wamphray, was a gay and reckless character. He was, in consequence, known as " The Galliard ". He had taken part in many battles against the hereditary enemies of his house—the Maxwells. He resented the truce made by his chief, and when he was not free to raid the Maxwell country, he crossed the Lowthers, and plundered the lands of the Crichtons at Sanquhar, driving the stolen cattle up one of the passes.

The Galliard was captured and hanged in one of these raids. Will o' Kirkhill, his chief lieutenant, who was standing by, swore that he would avenge his kinsman's death. Later he led his men to Sanquhar, and raided the countryside at his pleasure. The Crichtons followed them over the hills, and came on them near the head of Evandale. There were few Crichton survivors from the fight which followed.

The Crichtons complained to Lord Maxwell, the Lord Warden of the Marches, but he would do nothing because the Johnstones were his allies. But the Crichtons were not to be silenced. They sent a deputation to King James VI in Edinburgh. That deputation carried the bloody shirts of their dead kinsmen through the streets of the capital, where popular feeling was roused. King James commanded Lord Maxwell to bring the Johnstones to justice. He had, therefore, to obey, but before he did, he entered into a pact with the Crichtons.

The Johnstones routed the combined forces of the Maxwells and the Crichtons in the last Border clan battle. The skirmish on the slopes of the Lowthers over the hill from Nunnery is, therefore, of more than passing interest, in that it led to the last of the deadly fights which had wrought so much havoc among the Border families.

The Clyde, which rises among the hills on the opposite side of the main road south, is the smallest of the three streams which meet near Elvanfoot. Yet it has given its name to the river. I have not been able to find a reason for the loss of the names of the Daer and the Powtrail after the union.

There is an old rhyme about this watershed which every child in this region is taught before going to school:

Watermeetings

Annan, Tweed, and Clyde
A' rise oot o' ae hill-side,
There was a ploy 'mang the three,
Wha wad first get to the sea:
Slow and smoothly flowed the Tweed,
Annan wan wi' greater speed,
Clyde fell doon wi' muckle din
And broke its neck owre Cora Linn.

I was sorry to leave Watermeetings, but Crawford was six miles away, and the day was nearly spent.

Burns occasionally visited this region when he was an exciseman. He was wont to rest in the old toll-house of Glengeith near Elvanfoot, and it is said that he wrote some verses on a pane of glass there. No trace of them remains, but he has left a song which reveals his knowledge of the district:

Yon wild mossy mountains sae lofty and wide,
That nurse in their bosom the youth o' the Clyde,
Where the grouse lead their coveys thro' the heather to feed,
And the shepherd tents his flocks as he pipes on his reed.

Not Gowrie's rich valley, nor Forth's sunny shores,
To me ha'e the charms o' yon wild mossy moors;
For there, by a lanely, sequester'd clear stream,
Resides a sweet lassie, my thought and my dream.

Amang thae wild mountains shall still be my path,
Ilk stream foaming down its ain green, narrow strath;
For there, wi' my lassie, the day lang I rove,
While o'er us unheeded fly the swift hours o' love.

CHAPTER XX

The Birth of a New Age

A great change stole over the face of Lanarkshire a century ago. From a purely pastoral county it became one of blazing furnaces, black-throated stalks, slag heaps, and refuse dumps. There took place one of those social and industrial movements which George Eliot loved to describe, with a fancy touched to pathos for the old, and yet not without sympathy for the new.

At the beginning of the nineteenth century the district between the Lowther Hills and the Campsie Fells lay in unbroken stretches of fertile corn land. The only features which withdrew the eye from the contemplation of pure rural beauty were the comfortable homesteads of the farmers, and here and there an irregular hamlet.

The railways had not come. Travellers jogged about the quiet roads on horseback, or were heaved uncomfortably against their neighbours in a swinging mail-coach. The natives were a comfortable and easy-going race of men, whose keenest interests lay, perhaps, in Church disputes and the rights of eldership.

The agricultural labourer was poorly paid, but contented. He was not a harsh critic, except of sermons. Occasionally there leaped into his mind revolutionary ideas of disestablishing the parish church.

Thus the country slept on until the Dunlops, the Mushets, the Neilsons, and the Bairds discovered the hidden treasures under the soil of the county. Then began the irresistible transformation, not by the waving of a wand by any means, but at the impulse of the commercial instincts. Year after year more of the farmers' fields were broken into for the sake of the black harvest. Mountains of refuse arose, on which no plant can thrive. The landscape became loaded in places with the black grimy buildings which house furnaces and mark the scene of a colliery, while fires from shafts and smouldering refuse-heaps blazed and reeked day and night.

The old villages grew, and new settlements arose, with their long rows of depressing brick buildings and dismal tenements of the type which denotes the subordination of man to drudgery. The social habits changed. Language changed. The common people of Lanarkshire talked the pure Lowland Scots of Burns's day, but soon the pleasant-sounding vernacular was mixed with the tones of Irish.

Thus, in the blind forward heave of things, wealth and population advanced. From a simple society of tillers of the fields sprang a composite race, concerned not only with prices of grain and feeing markets, but with strikes, sliding scales, and periods of unemployment. All over the Middle and Lower Wards of the county particularly, there was an eruption of pits and their squalid accompaniments.

Strangely enough, the first traces of this development are found in the more peaceful Upper Ward. Ironworks were begun at Wilsontown by two brothers named Wilson in 1779. They prospered for a time, but were doomed when seemingly limitless supplies of ironstone were found in the Monklands. Moreover, the newcomers to the industry had plenty of money to back them up, while the company which began at Wilsontown was weakened by domestic differences and costly litigation. They were unable to compete with their rivals, and their industry began to decline. A severe depression increased the embarrassment, and the works were closed. The coal-field, however, is still being worked.

Tobacco and coal both end in smoke. They brought a fortune to the Dunlops of Tollcross. Colin Dunlop was one of the " Tobacco Lords " who made Glasgow famous in the eighteenth century. He bought the lands of Carmyle, in which he was succeeded by his son James, a man of great business capacity and energy.

James Dunlop had to find new outlets for his energy. He made himself master of coal-mining, and worked the minerals on his estate with great success. This success made him reckless in his dealings. He was caught in the general collapse of 1793, and foundered. It looked for a time as if he would be left penniless, but some of the people whom he had helped to fortune in other days did not forget him when he was under a cloud. They came to the rescue, and he was able to retain the Carmyle minerals, which he worked with fair success.

It was his son Colin who, though trained for the Bar, made the products of the Tollcross Ironworks famous throughout the world. Ill-luck dogged his footsteps for a time, and he lost his works. But he was able to buy them back in a few years, and in 1828 laid the foundations of a large fortune.

It was in that year that another bright star began to shine in the firmament. James Beaumont Neilson then introduced the hot-air blast to furnaces where a blowing apparatus was required. That invention was really the beginning of the Iron Age.

Neilson's father was an engineer at Govan Colliery, where Neilson had been set to work before he was fourteen. Showing a turn for mechanics, the lad was later apprenticed to his elder brother, who was an engineman at Oakbank. At the end of his apprenticeship he was appointed engineer to a colliery at Irvine, but his employer failed, and he came to Glasgow, where he became superintendent of the first gasworks in the city. Although he knew nothing of gas-making when he entered the service of the company, he soon mastered it in all its branches, and introduced many important improvements into the manufacture and utilization of gas.

His attention was drawn to the smelting of iron in 1824, especially to the fact that the action in furnaces was irregular, and that the output in winter was generally greater than the output in summer. He began a search for some means to improve the blast employed to excite combustion in the furnaces. It was suggested to him that the blast might be submitted to some purifying process, but he thought the action of the oxygen in the air should be increased to free the blast from moisture.

Neilson was now a Daniel in a den of lions. Ironmasters and men of science were agreed that the cold blast was the better. So strongly were some of the smelters convinced of the truth of this theory that they had adopted devices for the artificial refrigeration of the blast. Neilson rejected that theory. He was sure that the superior yield in winter was caused by the lack of moisture.

The poor results obtained in one instance where the

blowing engine was half a mile from the furnace, attracted his attention to the experiments which ultimately led to his invention. He came to the conclusion that the effects of distance between furnace and bellows would be overcome if the blast were heated by passing it through a red-hot vessel, by which its volume, and, consequently, the work it could do, would be increased. He discovered by experiment that the blast could be made more efficient by heating.

It was not easy to persuade the ironmasters to accept this view. It was even more difficult to induce any of them to test it. Eventually Colin Dunlop of the Clyde Ironworks at Tollcross agreed, with the result that the financial backing necessary to exploit the patent was immediately forthcoming.

This discovery revolutionized the whole industry. Previously Scottish coal could not be used in smelting without coking, and it was not suitable for this process. But by using the hot blast the coal could be used in the raw state.

That was not, however, the only economy. With the hot blast the same amount of fuel produced three times as much iron, while the same amount of blast did twice as much work as the cold blast did formerly.

The process was in general use by 1835, and it could be truthfully said that Neilson had done as much for the iron industry as Arkwright did for the cotton trade fifty years before.

Like Arkwright, Neilson was not allowed to enjoy undisturbed the fruits of his invention. From time to time ironmasters tried to destroy his patent, but in every case they failed. Some of them had even made improvements on the original, but the specifications of Neilson's patent, which had been prepared by Lord Brougham, were so generally worded that they could not circumvent them and claim relief from paying royalties. A systematic attack was made on the patent rights. Nothing was omitted that persistence or lavish expenditure of money could effect, but all was in vain. Cases were carried from court to court both in Scotland and England, but they only served to establish the merit and the claims of the inventor and his guarantors.

Neilson was greatly discouraged by these proceedings, but the firmness and determination of his colleagues carried him through his difficulties, and he realized a small fortune. He retired soon after these battles had been won.

Meanwhile the works at Tollcross grew in extent and fame. One man who had helped to bring success to them and to the iron industry in Lanarkshire as a whole, and who had been dismissed for his zeal, was David Mushet. He was an accountant, but in his spare time he carried out some research work with apparent success. His employers were jealous of his success, and dismissed him. He joined a partnership on the banks of the Calder, and while a furnace was being built there he discovered the Black-band Ironstone, and showed that this so-called " wild-coal " was capable of being used economically.

That discovery in the Monklands brought another man into the business. This was Alexander Baird.

Baird began life as a farmer, but found the precarious livelihood insufficient to maintain his large family of eight sons. He acquired a lease of a colliery in Dalserf, which he managed in addition to his farm. Seven years later, the year after Waterloo, he took a coal-field near

Airdrie, entrusting the management to his eldest son, William. The family had soon six pits working in the Gartsherrie district, and in 1828 they leased the ironstone seams adjoining these collieries. Their first furnace was built in 1830. By 1842 sixteen were in full blast.

When the Bairds entered the iron business there were only seven blast-furnaces in Scotland, with an annual production of little more than 10,000 tons. They carried out many improvements in production methods, and output increased by leaps and bounds.

A business of such dimensions required a large quantity of raw material. It was important to have the supplies near at hand, and so the surrounding mineral fields were bought one after another, including the site of Coatbridge. Still that was not enough. There was a danger of the seams being exhausted. New territory must be tapped.

Works were built at various centres in Ayrshire, but Gartsherrie remained the head-quarters of the company, even when, under the name of the Eglinton Iron Company, they extended their operations into other counties as well. Within twenty-five years this company attained a degree of prosperity never before equalled by any industrial concern in the world.

The prosperity was a family affair. Every member pulled his weight. It is not easy to cite another example where so many members of one house have worked to-gether as a team with such success. Much of their money was put into real estate, and as landed proprietors they attained a pre-eminent position in Scotland. One estate after another was bought, until they held land in many counties from Aberdeen to Dumfries and from Inverness to Roxburgh.

The story of their rise to fame is one of the finest examples of what has been achieved by men of humble origin endowed with natural abilities of a high degree, an unbounded capacity for work, and a determination to succeed.

These were the men who laid the foundations for the throne of His Industrial Highness, which their successors have strengthened.

The century which has run its course since the birth of the hot blast will for all time be marked out in history as the most wonderful, the most thrilling period the world has ever experienced. Civilization is even now on the threshold of great discoveries, but it seems unlikely that the next hundred years will have crowded into them so many astounding events and discoveries as have characterized the century which has passed.

Think for a moment what has been crammed into that period. Gas and electricity have taken the place of the candle and oil-lamp. Railways and luxurious trains have ousted the mail-coach and its teams of horses. Ironclads have superseded the old wooden walls of the navy, and floating palaces have driven out uncomfortable sailing ships.

The world has been circled by aeroplane and airship, and air-line services have been run with the regularity of railways between most of the chief cities of the world. Motor vehicles have revolutionized inland transport.

Telegraphy and telephony have broken down distances, and in these realms one miracle has followed on the heels of another with breathless haste, until now, without the aid of wires, we listen to the world's concerts, see events at the other side of the Atlantic, and receive messages from ships as they pass in the night.

Engineers, with the inventive and scientific co-operation of the iron and steel makers, have, in short, marched steadily from one triumph to another, and have swept victoriously forward and upward from one peak to another.

All these developments had their foundations in the iron and steel industries, all owe their origin to the enterprise of the Clydesdale pioneers of the early years of the nineteenth century. Those industries were the solid rock on which Scotland's industrial greatness has been built. Her sons and their products have made Clydesdale famous, have given the region a place in the annals of the world from which it will never be ousted.

What of the future? Still greater glory. Clydesdale men and women are proud of the achievements of their fathers, but they are prouder still of their youth, who have the same enthusiasm, energy, initiative, enterprise, and a dash of discontent which impel them forward to the achievement of something better. In their hands the future is safe.

BIBLIOGRAPHY

I found the following books useful. Some of them are rare; they may be found in second-hand bookshops or consulted in the libraries in the districts concerned.

Ure's *History of Rutherglen and East Kilbride.*
Lives of the Lindsays, by Lord Lindsay.
Memoirs of the Maxwells of Pollok, by W. Fraser.
A History of Cambuslang, by J. A. Wilson.
By Bothwell Banks, by G. Henderson and J. Jeffrey Waddell.
Annals of Blantyre, by S. Wright.
Memoirs of the House of Hamilton, by J. Anderson.
Naismith's *Handbook of Hamilton.*
Historical Sketches of Cambusnethan, by P. Brown.
Stonehouse, by R. Naismith.
Sketches of Strathavon, by M. Gebbie.
The Covenanters, by J. B. Dalziel.
Gleanings among the Mountains, by R. Simpson.
Annals of Lesmahagow, by J. B. Greenshields.
Notices Relating to Carluke, by D. R. Rankin.
Memoirs on the Affairs of Scotland, by George Lockhart.
The Talisman, by Sir Walter Scott.
Old Mortality, by Sir Walter Scott.
History of Lanark, by W. A. Cowan.
History of Lanark, by W. Davidson.
Descriptions of Lanark and Renfrew, by W. Hamilton.
The Upperward of Lanarkshire Described and Delineated, by C. V. Irving and A. Murray.
Notes by the Way, by A. McMichael.
Adventures in Socialism, by Alexander Cullen.
The Clyde, by M. Y. and J. Y. Hunter and Neil Munro.
Clydesdale, a Poem, by A. Beveridge.
Clydesdale, by A. MacCallum Scott.
The Clyde, by John Wilson.
The Douglas Cause, edited by A. F. Stuart.
The Douglas Book, by W. Fraser.
The House of Douglas, by Sir Herbert Maxwell.
Memorie of the Somervilles, by Lord Somerville.
An Account of the Baronial House of Somerville, by James Somerville.
Biggar and the House of Fleming, by W. Hunter.
Crawfordjohn, by Thomas Reid.
Domestic Annals of Scotland, by R. Chambers.
Scenery of Scotland, by Sir Archibald Geikie.
Flemish Influence in Britain, by J. Arnold Fleming.
Lamington, Past and Present, by Mrs. Ware Scott.
The Call of the Pentlands, by Will Grant.
Crawford, by W. C. Fraser.

INDEX

195